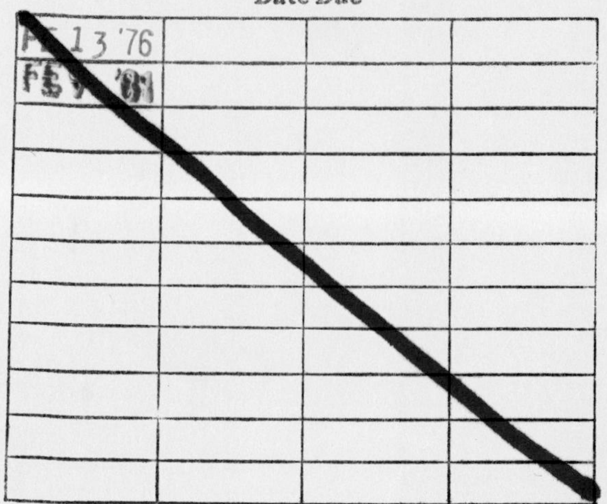

Recreation FOR THE Physically Handicapped

Janet Pomeroy
Founder and Director
Recreation Center for the Handicapped, Inc., San Francisco, California

Recreation FOR THE Physically Handicapped

The Macmillan Company
Collier-Macmillan Limited, London

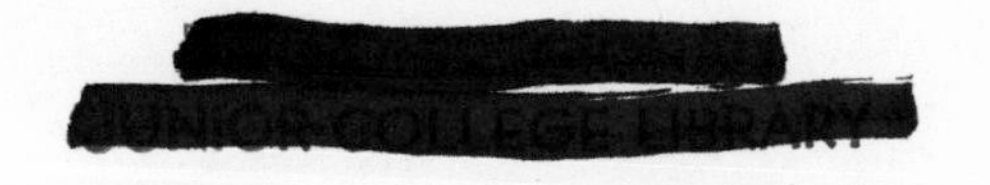

To the children and adults of the Recreation Center for the Handicapped whose enthusiastic response to the program and whose willingness to share their experiences inspired the writing of this book.

Library of Congress catalog card number: 64-10971

Seventh Printing, 1971

THE MACMILLAN COMPANY
866 THIRD AVENUE, NEW YORK, NEW YORK 10022
COLLIER-MACMILLAN CANADA, LTD., Toronto

Printed in the United States of America

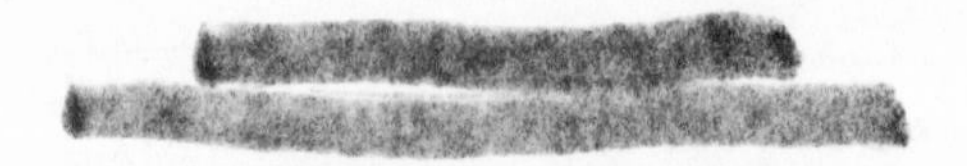

Preface

This volume is designed to interpret the widespread need by the physically handicapped for opportunities to engage in satisfying and constructive recreation activities. It indicates the possibility of providing recreation for this group, lists principles that should underlie recreation programs, and describes procedures that have proved effective in serving the recreation needs of physically handicapped individuals and groups. The book should therefore be useful to agencies and communities concerned with providing recreation and other services for the handicapped.

An increasing awareness of the needs of the physically handicapped has stimulated the development of greater health, education, and welfare services for them. On the other hand, their need for recreation and the benefits it can bring them have received relatively little attention. The evidence presented in this volume as to the values resulting from participation in recreation by persons with physical handicaps should awaken public interest in extending recreation opportunities to this large and relatively unserved segment of our population. The meagerness of published materials on the subject heightens the importance of this publication.

The suggestions relating to principles, policies, and procedures for initiating and conducting a recreation program for the physically handicapped and the descriptions of activities of various types and their adaptation to the needs of this group are based primarily upon experience at the Recreation Center for the Handicapped, in San Francisco. (Throughout this book, in the interest of brevity, it is referred to as the Recreation Center.) This Recreation Center was founded by the author, who has served as its full time director without salary for more than a decade. She has also drawn on her training and experience as a professional leader in community recreation programs, her observation of activities in many cities, and her participation in a variety of conferences and workshops.

The book is intended to serve the needs of several groups:

1. *Public recreation and park departments.* Since these departments have the responsibility for providing recreation service for all the people, they need and can benefit from the information in this volume.

2. *Teachers and students in the increasing number of colleges and universities offering courses in recreation.* Understanding of the special problems and procedures useful in providing programs for the physically handicapped is an essential part of the preparation of students for professional recreation leadership. It also has a place in curricula for students preparing for social work, medicine, education, nursing, rehabilitation, and related fields.

3. *Public and private health and welfare agencies.* Most health and welfare agencies are concerned with the needs of the handicapped; some of them are organized primarily to serve this group. Typical of these agencies are public health and welfare departments, hospitals, associations for handicapped groups such as crippled children and the cerebral palsied, nursing organizations, and institutions of various types.

4. *The many community organizations sponsoring or supporting programs for the handicapped.* Luncheon clubs, parent-teacher associations, businessmen's groups, and women's clubs are typical of the many organizations that can find this book useful as a guide in developing service projects.

The information in this publication is grouped in three divisions. Part One deals briefly with the nature and extent of the handicapped, their need for recreation, and the values resulting from recreation programs under qualified leadership. Part Two describes in considerable detail principles, policies, and procedures that have been adopted successfully in initiating and conducting recreation programs and in dealing with essential factors such as leadership, finance, transportation, and public relations. Many of these can be used with equal success in providing recreation for persons other than those with physical disabilities. Part Three is devoted to operating of the major aspects of the recreation program, the types of activities comprising it, and the adaptations that are necessary in helping seriously handicapped persons to engage in them. It includes examples of activities that have proved popular and successful. The book is not intended to be an activities manual, however, as there is an abundance of literature dealing with the conduct of specific activities.

A few comments are offered on the basic assumptions underlying the volume. One is that recreation is a universal human need which should be satisfied by activities and experiences freely chosen by the individual —not prescribed as therapy. Another is that public recreation agencies have the primary responsibility for providing recreation for the handicapped, who should be treated as individual citizens and not as "patients" in an institution. A third assumption is that whenever and wherever possible the physically handicapped should be helped to participate in recreation activities with nonhandicapped groups. Integration of programs cannot always be achieved, especially in the case of some persons with serious or multiple handicaps, but it should be an ultimate objective.

In view of the importance attached to program integration, one might question why much of the material in this book is based upon a center for the handicapped. Valid reasons can be offered in explanation. When the Center was established little was known about the ability of the handicapped, especially those with serious physical defects, to participate in recreation activities. Very few agencies, particularly public recreation departments, were providing recreation programs for them. The Recreation Center was a pilot project. An attempt was made to determine by experience the degree to which it was possible for individuals with physical defects to take part in forms of recreation and the ways by which activities could be adapted so the handicapped could participate in them. Increasingly, handicapped individuals and groups were given opportunities to share in recreation programs with the nonhandicapped, and several examples of successfully integrated programs are recorded in this volume. The Recreation Center is still used primarily by the handicapped; but playground children, scout troops, and other nonhandicapped groups frequently share in its program. Based upon experience at the Center, the author has consistently advised agencies and communities to initiate integrated programs and activities rather than to start a special center for the handicapped.

Recreation for the Physically Handicapped will have achieved the purpose for which it was written if it helps bring about a better understanding of the recreation needs of this group and encourages communities to establish recreation programs which provide the physically handicapped with constructive and satisfying activities.

JANET POMEROY

Acknowledgments

Grateful acknowledgment is due to the many individuals and agencies whose cooperation and assistance made this publication possible.

Sincere gratitude is due to Mrs. Jeanne Cherry of Carmel, California, who, on her own initiative, made the financial grant under which the Recreation Center for the Handicapped was established. Her encouragement and support over the years have continued to be an inspiration to the author.

A special expression of appreciation is due to Mr. George D. Butler, for years a member of the National Recreation Association staff, for his invaluable assistance in the preparation of this volume. Over a period of years, this recognized authority has given freely and generously of his time and knowledge of recreation in assisting and encouraging the author. His experience as an author has enabled him to give guidance in the organization and presentation of the material. Satisfactory completion of the book was made possible in no small measure by his willingness to edit the completed manuscript.

I am deeply grateful to the Recreation Faculty of San Francisco State College for its many years of encouragement and guidance, especially in the development of principles and procedures for program and personnel. Many of these were applied at the Center and are recorded in this volume. In particular, I wish to thank Carol Brown, Instructor in Recreation at San Francisco State College, for her technical advice on the music in Chapter 16 and for permitting me to include several songs which she had notated.

The Center's Board of Directors, committee members, and volunteers have rendered services of inestimable value, many of which have afforded the basis for material used in various chapters.

The large number of contributors whose financial support has enabled the Center to carry on the experimental program reported here also merit sincere appreciation. This effort was due in no small measure to the cooperation received from many individuals representing San Francisco newspapers, television and radio stations, and other publicity media in interpreting the Recreation Center program to the general public. In acknowledging this cooperation, special appreciation is due to Mrs. Anita Day Hubbard, whose advice and guidance were most helpful during the early development of the program.

No acknowledgment of my appreciation and gratitude would be complete without special mention of "Mr. Anonymous," whose continued interest in and generous support of the Recreation Center's program has earned for him the title of "Angel of the Center."

Many suggestions received from members of the Center's staff and materials presented at conferences or appearing in other publications have proved useful to the author.

The San Francisco Recreation and Park Department merits special gratitude for its indirect but outstanding contribution to this book. It not only made available the use of the building and day camp in which the Center's program was largely carried on but also provided maintenance, supplies, and leadership for an aquatic program. Members of the Department's staff offered valuable advice and suggestions used in the book.

Sincere thanks are also due to Mrs. Miriam Pedeuboy for the patience, time, and devotion she volunteered in transcribing and preparing the rough draft of the manuscript.

Finally, my husband, Morris Pomeroy, merits my sincere gratitude because of his willingness that I devote much of my time over the years to the founding and operation of the Recreation Center and for the preparation of this book. His deep interest in, and financial support of these projects deserve consideration.

JANET POMEROY

Contents

Recreation FOR THE Physically Handicapped

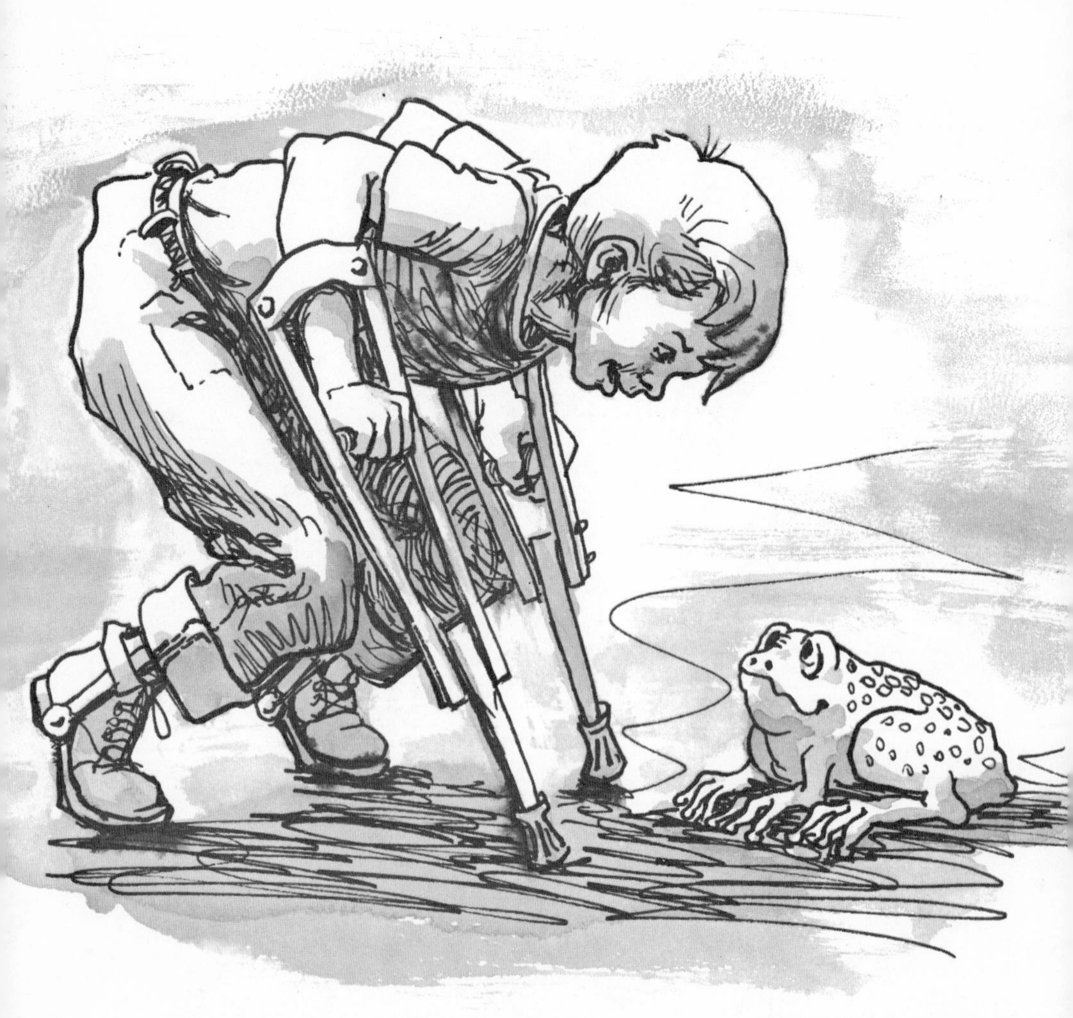

"The handicapped child has a right to grow up in a world which does not set him apart, which looks at him not with scorn or pity or ridicule but which welcomes him, exactly as it welcomes every child, which offers him identical privileges and identical responsibilities." (White House Conference on Child Health and Protection, Committee on Physically and Mentally Handicapped, *The Handicapped Child* (New York: Appleton, 1933), p. 3.)

PART ONE

The Handicapped and Recreation

This section of the book provides the background for the sections that follow. It indicates briefly the types of physically handicapped and their number, traditional attitudes toward this group, significant developments in dealing with them, and the challenge they present to recreation leaders. It describes the various human needs and desires that can be served or fulfilled by recreation and the additional values for the handicapped individual and to society resulting from participation in recreation activities.

CHAPTER 1

Understanding the Physically Handicapped

The word *handicapped* is a broad term used today to describe persons who differ from their fellow men to a marked degree, physically, psychologically, or socially. Many definitions have been suggested as to what constitutes a person with a handicap, but one recommended for handicapped children and youth at the White House Conference on Children and Youth in 1960 is highly acceptable. It defines a handicapped child as one who "cannot play, learn, work, or do the things other children of his age can do; or is hindered in achieving his full physical, mental and social potentialities; whether by a disability which is initially mild but potentially handicapping, or by a serious disability involving several areas of functions with the probability of life-long impairment."[1] In large measure this definition can be applied to handicapped adults.

Types of Handicapped

There are many subgroups included within the broad definition of handicapped persons. One such group, which is considered in this book, comprises persons who have a physical disability. Individuals with a physical disability have been variously referred to as crippled, orthopedically handicapped, physically disabled, or limited, and exceptional, among other terms. A "crippled child" has been defined as "an individual who at birth, or by reason of illness or injury, is deprived of normal functions of his neuromuscular and associated skeletal system."[2] The Department of Health, Education and Welfare points out that while historically the term *crippled children* has meant children with orthopedic handicaps, today it is applied to children suffering from impairments in speech, hearing and vision, heart defects, defects in metabolism, mental and neurologic functions, and other defects.[3]

The term *exceptional children,* which is used more and more frequently, particularly in special education, is an umbrellalike term which encompasses many medical and psychological groupings of children, including the physically handicapped and crippled.

[1] *Conference Proceedings,* Golden Anniversary White House Conference on Children and Youth, Washington, D.C., 1960, p. 381.

[2] *Focus on Children and Youth,* Golden Anniversary White House Conference on Children and Youth, Washington, D.C., 1960, p. 255.

[3] "Child Health and the Nation's Handicapped Children," Department of Health, Education and Welfare, Social Security Administration, Children's Bureau, Washington, D.C., 1960, p. 4. (Mimeographed.)

Whereas the words *crippled* and *physically handicapped* are commonly used interchangeably and appear to be synonymous, the term *physically handicapped* seems to be more acceptable in present-day usage than others to describe this specific group of persons. As used here, it denotes persons who have a physical disability. Within this large category are a number of separate and distinct groups which Cruickshank and Johnson classify as persons with impaired vision, impaired hearing, speech handicaps, and orthopedic and neurological impairments.[4] These authorities have classified and described the handicaps somewhat as follows:

Impaired Vision consists of two major groups—the partially sighted and the blind. The partially sighted are those whose vision is between 20/70 and 20/200 in the better eye with correction. The blind are those whose vision is less than 20/200 with corrections, or whose field of vision is significantly restricted.

Impaired Hearing ranges from hard of hearing to deaf. Deafness may be classified as congenital or acquired.

Impaired Speech results from developmental, functional, and organic causes.

Crippling Conditions result from various factors, such as:

1. Congenital abnormalities: cerebral palsy, erbs palsy, spina bifida, bone imperfections, hemophilia, and others.
2. Infection: poliomyelitis, tuberculosis, arthritis, myositis, epiphysitis.
3. Metabolic disturbances: muscular dystrophy, myesthenia gravis.
4. Traumatic conditions: fractures, accidents, burns, etc.
5. Unknown or miscellaneous causes: multiple sclerosis, tumors.

Physical disabilities, therefore may be the result of a variety of diseases, accidents, or congenital defects, may happen to persons of every race, color, and creed, and may range from a very slight to a total disability. Some persons, for example, are partially sighted or hard of hearing. Others, particularly those with cerebral palsy, are often multiple handicapped. They may have a speech impairment, hearing loss, and a great deal of involuntary motion of parts of the body such as the hands, arms, legs, and mouth. In rare instances, they may also be totally blind.

Number of Handicapped

The exact number of physically handicapped persons in the United States is unknown. However, it has been stated that approximately 10

[4] William M. Cruickshank and G. Orville Johnson, *Education of Exceptional Children and Youth* (Englewood Cliffs, N.J.: Prentice-Hall, 1959), p. 5.

percent of the children in the United States have an appreciable physical or mental disability.[5] The Children's Bureau, Department of Health, Education and Welfare, Washington, D.C., has published national estimates for 1960 and 1970 on the basis of available data resulting from studies of the prevalence of these disabilities in recent years. The table that follows records these estimates, a number of which are seen to be restricted to a limited age group.

ESTIMATED NUMBER OF PERSONS WITH SPECIFIC HANDICAPS IN THE UNITED STATES

	Estimated Number In	
Type of Handicap	*1960*	*1970*
Epilepsy (under 21)	360,000	450,000
Cerebral palsy (under 21)	370,000	465,000
Eye conditions needing specialist care (5–17)	10,200,000	12,500,000
Hearing loss (under 21)	360,000 to 725,000	450,000 to 900,000*
Speech handicaps (5–20)	2,580,000	3,270,000
Cleft palate and/or harelip	95,000	120,000
Orthopedic (under 21)	1,925,000	2,425,000
Rheumatic fever (under 21)	880,000	1,100,000
Total (Estimated)	16,952,500	21,005,000

* Average used for total.

While the above figures are admittedly estimates, the known number of physically handicapped persons is large enough to have special significance for the nation and to present a challenge to recreation leaders in every community. In order to interpret adequately the role of the recreation leader and his responsibility toward the physically handicapped, it is essential to review past and present social attitudes toward these persons and methods of treating them.

Traditional Attitudes

The recognition and general acceptance of the severely physically handicapped person as an individual, entitled to basic human rights and

[5] *Conference Proceedings, op. cit.*, p. 255.

privileges, is relatively new in our society. It was not until the twentieth century that these persons were considered by society as having any social or economic worth. History shows that in the seventeenth and eighteenth centuries people attributed severe physical disabilities to evil spirits and the curse of various gods. People in general, as is true today, viewed the handicapped with morbid curiosity and feared to come in contact with them.

"In ancient Sparta, for example, individuals with any type of physical ailment were placed on the mountain side and allowed to perish solely for eugenic reasons."[6] Some persons, now known to us as cerebral palsied individuals, were subject to cruel and inhuman treatment. Because of their involuntary movements, their grimacing, unsteady gaits and queer speech, they were often used as court jesters for the amusement of the people. Others were sacrificed to the gods as evil spirits, placed in asylums, or bound in chains. Apton contends that "down through the ages the physically handicapped constituted a neglected and tragic minority."[7]

The early history of the United States, notwithstanding the nation's establishing itself on a democratic concept, shows a neglect of the handicapped. Pioneers were too busy building a new social order to give much attention to persons who could not care for themselves. The first efforts to give any handicapped person dignity as a human being occurred in the early nineteenth century, when Horace Mann and Samuel Gridley Howe became aware of the needs of the mentally retarded child, while Reverend Thomas Gallaudit developed an educational program for the deaf, blind, and mentally retarded.

Programs for the crippled child, however, were not established until decades later. Previously, many doctors diagnosed multiple handicapped persons such as the cerebral palsied as mentally deficient and hopeless and recommended that they be placed permanently in institutions, where they were allowed to vegetate. Many children not placed in institutions were literally hidden in back rooms and attics because their parents were ashamed of them. This attitude of parents reflected not only a stigma placed upon the child but a commonly held belief that human deformities in the offspring were the result of parents' transgressions.

[6] Selma J. Glick, Hunter College Chapter, International Council for Exceptional Children, *Vocational and Recreational Needs of the Cerebral Palsied*, 1958, p. 12.

[7] Adolph Apton, M.D., *The Handicapped, A Challenge to the Non-Handicapped* (New York: Citadel, 1959), p. 11.

Significant Developments

Fortunately, after the turn of the twentieth century, certain developments contributed toward a change in attitude and in the over-all treatment of all types of handicapped individuals, which has continued to gain momentum up to the present. These developments, which have helped to create a better understanding and acceptance of the physically handicapped child, have been decribed in detail by Cruickshank and Johnson.[8] Several developments of special significance will be mentioned briefly.

Special Education Programs

The development around 1900 of the day school program for exceptional children was a movement away from the earlier concept that children with physical, intellectual, emotional, and social differences must be educated in residential schools. Although public schools began to provide special programs for some types of handicapped children, it was not until 1920 that special attention was focused on the crippled child. State commissions were created in the interest of crippled children, whose responsibility was to establish decentralized hospital-school facilities, diagnostic centers, and local clinics.

While children with relatively minor physical handicaps were educated in regular class rooms with the nonhandicapped, as they are today, many persons with severe disabilities had little or no opportunity for formal education. Some communities aware of this problem have established day schools designed especially for children with severe orthopedic disabilities, where special equipment, therapy, and transportation are included in the total program. Others have provided specially equipped units in public school buildings. These units tend to be preferable inasmuch as the handicapped are considered part of the total school body and are included in most of the over-all activities with the nonhandicapped.

The provision of special classes in public schools or special day schools for the multiple handicapped is a relatively recent development; in many communities they have been established during the past ten or fifteen years. Before this, most persons with severe disabilities had to rely on home teaching, if instruction was provided at all.

[8] Cruickshank and Johnson, *op. cit.*, pp. 12–40.

World War II Experience

The impact of World War II helped to change the attitude of people toward a disability. Thousands of men, seemingly normal and socially acceptable, who were rejected for military service because of physical disabilities, continued to be socially accepted and were considered normal. Many service men injured and crippled in World War II were generally accepted in their respective communities the same as they were before the disability occurred.

The need for all available manpower during the war helped considerably in the job placement of handicapped individuals. *Untapped Man-Power,*[9] a study published during World War II by the United States Civil Service Commission, showed that the handicapped were excellent workers and revealed that they had a better record than the nonhandicapped in absenteeism, turnover, accidents, and production. This study encouraged companies to hire handicapped individuals, and this in turn helped create a better understanding and acceptance of physically handicapped persons.

Parent Education

A gradual change of parents' attitudes toward handicapped children was another significant development. Shortly before and during World War II, parents of cerebral palsied and of mentally retarded children in particular organized themselves widely to encourage the establishment of centers for treatment and for research. Some of these parent groups, though small at first, grew into national associations concerned with the health and welfare of specific types of handicapped persons. Examples of these agencies are the United Cerebral Palsy Association and the National Association for Retarded Children. These agencies helped bring about extensive medical and psychological research, legislation, teacher education, transportation, and funds designed to serve the needs of the multiple handicapped.

Research Results

The development of prosthetic devices for crippled children, which enable them to function outside previously sheltered environments, illustrates how research and special education helped upgrade the treatment

[9] United States Civil Service Commission, *Untapped Manpower* (rev. ed.), United States Civil Service Commission, Washington, D.C., November 1943, p. 61.

of this group. To a large degree, public day school education for crippled children had to wait for the provision of special transportation, which is essential in moving these children about. In California, a state that recognizes transportation of crippled children to and from classes as a public school function, the School Code not only authorizes transportation for pupils assigned to special schools or classes for the physically handicapped but also states that "districts must provide such transportation for those pupils whose physical handicaps prevent walking to school."[10]

Research in medicine, psychology, physics, and chemistry has played, and will continue to play, an important role in aiding the physically handicapped. One example is the discovery of new types of vaccines which through the prevention or treatment of poliomyelitis will reduce the number of crippled children. Efforts to prevent causes of deformity have almost eliminated many types of congenital handicaps. On the other hand, advances in medical knowledge, combined with better standards of living, have enabled many infants and children to survive who would have succumbed at the beginning of the twentieth century.

Growth of Specialized Agencies

Technological advances and a broader understanding of exceptional children have created growing demand for specially prepared teachers. Although many colleges and universities are offering curricula designed to prepare men and women to teach exceptional children, including the multiple handicapped, the gulf between the supply and the demand is still significant.

The establishment and growth of specialized agencies for the exceptional child have contributed immeasurably to the progress of the previously mentioned developments that led toward a better understanding and acceptance of all exceptional children. One such agency is the International Council for Exceptional Children, which represents a cross section of educational, psychological, and medical personnel. Through its journal and other services it fulfills a great need throughout the country for information regarding all types of exceptional children. Many voluntary organizations, too numerous to mention here, have had tremendous impact upon the health, education, care, and treatment of all types of exceptional children.

[10] California State Department of Education, *Education of Physically Handicapped Children,* Commission for Special Education, California State Department of Education, Sacramento, 1941, p. 71.

The National Society for Crippled Children and Adults, established in 1919, has contributed perhaps more than any other single agency to the positive care and over-all treatment of the physically handicapped, who make up a large segment of exceptional children. The Institute of Crippled and Disabled, established after World War I to help the disabled live a more normal life through a functional program of therapy, aided greatly in changing stereotyped social attitudes and encouraged physically handicapped persons to participate in community life. The Shriners and other fraternal organizations have made significant contributions toward the cause of crippled children, especially through the provision of medical care.

Rehabilitation Programs

The rehabilitation program for the physically handicapped in the public school has been broadened to include responsibility for the future of children with orthopedic disabilities. Services available through the government's Office of Vocational Rehabilitation now include medical, psychological, and vocational evaluation, specific and over-all guidance, medical services (if needed) to minimize the vocational handicap, training for specific occupation, and transportation and housing when indicated. In 1943 vocational rehabilitation legislation extended its services to handicapped adults of work age.

The rehabilitation concept for the physically handicapped recognizes personality adjustment and character development to be as important as the attainment of manual skills. To emphasize this concept, Dean W. Roberts, M.D., states: "Increasing concern with the nonmedical problems of the handicapped child has resulted in the formulation of a more mature concept and practice of rehabilitation that emphasized the overall needs of the child as opposed to a limited focus on correction of the physical defect."[11]

Increasingly, educators too state that the need for moral and spiritual maturity may be even greater for the physically handicapped child than for one without such handicaps, to aid him in his adjustment of life with a disability. In addition, the constructive use of leisure time is more and more recognized as an essential aspect of the total growth and development of these children.

[11] *Conference Proceedings, op. cit.*, p. 258.

A Creed for Exceptional Children

The rights of all handicapped children, as well as of all other children, have been clearly delineated in a *Creed for Exceptional Children,* part of which reads as follows:

> We Believe in the American promise of equality of opportunity, regardless of nationality, cultural background, race or religion.
>
> We Believe that this promise extends to every child within the borders of our country no matter what his gifts, his capacity, or his handicaps.
>
> We Believe that the nation as a whole, every state and county, every city and hamlet, and every citizen has an obligation to help in bringing to fruition in this generation the ideal of a full and useful life for every exceptional child in accordance wtih his capacity: the child who is handicapped by defects of speech, of sight, or of hearing, the child whose life may be adversely influenced by a crippling disease or condition, the child whose adjustment to society is made difficult by emotional or mental disorders, and the child who is endowed with special gifts of mind and spirit.[12]

The Present Status

As the preceding paragraphs indicate, society has come a long way in the positive acceptance and over-all treatment of the physically handicapped. All states today offer aid to crippled children, and most states have legislative provision for them in special educational facilities. In increasing numbers severely handicapped youngsters are attending special or regular schools, and those unable to leave their homes are receiving home instruction. The development of prosthetic devices has helped the physically handicapped to function more normally, and the rehabilitation concept encompasses all aspects of their life. As a result of public awareness and an increasing interest in all exceptional children, many services have been developed for them.

In spite of this progress since the beginning of the twentieth century, the needs of great numbers of physically handicapped are largely unmet. For example, when many special schools or classes were established, large numbers of adults were too old for special educational benefits. As a result, some young adults and many older persons with physical handicaps have extremely limited backgrounds in education. Indeed, there are cases of bedfast persons who have had no opportunity for formal education at all. Some multiple handicapped children are released

[12] Department of Health, Education and Welfare, *Creed For Exceptional Children* (Washington, D.C.: U.S. Government Printing Office, 1954).

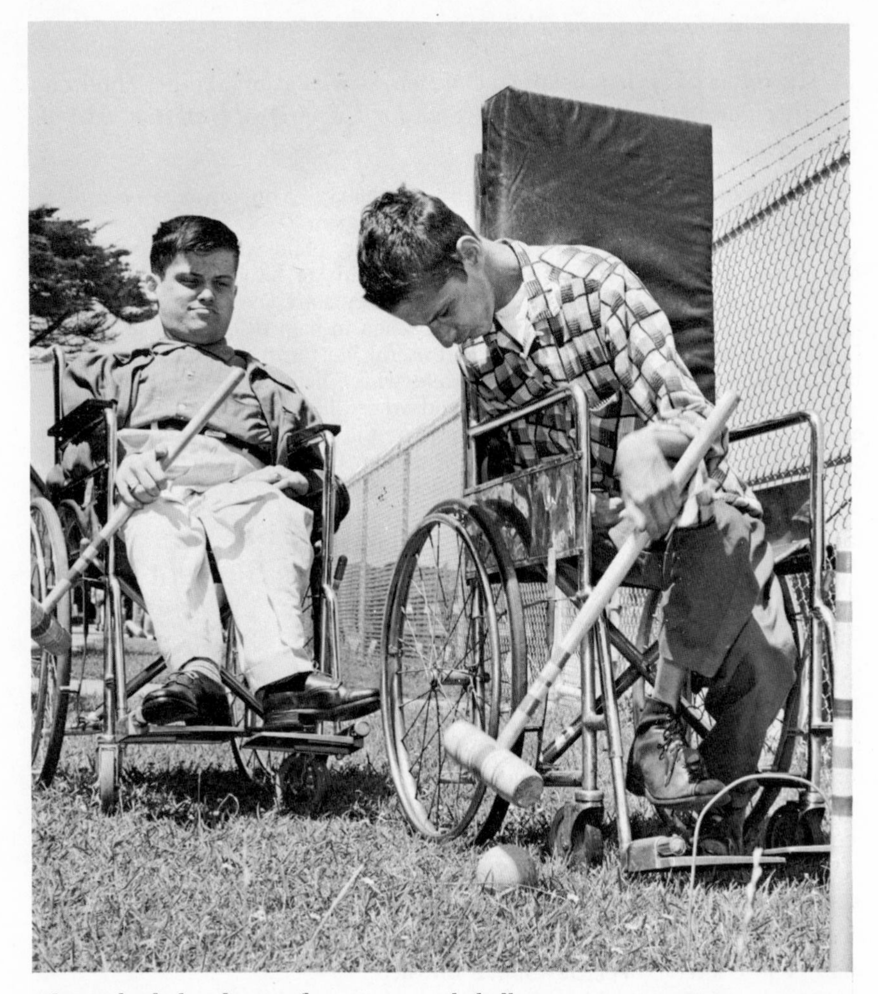

The multiple handicapped present a real challenge to an imaginative recreation leader.

from special schools today before they reach the age of eighteen, the age at which special educational benefits are generally terminated. Lack of suitable available transportation is one of the most serious problems facing agencies desiring to develop programs for this group. Educators point out that less research and understanding exist with respect to the multiple handicapped than to any other type of exceptional child.

The need for special services for the multiple handicapped was confirmed at the 1960 White House Conference on Children and Youth, which recommended that legislation, appropriate educational facilities, community services, and comprehensive research be provided for this group. Specifically it stated that, "Institutional facilities and community services should be developed, in particular for the child with multiple severe handicaps who cannot benefit from restorative or rehabilitative services and the young adult who at the age of 21 is no longer eligible for crippled children's services and by reason of severity of his handicap has no reasonable expectation of a vocational objective."[13]

The Challenge to Recreation Leaders

In spite of the progress achieved in public understanding of the physically handicapped and in their care and education, opportunities for them to engage in organized recreation programs exist in few communities. This neglect arises primarily from the misconceptions that are still widely associated with handicapped persons. The scarcity of recreation programs for this group is doubly unfortunate not only because their recreation needs are similar to those of nonhandicapped people, but because they have so much free time, which becomes a burden unless filled with constructive activity. It is not surprising that established goals for serving the needs of this group include the provision of leisure time activities. There is no justification for excluding upwards of twenty million human beings from normal social intercourse through recreation because of mistaken ideas as to their ability, interests, and needs. No greater challenge faces public and voluntary recreation agencies than that of educating the public as to the need for diversified and creative recreation programs for this neglected sector of our population and of marshaling community resources in support of such programs.

The recreation worker has the same unique professional role to play in the life of the handicapped as in that of the nonhandicapped. It is of great importance that he understands that his relationship to both groups should be the same. Experience has indicated, however, that the challenge may be even greater in working with the handicapped, as he is often called upon to use all of his personal resources in human relationships and understanding, in addition to his technical ability in recreation. In order to comprehend fully his role as a recreation worker with the handicapped, he should know the common misconceptions about them and be familiar with the attitudes that are considered essential for all people to acquire toward them.

[13] *Conference Proceedings, op. cit.*, p. 260–261.

for the physically handicapped, a report to the New York Board of Education stated that "oversolicitude of parents and teachers concerning the education and the physical activities which handicapped children might engage in, is a hindrance to their eventual adjustment."[19] In the majority of instances, oversolicitude is a compensatory attitude similar to that of pity.

Mild dislike is considered to be a form of rejection, although many persons who feel this dislike are unable to explain their reactions. They are aware, however, that they feel uncomfortable and ill at ease among physically handicapped persons. Persons who feel mild dislike will, if at all possible, avoid coming in contact with handicapped persons, as they find themselves unable to develop a rapport with them.

Repugnance and complete rejection have been acknowledged by some persons. Experience indicates that this attitude is more common than one would think.

Fear is a common reaction usually expressed for one of two reasons. Most people fear the unknown, and a person's handicap may be seen as an unknown threat to themselves. Children, as well as adults, often fear that a handicap is "catching." More common than this, however, is a feeling of inadequacy. Many persons do not know what to say or how to react for fear they may not do the right thing.

Common Misconceptions

Notwithstanding the progress made in public understanding, a number of common misconceptions about the physically handicapped persist in our society. Some of these mistaken beliefs have in particular affected the development of recreation for these persons. The concept that physically handicapped persons are ill and should be treated as patients tends to bring about a chain reaction which not only excludes them from community recreation programs, but also retards the development of special programs.

A severely physically handicapped person in a wheel chair or on crutches may not be ill, yet people often associate such a handicap with a crippling disease and either think of the person as ill or as a patient who is recuperating. According to *Webster's New International Dictionary* the word *patient* means "a sick person, now, commonly, one

[19] Board of Education, *Physically Handicapped Children in New York City,* Committee for the Study of the Care and Education of Physically Handicapped Children, New York, 1941, p. 15.

under treatment or care by a physician or a surgeon or one in a hospital, hence a client of a physician." This definition does not apply to a large number of handicapped people. It is entirely possible that a severely physically handicapped person, even though he may be bedfast, has never spent any time in a hospital and that his only experience as a "patient" was the time he had the measles or some other illness common to children. His handicap could have been caused by a birth injury that resulted in cerebral palsy, for example, and is therefore a condition rather than an illness. Even if his handicap had been caused by a crippling disease, however, such as poliomyelitis, he would be considered, following his recovery, merely physically handicapped.

Some health and welfare agencies associated with the severely physically handicapped have contributed, no doubt unknowingly, to the general misunderstanding by creating stereotypes through the use of medical labels. For example, cerebral palsied persons are referred to as "C.P.'s" or "spastics." Recreation activities conducted by some of the welfare groups have been called "spastic activities" or "group activities for C.P.'s." This type of label tends to surround these persons with a medical aura which, in turn, mistakenly implies the need for "medically oriented" leadership.

Such misconceptions concerning severely handicapped persons have understandably affected the community recreation leader. A leader who is trained in general community recreation unfortunately tends to believe he is not qualified to work with such persons, whereas in reality he may be a most desirable worker. Working in recreation with persons who are truly ill requires specialized training, but it does not follow that the community recreation leader needs to be medically oriented in order to be successful with physically handicapped persons who are well. The professionally prepared recreation leader's very lack of specific medical orientation may actually be an advantage. As Ralph W. Meng, M.D., recently stated: "To make therapeutic use of himself, it isn't necessary for the professional recreator to know a great deal about sickness. Nor is it necessary that he be a psychoanalytically oriented psycho-therapist."[20] If the recreation leader is not involved with the medical background of individuals, he will tend to accept and treat these persons as participants in a regular recreation program. If he is not hampered and confused by their presumed "limitations" he does not set up mental blocks in his own mind concerning their abilities and potentialities. Moreover, medical

[20] National Recreation Association, *Recreation,* National Recreation Association, New York, October 1960, p. 360.

opinion on these so-called "limitations" is varied and continually changing.

A person with severe physical handicaps needs to be able to express himself naturally through interest or other normal motivation, without worrying about what muscle he must move or exercise because it is "good for him." If he knows that the recreation leader is dealing with him as a normal person, he is more relaxed and at ease as a participant. Therapy is essential for most severely physically handicapped individuals, but the recreator is not a therapist; he is a leader who provides them with incentives and opportunities to exceed their "limitations," and his services often result indirectly in desirable therapy. Special information and skills that will help the recreation leader, particularly in communication and in the physical handling of the severely physically handicapped, are indicated in Chapter 5.

CHAPTER 2

Objectives and Values of Recreation for the Handicapped

There are certain major principles that should be considered in providing recreation for the physically handicapped.

First of all, it should be understood that the handicapped have the same basic needs, desires, and rights as all other people. Therefore, they need, and are entitled to have, the same opportunities for recreation, which is defined as "a worth while socially accepted leisure experience that provides immediate and inherent satisfaction to the individual who voluntarily participates in an activity."[1]

Secondly, the physically handicapped should have the opportunity to participate in recreation activities with the non-handicapped whenever this is possible. Some of the severely handicapped may not be able to integrate completely with the non-handicapped and therefore need specialized programs. Such activities, however, should be oriented toward the eventual integration of these persons into recreation programs in their own neighborhoods.

A third principle is that activities should be as nearly like those for the nonhandicapped as possible. When necessary, they should be adapted so that each person, regardless of his limitations, may participate actively and to his fullest capacity.

Specific Objectives

The specific objectives of a recreation program for the handicapped may be summarized as follows:

1. To provide opportunities for creative use of leisure time for those handicapped individuals who are physically unable to participate in recreation activities with nonhandicapped groups.

2. To provide activities that assure each individual, regardless of his handicap, a chance to participate actively, thereby encouraging him to accept his handicap and establish a potential capacity for social integration in his own neighborhood or community.

3. To encourage various means of self-expression through adaptive recreation activities; and to provide instruction in the techniques and skills necessary for each individual to find satisfaction in recreation.

4. To provide a variety of opportunities for investigation and continued application of learning experiences—to motivate each individual so he will discover his latent abilities and potentialities and develop

[1] John L. Hutchinson, *Principles of Recreation* (New York: Ronald, 1951), p. 2.

interests and hobbies that he may pursue during his leisure time at home and throughout his life.

5. To foster the growth of independence and self-direction in each individual, regardless of his limitations, and to enlarge and deepen his personal interests so that he may have a more richly satisfying life.

Needs and Desires

As previously stated, the handicapped have the same basic needs for experiences which contribute to spiritual, emotional, social, physical, and mental growth as the nonhandicapped. Recreation programs can provide opportunities for fulfilling many of these needs. Butler states that all persons have certain fundamental desires and that many of these desires can be satisfied through participation in recreation activities. He further contends that some of the satisfactions which people obtain through recreation are the "joy of creation, fellowship, adventure, a sense of achievement, physical well being, use of mental powers, emotional experience, enjoyment of beauty, and a sense of service and relaxation."[2] In providing recreation for the handicapped, objectives should include the fulfilling of these fundamental needs and desires.

The Joy of Creation

The opportunity to create is a very rare experience, particularly for the severely handicapped individual. Well-meaning persons tend to do too much for them—partly because they lack the imagination to realize that there are many ways in which such individuals can express themselves and partly because it takes time, patience, and ingenuity to encourage and allow the handicapped to participate actively within their limitations. Some handicapped persons who are unable to use their hands to express themselves, in painting, for example, can learn to use their toes and feet instead. Similarly, persons without arms have learned to hold tools in their mouths in order to create in various media such as sketching, block printing, and painting. In these instances, it is not the device that matters; what matters is that the need for expression be satisfied. Through recreation, handicapped persons should have the opportunity to find ways for creative self-expression in spite of their limitations.

[2] George D. Butler, *Introduction to Community Recreation* (New York: McGraw, 1959), pp. 225–234.

Fellowship

Loneliness is one of the most common conditions found among the handicapped. They lack opportunities for companionship and for social relationships with persons their own age. Many have no alternative but to spend a sheltered life at home, where day in and day out they are alone most of the time. The need for fellowship is demonstrated in the case of a twenty-four-year-old, severely handicapped young man. He stated that he had nothing at all to live for. Day after day he sat at the window watching the crowds go by. He had no job, no hobby—only his radio to keep him company. He remarked that sometimes he talked just to hear his own voice. Though there were others in the family, he wanted to be with someone his own age who could discuss things like baseball and football. Very shy and withdrawn, he kept reminding the interviewer that all he wanted was something to do, something to live for.[3] Experience has demonstrated that for handicapped persons just to sit and chat with one another is a very simple but a very popular activity. This means that there are limitless possibilities for offering new adventures to them. Because of the lack of previous opportunities and because of certain physical limitations that create a sense of failure, some handicapped persons need to be encouraged to try new experiences. Nonetheless, there does lie within the handicapped that same desire for adventure and new experiences that all people have, and recreation activities can provide the opportunities for fulfilling this desire.

Sense of Achievement

Some handicapped persons are denied even minimal attempts at achievement. Normal situations involving the solving of problems or attaining any degree of accomplishment are not part of their experience. They need to be provided with activities that are within their powers. Despite severe limitations, they can find in recreation activities many opportunities to realize a sense of achievement. Much of the value of group activity for the handicapped is due to the fact that achievement on the part of the group is shared by the individual members, some of whom may not be able to gain individual success. Yet there still remain certain adapted activities of considerable value which will enable them as individuals to attain a degree of success.

[3] Selma J. Glick, "Vocational, Education And Recreational Needs of the Cerebral Palsied Adult," Hunter College Chapter, International Council for Exceptional Children, United Cerebral Palsy of New York City, Inc., New York, 1953, p. 45.

Physical Well-being

Physical activity is widely recognized as a fundamental function of life. There are many ways in which the physically handicapped can participate in and gain satisfaction from forms of recreation involving physical activity. Even though games and sports must be adapted to their physical limitations, handicapped persons may derive great pleasure out of playing them in wheel chairs, on crutches, or even from their beds. Since part of the satisfaction of sports is derived from the fellowship accompanying them and from the opportunities for achievement they provide, participation in such adapted activities has values in addition to affording satisfying outlets for physical energy. This is particularly true for persons who have been severely handicapped from birth and cannot achieve total physical participation. Dancing and dance movements, for example, can be performed very satisfactorily through use of arms, head and shoulders while sitting in a wheel chair or lying in bed. Swimming offers an excellent physical activity for even the most severely handicapped individuals. In a discussion of the psychological values of swimming for the handicapped, the Red Cross states: "Fortunately, water, because of its buoyant effect, offers people an opportunity to satisfy their desire for physical activities."[4] Persons who are permanently bedfast have learned to swim. Some handicapped persons are no more interested in strenuous physical activities than are certain nonhandicapped persons, but for those who wish to participate, many activities can be adapted to provide wholesome pleasure and the opportunity to release physical energies.

Use of Mental Powers

The development and use of mental powers is often the primary means of preventing excessive boredom in the life of handicapped persons. Many with high intelligence, who are severely handicapped, find that the use of their mental powers is their sole salvation against idleness and sheer boredom and that it provides a primary means of enrichment of everyday living. Many hours can be spent in pursuing interesting hobbies such as creative writing, reading, music, and art. Many handicapped adults who lacked the opportunity to go to school when they were children are unable to read and write; some who can, lack

[4] American National Red Cross, *Swimming for the Handicapped, Instructor's Manual,* The American National Red Cross, Washington, D.C., 1955, p. 3.

Tobogganing from a wheel chair can be a thrilling experience.

background knowledge to make those skills fruitful. Such persons should be encouraged and shown that it is never too late to learn. Their recreation programs should include opportunities for reading, writing, and other forms of activity such as discussion groups or book clubs to stimulate and bring into play the use of their mental powers.

Emotional Experience

Because of the sheltered life they have lived the handicapped have a special need for emotional experience. The thrill of tobogganing from a wheel chair and the satisfaction gained from performing in a play, in spite of a severe speech impairment, were outstanding emotional experiences remembered by two severely handicapped individuals. Too often the handicapped person has had to seek emotional satisfaction as passive observer rather than as active participant. Recreation leaders should be aware that the emotional appeal is enhanced when activities include both sexes. In addition, opportunities for socializing with those having similar difficulties give the handicapped a more realistic understanding of their problems. Love and marriage among even the most severely handicapped have proved to be successful ventures.

Enjoyment of Beauty

Many handicapped persons have had limited opportunities not only for creating beauty but for enjoying beauty in its various forms. For this reason, recreation leaders should find it a challenge to provide opportunities for these experiences. Even though persons may be virtually helpless, they may still be able to create objects of beauty. A boy of twelve, unable to use his hands, learned to paint beautiful seascapes and landscapes with his toes. Another youth, unable to speak or to use his hands or feet, designed a handsome mosaic. He did this by indicating with various nods of his head the desired shape, color, and placement of the various bits of material. Handicapped persons should also be given opportunities to enjoy places of unusual beauty such as the mountains, parks, museums, and botanical gardens. Even bedfast persons have been transported to theaters and indoor and outdoor recreation places, where they enjoy the grace and rhythm of the dancer, as well as the skill and precision of the athlete. Looking at or caring for flowers contributes to the appreciation of beauty, inside the home or in the garden.

Sense of Service

Experience has indicated that one of the greatest unfulfilled needs of the handicapped is the chance to help others. They spend a great part of their lives in receiving help but do not have the opportunity for helping others. Because it takes time and patience to help them to be of service, parents and others tend to rob them of the chance to enjoy the satisfactions resulting from service to others. Fortunately, in recreation there exist numerous opportunities for the handicapped to realize them. In group programs, as junior leaders or as program aides to the staff, they can help one another. Developing community service projects has proved to be one of the most highly stimulating and satisfying activities that are possible for groups of severely handicapped persons.

An illustration of this concerns a group of handicapped teen-age girls who had never had an opportunity to "do something for others" until they undertook to make dolls for a nearby infant shelter. Each girl contributed to the total activity to the extent of her capabilities. Some participants were able to sew up cloth bodies by machine; others stuffed them with cotton, sewed on button eyes, or braided yarn for hair. Those who could embroidered the eyes and mouths of their dolls. One bed-ridden girl, who could not use her hands, held the yarn in her toes and feet for others to braid. She also participated in the activity by selecting buttons for eyes and by choosing colors and materials for the clothing and hair for her doll. The fact that it took several months to complete the dolls did not matter; enthusiasm was the important factor, and it was evidenced constantly. After the dolls were completed the group visited the infant shelter and presented them to the children. The satisfactions gained from the experience of serving others were most profound and evident in every participant.

Secondary Objectives

Joy and happiness should be the primary aims of recreation for the handicapped; however, many by-products and social values are certain to result from well-organized programs. Among them are physical, mental, and emotional health; self-realization, social adjustment; democracy and good citizenship. Evidence of the benefits of recreation should encourage recreation authorities to establish programs for the handicapped and should justify their continued support.

Health

Participation in wholesome, suitable forms of recreation contributes to the physical, mental, and emotional health of all persons, including the handicapped. Heretofore, this by-product of recreation has been largely overlooked in the treatment of the handicapped. In the same manner in which joyous activity and emotional release contribute positively to the development of health for all persons, they also contribute to the health of the handicapped. As an example, persons who have a great deal of tension, as do the cerebral palsied, can best release this tension in a relaxed and harmonious atmosphere. Many such persons have testified that participation in recreation activities that bring them sheer joy and pleasure helps immeasurably to release tension and emotions. One boy wrote, "There is no tension at the Recreation Center [Recreation Center for the Handicapped, San Francisco]. This makes it easier for us to walk and talk."

Self-Expression

Because their occupation limits their opportunities for self-expression, more and more persons must depend upon recreation as a means of developing their potential for creativity. Many handicapped who were born twenty or thirty years ago had little chance for such development to take place at all, since they lacked the opportunity for either formal education or creative experiences in play. The severely handicapped child was often deprived of the chance to explore, to investigate, and to play in creative and imaginative activities. Hence, the opportunity for self-realization was greatly limited. For such persons who are now adults, recreation is the primary means for any kind of development, both in education and self-realization.

The limitation on self-expression resulting from certain types of occupation is particularly true of handicapped persons whose jobs in sheltered workshops are assigned to them because of their physical capabilities, rather than for their vocational interest. In these situations, they have little opportunity for self-expression or for discovery of a creative ability. Persons thus occupied therefore need well-planned leisure time programs to help them discover latent talents and to give them opportunities for self-realization.

Activities that can provide these opportunities are limitless; but especially to be mentioned are literature, creative writing, journalism, history, drama, music, and art. The statement that "persons may literally be born anew by the discovery of a creative capacity in one of the field of art, music, literature and the drama"[5] was proven with a group of young adults at the San Francisco Recreation Center for the Handicapped.

One participant, a girl of twenty-seven, quite severely handicapped from arthritis, discovered a latent capacity for creative writing. Experience gained at the Center helped her to obtain a position writing a gossip column for the local newspaper of her town. Eventually, she wrote an article which was published in a national recreation magazine. The article described a party she had helped to plan and conduct at the Recreation Center. The development of this interest in creative writing helped her to gain confidence in herself and provided the incentive for her to go to college, even in her wheel chair, in order to develop this ability further. Self-realization has helped her to make a social adjustment. She is now participating more and more in the affairs of her own community and is attending the Center less and less.

The whole field of drama has probably been the greatest single contributor to self-realization for a group of handicapped young adults at the Center. Writing, producing, and acting in their own plays have

[5] George Hjelte, *The Administration of Public Recreation* (New York: Macmillan, 1940), p. 17.

presented an opportunity for many of them to discover a creative capacity, and have been the motivating force for personal development. As a result of their participation in dramatics, a number of individuals have improved in speech and diction. Through character interpretation they have literally forgotten themselves and their limitations—the stammerer forgets to stammer, and the person with a great deal of involuntary motion in his arms and hands is able to steady them sufficiently to express the proper gestures necessary to interpret his role in the play. Several persons have written plays and poetry and have become intensely interested in making scenery, props, and costumes. One person developed an interest in mural painting through his experience in making scenery.

An important consideration about recreation for the handicapped is that it may be the means for discovering a creative talent which they can carry over into their homes. Thus, many hours which otherwise would be idle may be spent in pursuing an interest which could bring them the joy and satisfaction of self-realization.

Social Adjustment

The potential of recreation for helping individuals to achieve social adjustment is most apparent in the progress made by handicapped adults who were denied recreation opportunities in early life. In play children learn to adjust to a group—to share, to take turns, and to have consideration for others. This recognized and important segment of total growth and development is commonly taken for granted, but many handicapped individuals never belonged to a group as they grew up. Their chance to express the emotions and desires common to all children was very slim. In addition, the opportunities normally afforded for realizing achievement—so important for gaining self-confidence—were lacking in their lives. To observe the actions of such adults is to become keenly aware of the social needs of human beings and of the importance of play and recreation as means of satisfying these needs.

At the Center was a young man thirty years of age, severely handicapped by cerebral palsy. As an only child he had been sheltered in his home most of his life. His first group experience was when he took part in the recreation activities of a group of handicapped young adults. More than anything else, he wanted to be friendly and talk to the girls, but his only way of going about this was to be aggressive. The girls responded negatively and would walk away from him when he came near. Once when he sat down beside a girl and she got up to move away, he tripped her with his crutch. This type of behavior has been apparent in several handicapped individuals who lacked previous opportunities for companionship, social relations, and membership in a group. They repeatedly excused their actions by saying "I only want to make friends." Participation in recreational group activities shows these individuals more desirable ways of gaining social acceptance; especially does it teach them that they need not use force to get attention.

Handicapped persons are apt to become adults before they have any opportunity to develop such basic human virtues as courage, justice, patience, tolerance, and fairness. Notwithstanding this fact, it is never too late to give them recreation activities that provide a setting for the development of these virtues. This is seen in the following letter, written by a cerebral palsied woman of twenty-nine who, through four years of participation in recreation activities, gained a courage and confidence in herself that resulted in a social adjustment for her. She writes:

> What am I getting out of recreational activities at the Center? In the first place, what do you mean by that—physical or mental? From a therapist's viewpoint I am getting very little in physical training. I am not learning to walk; I am not getting speech therapy and I am not being shown how to relax. Now is this good or bad? To a child, this would be harmful, but to me, going on twenty-nine, it isn't bad. For twenty-five years I have been working on my body—now I want to work on my mind a little. I want to enjoy life from a wheel chair instead of always hoping things will be different. Oh, I am not saying I am not improving because I am. The things I am doing at the Center are giving me better control over my muscles. I am storing up a source of information to write about. I am learning to take responsibilities on my shoulders and I am enjoying the whole program very much. But, besides all these things, I am learning one important thing; I am learning self-confidence. I am learning to go out among people without worrying about how I am going to act. I don't have to think twice before accepting an invitation. I am developing the attitude of not caring if I shake or don't shake. Believe me, mental attitude is as important to the cerebral palsied as teaching him to walk, but he couldn't do anything without his self-confidence. I, for one, am very happy to be at the Center, and I hope the program goes on just as it has been.[6]

The fact that the handicapped have a great many more leisure hours than the average person makes it even more important to help them find ways of spending them advantageously to themselves and to society. In the past, handicapped persons have not been given the opportunity to develop interests or to acquire the tools necessary for spending their leisure time constructively. Left simply to face a life of loneliness and frustration, they tend to develop unrealistic and immature attitudes.

[6] "Creative Writing," Recreation Center for the Handicapped, San Francisco, 1954. (Mimeographed.)

Through recreation, these persons can be motivated to develop social and cultural interests which they can continue to pursue in their leisure time.

Because many of the handicapped have lacked the opportunity to learn accepted principles of social behavior, they tend to be self-centered and use their handicap to get attention. Recreation provides limitless opportunities for teaching them good manners, personal grooming, and proper conduct in public. Consequently, it not only aids in their acceptance of self and their social adjustment, but it contributes toward a better understanding of them by the public in general. That this is so is shown by the results with a group of severely handicapped young adults who had no previous social experience. By participating in the recreation activities of the Recreation Center for a number of years, the members of this group gained enough confidence in themselves and enough social maturity to appear as a panel before college students, recreation administrators, and delegates to state conferences to discuss the social problems of the handicapped. They have done much to create a better understanding between the handicapped and the nonhandicapped. Discussing themselves and their problems also gives them a better understanding of their responsibilities as citizens.

Democracy

Recreation for the handicapped dramatically demonstrates the essence of democracy, for it provides activities which recognize the essential worth and dignity of the handicapped as individuals, together with their right to the pursuit of happiness. The following example demonstrates this principle. At the inception of a recreation program for a group of handicapped young adults, the first day was spent in discussing and exploring the program possibilities. These individuals, all of whom had lacked opportunities for previous recreational or social experiences, were amazed to discover that their opinions, desires, interests, and needs were considered in the planning of the total program. "This is the first time in our lives that anyone has really listened to what we have to say, to hear us out—to take time to let us talk and express our own ideas," they said.

This group composed an original planning council, which, over the years, has assumed a great deal of responsibility in planning and conducting the activities of a total program in a recreation center for the handicapped. This member-constituted advisory council is representative of all age groups. It has been one of the primary sources for affording experiences in the democratic process and in the give and take of successful group action. The council has provided many of the participants their first opportunity to assume committee responsibility and to understand and actually see democracy in operation. The liberty to choose their own activities has been for many their first experience with freedom as such or, indeed, with the opportunity to make any sort of choice. The fact that this has contributed greatly to their self-assurance, maturity, and independent thinking has proved to be a challenge for parents who tend to protect and shelter their son or daughter from life and reality. At the Recreation Center, one handicapped woman of twenty-seven said:

> It is wonderful to be treated as an adult with opinions, suggestions and ideas of my own, instead of as a child who should be seen and not heard. Before I went to the Center I was very shy, and since all I did all day was to lie on my bed, my speech and walking became pretty bad; but after being around people who didn't think I was still a child, and made me feel that my suggestions and ideas amounted to something after all, my shyness vanished and my confidence in myself was built up. When I was chosen to announce our Christmas program in front of an audience, I was really happy and proud of myself, for this meant that I spoke well enough to be understood by an audience.

Citizenship

The objectives of education can also be brought into play while teaching good citizenship through the medium of study clubs in areas such as history and government. For example, a group of twelve handicapped young adults, realizing that they lacked an understanding of government, requested a course in California history. In their study of this topic, they were encouraged to relate the knowledge gained in the general discussion sessions to the activity periods devoted to arts and crafts, pottery, music, writing, dramatics, and singing. For example, members of the group made pottery as the early California Indians did; they learned songs and music and they wrote plays based on the early history of California. In arts and crafts they undertook, as a joint project, to make a papier-mâché relief map of California and spent many joyful hours creating mountains, rivers, cities, parks, and highways. After they had finished the map and had learned much geography, they became interested in making products for the map. Oranges, grapes, apples, lemons, and other fruit were made from papier-mâché or clay. Wild animals, too, such as deer and bears, were made from clay or wood. During the project, the group visited missions, state parks, historical sites, and many other monuments of California. In the study of government, the group learned their rights, privileges, and responsibilities as voters. Many of them learned for the first time that they had the right to vote and were told how to go about voting.

Relationships with Others

In addition to its direct contribution to the handicapped as individuals and as groups, a recreation program has significant by-products of value to other members of the community. Group programs may aid in educating the general public in understanding and accepting the handicapped. By providing opportunities for the handicapped to go out into the community and to participate in its recreational and other affairs, they offer the public a chance to see handicapped people having fun and to talk with them. Encouraging and preparing the handicapped to discuss their handicaps also helps them to break down the barriers between themselves and the nonhandicapped and gives them self-assurance and self-confidence.

A recreation program also offers a pleasurable and acceptable opportunity for the handicapped to prove to the public that they are more like others than unlike them by demonstrating that they have the same recreation needs as any other group of people. Moreover, when people see the handicapped having fun, they accept them more readily and cease to pity them.

The provision of recreation programs for the handicapped can aid greatly in strengthening family ties and family relationships. For one thing, a program affords parents an opportunity to be away from their children for a while. Because the handicapped acquire interests and skills that can keep them happily occupied, parents are relieved of their constant responsibility and care. Finally, since a recreation program enriches the interests and social life of the handicapped person, he is better able to function as a regular member of the family group.

PART TWO

Organization and Operation

This section considers the various steps that need to be taken in initiating, organizing, and conducting a recreation program for the physically handicapped. Among the specific topics discussed are methods of determining the need for such a program and the agency that should sponsor or administer it, financial aspects, program planning principles, and the types of leadership personnel, their qualifications, and duties. Consideration is given to public relations, facilities and equipment, and the types of records that are essential for effective operation. Practical suggestions are offered for dealing with problems that are of special importance in programs for the handicapped, such as transportation, physical handling, and relationships with the parents of handicapped children.

CHAPTER 3

Preliminary Steps in Starting a Program

The need for recreation for the handicapped exists in every community where there are handicapped people. It is necessary, however, to interpret the fact that recreation as a basic need and welcome opportunity for the handicapped cannot be supplied by the usual prescribed and recognized therapies. The recreation profession and others concerned with the handicapped must therefore interpret recreation not only as an essential aspect of life, but also as a complement to the established and accepted medical and therapeutic treatment for this group.

Consequently, a preliminary step in considering a recreation program for the physically handicapped is recognition of the fact that handicapped persons have recreational needs the same as all other persons and that ways of discovering and serving these needs are available in every community. Awareness alone, however, does not assure action. A recreation program for the handicapped, like every other worthwhile enterprise, is established when an individual or group is convinced of its importance and takes the initiative in seeing that something is done about it. Suggested procedures for accomplishing this action are described in the pages that follow, although local conditions will, of course, determine the most effective methods to be followed in any particular city.

Determining the Need

A community will develop a readiness to provide recreation service for the handicapped only when it learns of the need, and a community survey is an effective means of making the people aware that it exists.

In many communities facts are lacking about the handicapped, their age and sex, their type of handicap, the programs already available for them, and the recreation services they should have. Moreover, many public recreation departments are not aware that they have a responsibility toward the handicapped, and even if they are aware, some are not quite sure just how to initiate recreation services for them. Parents of the handicapped often do not know that their children have a right to participate in all community activities, nor do they know how to go about helping their children take an active part in community life. Many handicapped adults need to be informed, encouraged, guided, and assisted in order for them to participate in community recreation programs.

The individual or group that decides to do something to provide recreation for the physically handicapped needs to know the facts about the handicapped in its community before a plan of action can be developed. They can be determined by a single organization, but since greater interest in the project and more widespread support are likely to result if many individuals and agencies participate in it, it is generally desirable to enlist the cooperation of other groups. An effective means of initiating a project is to call a meeting to which all agencies and groups that might be interested or that have any responsibility for the handicapped are invited to send representatives. Among the specific groups and agencies that could assist in finding out the facts about the physically handicapped in a community and that would welcome an opportunity to share in the survey are:

1. Public Departments and Agencies.
   a. Municipal Recreation Department
   b. Public Health Department
   c. Welfare Department
   d. Public Schools, including schools for the handicapped
   e. Public Libraries
   f. Bureau of Vocational Rehabilitation
   g. Visiting Nurse Services
2. Private Health and Welfare Agencies.
   a. American Red Cross
   b. Arthritis Foundation
   c. Lighthouse for the Blind
   d. Local Medical Societies—local physicians
   e. Muscular Dystrophy Association
   f. Multiple Sclerosis Association
   g. Society for Crippled Children and Adults
   h. Poliomyelitis Foundation
   i. United Cerebral Palsy Association
   j. United Crusade
   k. Other agencies working with the blind, deaf, mentally retarded, and so on.
3. Voluntary Agencies.
   a. Boy Scouts of America
   b. Boys Clubs of America
   c. Camp Fire Girls
   d. Catholic Youth Programs
   e. 4-H Clubs
   f. Girl Scouts of U.S.A.
   g. Jewish Youth Programs

h. Junior League
i. Settlements
j. Y.M.C.A.
k. Y.W.C.A.

4. Parents and parent organizations, i.e., P.T.A.'s, and so on.

Special arrangements should be made for representatives of the local press, radio and television stations, and other influential community leaders to be present.

The purpose of meeting should be to interpret the need for recreation for the physically handicapped, to propose that a study be made to determine the feasibility of establishing a program, and to enlist the interest and cooperation of the agencies represented. Desirable outcomes of the meeting would include approval of a survey, general agreement as to its nature and scope, selection of an agency or group to conduct it, a plan for financing it, and a tentative date for submitting the survey report. In many cases these decisions will not be reached at the first meeting, so a temporary committee might be appointed to study the situation and to submit to a second meeting its recommendations with reference to the survey. More than two meetings may be needed to develop a satisfactory plan and to assure adequate agency support. It should be made clear that approval of the plans for a survey implies a readiness on the part of the participating individuals or agencies to cooperate with the group that accepts responsibility for making it.

A community survey, particularly if all appropriate public, private, and voluntary agencies are involved, and if it is highly publicized, can serve many useful purposes. It is a tool for informing the average citizen that the handicapped persons exist, that they have the same recreation needs and rights as the nonhandicapped, and that these needs should be fulfilled. It also provides the basis for determining the best procedure to follow in initiating a recreation program.

Conducting a Survey

A survey committee, composed of representatives of the groups that have shown a genuine interest in the project and have indicated a willingness to support it, should be appointed to gather the necessary facts on which it is to base its recommendations. Its chairman should be a person who has the ability to enlist cooperation and to assure satisfactory completion of the survey by the date set. Assignment of responsibility to subcommittees for specific aspects of the study is generally advisable, but regular meetings of the entire committee are essential in order to assure coordinated action. All recommendations in the final report should have received the approval of the survey committee. In some instances responsibility for conducting the survey may be assigned to a single agency such as a public recreation department or a voluntary organization. In such cases a representative advisory committee is usually appointed, since it can help enlist cooperation, and the recommendations are more likely to receive wide approval if many groups have shared in the survey process. Employment of a survey director is seldom necessary; technical advice can usually be secured from the staff of participating agencies or from other available sources.

Selected Examples of Surveys

A community study on recreational needs of the handicapped was initiated by the San Francisco Recreation and Park Commission in October, 1958, and was completed in February, 1961. Thirty persons, who were representatives from public, private, and voluntary agencies in recreation, education, and health and welfare, participated in the study. The general chairman, a member of the Commission, appointed three subcommittees from this group whose respective responsibilities were as follows:

1. To determine as nearly as possible the actual numbers of handicapped persons residing in San Francisco who might require special recreation services. This phase of the study was conducted by the San Francisco Public Health Department with the cooperation of the public and parochial schools and the voluntary health and welfare agencies.
2. To determine the type of recreation programs already in existence in San Francisco for the handicapped and the type of program needed both for short-range and for long-range planning.
3. To utilize the information obtained from the other subcommittees and to make definite determinations of the needs in the field of recreation for the handicapped; "to determine how these needs are to be met, and to outline not so much by recommendation but by actual detailed program."[1]

Although the study was in progress for almost three years, the time and effort spent in determining the facts about the handicapped in the

[1] San Francisco Recreation and Park Department, *Study on Recreation for the Handicapped,* San Francisco, February 1961, pp. 1–2. (Mimeographed.)

community not only informed the general public of the recreational needs of these persons, but also encouraged them to assume some responsibility for fulfilling these needs. It is expected that this study will be published and made available to those interested.

Another such community survey on recreation for the handicapped was conducted in Kansas City, Missouri, where it was discovered that there were 14,000 orthopedically handicapped. Out of a cooperative conference of some twelve agencies, there emerged the Kansas City Council on Recreation for the Ill and Handicapped. This council works with the Public Recreation Division in meeting the recreational needs of the city's handicapped.[2]

Scope of the Survey

The group initiating the project should give the survey committee a general indication of the nature and scope of its study, but one of the first matters to be decided by the committee is the precise types of information it needs to gather. Accurate and adequate data on which to base sound proposals for action must be secured. Of primary importance is obtaining the following information about each handicapped individual in the community:

1. Name, address, age, sex, and type of handicap.
2. Type of services already being received: i.e., recreational, vocational, education, therapy, and so on.
3. Formal education, past and present; social experiences.
4. Current or past membership in or association with organizations, agencies, or clubs.
5. Individual interests, hobbies, and skills.
6. Transportation needs and resources.
7. Economic status of family.

Information should also be acquired about agencies serving the handicapped in the community. For each agency facts should be gathered concerning the numbers, ages, and types of handicapped served, the kinds of recreation activities offered, the recreation facilities available, the number and qualifications of paid and volunteer recreation leaders, the basis of financial support, the transportation used, and related matters.

[2] *Recreation In The Age Of Automation,* The Annals of the American Academy of Social Science, Columbia U. P., September 1957, pp. 87–88.

Time schedules of programs, frequency of activities, and fees and charges for services are also important facts to be secured. One subcommittee might be assigned to investigate possible sources of funds for financing a program; another to locate suitable sites or facilities for a program; and another to gather data on available transportation. An attempt should be made to secure comments from appropriate public and private agencies as to the most suitable auspices under which to launch a program and as to their readiness to cooperate with an organization that might be asked to sponsor it.

A survey committee would gain valuable information by visiting other cities where recreation programs for the handicapped have been established or by writing them for data as to their experience. Help in developing forms to be used in the survey and in planning its work can be secured from local sources or from state and national organizations concerned with recreation for the handicapped.

The Survey Report

The data assembled by the various subcommittees provides a picture of the local situation, and this enables the survey committee to determine the amount and types of recreation services needed and to propose appropriate means of providing them. In its report the survey committee summarizes its significant findings, draws pertinent conclusions, and makes specific recommendations for action based upon its study. Proposals naturally vary from one city to another, but they usually cover such items as the specific handicapped groups that should be served, the types of facilities and activities that should be provided for their use, the leadership required to provide the services, the agency that should sponsor or administer the program, and the methods of financing it. Since it is seldom possible to provide all desirable services, priority should be given to those areas or groups that have the greatest need or that will gain the greatest benefit from the proposed action. For example, the San Francisco Recreation and Park Department found in its previously mentioned study so many areas of need that it was necessary to set up priorities for realistic planning and service. The two major areas of service were for:

1. handicapped persons who can be integrated into an "ongoing" recreation program, and
2. handicapped persons who would require special recreation services.

The Department decided that it could begin immediately to implement the first area of need by conducting an in-service training program for its staff. This would better prepare them to integrate some of the lesser handicapped persons into ongoing recreation programs. Obviously, the other major area of need required long-range planning in the realm of public information and education, and the provision of funds, facilities, leadership, and other considerations.

In all cases, the survey should provide the data necessary to develop a long-range plan for meeting the recreation needs of all handicapped in a community.

Implementing the Report

The survey has little value except as it results in intelligent action that brings beneficial recreation services to the handicapped. Because such service costs money and effort, its value must be demonstrated. Recommendations usually call for the appropriation of public funds or the allocation of community chest funds, or both; hence community support is essential. Every appropriate means of publicizing the findings and proposals must therefore be utilized—the press, television, radio, talks before local clubs and organizations—in order that the significance and importance of the proposals may be fully understood and their values demonstrated. The members of the group that sponsored the survey and that presumably endorsed the recommendations of its survey committee should appear before their organizations and other local groups to explain the purpose of the study and the reasons for the suggested action. If representatives of the press, radio and television stations, local governing authorities, and influential organizations are included in the group initiating the project, understanding and support are more readily assured. The group originally authorizing the survey has the responsibility for assuring that every effort is made to secure favorable action on the recommendations in the report. Such action is almost certain to require the cooperation of several agencies.

CHAPTER 4

Establishing Recreation Services or Programs

the general public's understanding of handicapped persons. It has furthermore promoted good will for the department and increased recognition for the recreation movement.

A Special Service Division

Several studies concerned with recreation for the handicapped point up the need for public departments to develop a special service division where a "special" recreation supervisor and other staff members would be responsible for coordinating and providing year-long recreation for all children with handicaps.

Specific duties suggested by one study would be to:

1. Establish an educational program designed to interpret the importance of recreation for the handicapped to their parents as well as to the general public.
2. Coordinate existing recreation programs for the handicapped.
3. Establish training programs concerning the needs of the handicapped for public and private recreation agencies and camping staffs.
4. Establish integrated programs for the handicapped and nonhandicapped.
5. Establish special programs for the severely handicapped.

Studies made by the San Francisco Recreation and Park Department and the Baltimore Hearing Society recommended the establishment of a special service division and proceeded to implement this idea. Some public recreation departments have already created such a division while others are exploring the possibility. The creation of such a unit and the employment of a special recreation supervisor are essential to the development of a comprehensive plan for integrating the handicapped with the nonhandicapped and for providing special year-round recreation programs where needed.

Welfare Agency Sponsorship

Because few public recreation agencies had initiated recreation services for the handicapped, the majority of recreation and camping programs for such persons were operated until recently by voluntary health and welfare groups. These agencies have been concerned primarily with providing summer activities rather than with comprehensive year-round programs. Special summer camps, in particular, have been established throughout the nation for various types of handicapped persons, including crippled children, the blind, and the mentally retarded.

Some welfare agencies and groups have assumed as a primary function the entire responsibility for providing recreation for the handicapped; others have assisted recreation departments in providing this service. Welfare agencies serving only specific types of handicapped have conducted segregated recreation programs for a particular group, and in some cities recreation departments have assisted them by providing facilities and/or leadership. In other localities the welfare agency has found it advantageous to assist the public department in providing recreation for their clientele, since otherwise suitable and adequate activities might not be made available. By helping public recreation departments assume this responsibility, the private groups can concentrate on meeting other needs of the handicapped which are not recognized as public services, as is recreation.

Both Girl and Boy Scout groups, too, including the Sea Scouts, have established units especially designed for the severely handicapped. Weekly or monthly programs are frequently held in special schools. Resident and day camping programs are also conducted for handicapped units by the Scouts.

Cooperative Action

Many cities still have extremely limited recreation programs; and hundreds of unincorporated communities have none. In these situations, the community usually looks to the local youth-serving groups, welfare agencies, and civic organizations to initiate, conduct, and sponsor recreation for the handicapped. In addition to conducting a survey, as outlined in Chapter 3, such groups must employ leaders who possess a sound philosophy of recreation and understand how to put it into practice. The following account illustrates how total community resources can be mobilized for the purpose of providing recreation for the handicapped on a limited basis. Year-long programs can be conducted in the same manner.

In one community a citizens' committee was incorporated as a recreation unit of the County Society for Crippled Children and Adults. A survey showed that approximately seventy-five handicapped children and adults in the county were in need of recreation opportunities. Through discussion and by excellent publicizing of the results of the survey, enough funds were obtained to conduct a six-week summer program for children and adults. Transportation was provided by used car dealers. The only paid staff member was the professionally trained recreation director; trained volunteers carried out other leadership functions. The program was conducted in a multipurpose room of an elementary school building located in the central portion of the county. Private agencies and merchants of the community furnished needed equipment and supplies.

The New Agency Approach

Forming a completely new agency should be the last consideration in determining the basis for operating recreation programs for the handicapped. In some cases, it may be determined that a program—perhaps as a demonstration or pilot project—can best be initiated by a newly established organization created for this purpose. The extent of service received from the various agencies cooperating with the organization would be a factor in determining the composition of its administrative body. Agencies providing the major operating cost would no doubt wish to control the administration of the program through a board of directors.

The Recreation Center for the Handicapped, a San Francisco nonprofit corporation, was established in 1952 as a new agency with private funds and with an autonomous board of directors. Its purposes were twofold:

1. To fulfill an urgent need for year-round recreation activities for severely handicapped children and adults of San Francisco and the San Francisco Bay Area, and
2. To provide research and background materials for improved methods and techniques of organizing and administering recreation programs for the severely handicapped.

Likewise in Tulsa, Oklahoma, where no recreation program had previously existed for the handicapped, a new agency was established in 1957 by the National Council of Jewish Women. Its sole purpose was to provide "a recreational program designed to fit the requirements of physically handicapped persons in Northeast Oklahoma."[4]

Need for Advisory Committee or Board

Regardless of the type of department, agency, or cooperative group that accepts administrative responsibility for recreation for the handi-

[4] National Council of Jewish Women, *By Laws,* Tulsa, Oklahoma, November 8, 1957. (Mimeographed.)

capped, it can benefit from the services of a carefully selected advisory committee. Its professional and lay members can render valuable service to the recreation staff and board of directors. In particular, these persons are helpful in orienting and training the paid and volunteer staff, assisting with publicity and public relations, raising funds, securing transportation, and advising when special problems arise. Although the specific needs vary with each program, persons in each community who could be of great help as advisory committee members are:

1. Practitioners and technicians in services to the handicapped, such as social workers, therapists, physicians, and teachers.
2. Businessmen such as attorneys, insurance brokers, bankers, advertising agents, public relation directors, and certified public accountants.
3. Representatives from boards of education, health and welfare agencies, colleges, volunteer bureaus, and service and fraternal organizations.
4. Parents of the handicapped.

CHAPTER 5

Leadership Personnel

Qualified leadership has long been recognized as the most essential element in a successful community recreation program. It is of exceptional importance in recreation programs for handicapped individuals and groups. Without exception, outstanding recreation programs have been attained under qualified and devoted leaders. On the other hand, the employment of untrained, incompetent workers is certain to result in disappointment and failure of the program. An agency or group planning to establish a recreation program for the handicapped is faced by no more important task than the selection of qualified leadership personnel.

Personal Qualities

Leaders must have the same personal qualities expected of all professional persons dealing with human personalities. Among these qualities that are essential for recreation leaders are:

1. Belief in the worth and dignity of every human being.
2. An understanding of the interests and needs of people.
3. Concern with the growth of individuals through creative expression.
4. Sense of service above personal ambition.
5. Personal realization of the joy of life and the art of living.
6. Good sense of humor.
7. A pleasing, friendly personality.
8. Appreciation of leadership as an art.
9. Organizing ability.
10. Belief in democracy in recreation, as in government.
11. Productive energy and contagious enthusiasm.
12. Ability to get along with people, to accept others' opinions and personalities.
13. Sterling character and personal and professional integrity.
14. Good physical and mental health.[1]

Special Qualities for Leaders Working with the Handicapped

In working with the handicapped, some of the above-mentioned qualities that are essential for good leadership are of special significance.

[1] George D. Butler, *Introduction to Community Recreation,* McGraw Hill, New York, 1959, pp. 109–110.

In addition, certain desirable attitudes, skills, and attributes are required of leaders working with the handicapped. For example, leaders should:

Accept the handicapped person first as an individual who has the same basic needs, desires, and problems as other people. It is important to realize that the handicapped are more like others than they are different from them, and that they have the same basic needs for mental, physical, emotional, social, and spiritual development as the nonhandicapped.

Maintain a sympathetic understanding of each person's handicap, but not indulge in pity. Pity is a common reaction toward the handicapped and probably the most disliked by them.

Demonstrate a capacity for patience, imagination, and ingenuity. Adapting activities to persons who have severe physical limitations requires leaders who possess these qualities to a high degree. Special needs and limitations require new methods and techniques of using materials. The leader must not only develop ways and means for the handicapped to participate actively from wheel chairs, beds, crutches, and so on, but he must also inspire and encourage them to attain a higher level of interest and desire.

Recognize and be able to meet the specific and immediate social and recreational needs of the individual. Leaders must be able to set reasonable goals and standards for individuals and groups which will allow them a satisfying, pleasurable, and acceptable degree of achievement.

Help the handicapped to help themselves. A common reaction to the handicapped is to give too much help. It is much easier to do things for them rather than to devote the time and effort required to help them help themselves. For example, it takes a great deal of time to listen to and understand some persons with severe speech impairments and to let them discuss, plan, and carry out their own activities.

Be willing to do menial tasks such as feeding and lifting the handicapped, toileting, and handling wheel chairs and portable beds. Many severely handicapped persons are unable to feed themselves and require personal assistance in rest rooms. They must also be lifted in and out of wheel chairs when they are transported from place to place. Special schools for the handicapped, workshops, resident camps, and other programs employ "matrons" and "orderlies" to perform what is considered custodial care. However, recreation leaders have found that this type of treatment tends to create an institutional atmosphere, which is not appropriate for the recreation setting. They have been successful in handling these necessary duties with the help of additional staff and volunteers.

In order to perform some of these tasks leaders must possess a great deal of stamina and physical energy.

The importance which should be attached to the characteristics mentioned is illustrated by the following list of qualities which the staff of a recreation program for the handicapped agreed were the most desirable for effective leadership:

1. Emotional stability.
2. Self-confidence and security.
3. Patience, tolerance, and understanding.
4. Stamina and physical energy.
5. Ingenuity and imagination.
6. Selflessness.
7. Responsibility.
8. Mature judgment.
9. Enthusiasm and a sense of humor.

Training and Experience

Recreation leaders working with the handicapped must possess not only the essential personal qualities, but the technical skills necessary for good leadership. These require professional training and experience in recreation. Professional preparation should be in the field of community recreation and should include experience gained in work with the nonhandicapped, preferably in public recreation programs. College preparation for the field of recreation commonly includes: (1) an understanding of the nature, significance, and values of recreation; (2) familiarity with various program areas and personal skills in some of them, such as social recreation, games and sports, arts and crafts, music and others; (3) a knowledge of the techniques and methods used in organizing and conducting recreation programs; and (4) directed field work experience, which consists of observation and practice leadership.

Experience has demonstrated that in general recreation leaders who work successfully with nonhandicapped groups and individuals can work successfully with the handicapped. Moreover, in order to work successfully with the handicapped, recreation leaders must have previous experience with nonhandicapped groups. Furthermore, they are likely to be more effective in working with the handicapped if they are also interested in and are working with other groups.

As previously mentioned, it is not necessary for recreation leaders to have specialized training in psychotherapy or in medicine in order to work with the physically handicapped in the community. However, they need to have information that will help them in the physical handling of handicapped persons and in the over-all understanding and acceptance of them.

All agencies planning or providing recreation programs for the handicapped have a primary obligation to employ only such leaders as have the personal qualities, training, and experience that enable them to perform their duties effectively and successfully. Nevertheless a continuous in-service training program is essential in order to help assure the highest possible degree of performance on the part of all workers.

Types of Leadership Positions

The number and types of positions involving leadership functions in a recreation program for the handicapped vary with its nature and scope and are also influenced by the type of administrative agency. However, typical leadership positions in a recreation center providing a comprehensive program and the major responsibilities related to each are:

1. Center director. This worker is in complete charge of the center—its operation, program, and maintenance. His primary responsibility is to administer the center and its program in accordance with the policies established and approved by the board of directors.

2. Program director. This person plans, develops, and conducts a program of individual and group recreation, operating within the defined policies and subject to budgetary limitations and administrative review. The job combines program development, group work, and recreation leadership as well as certain limited administrative responsibilities.

3. Recreation leader. This title is applied to workers who are directly responsible for the leadership of one or more of the recreation activities that have been cooperatively developed under the general supervision of the program director. In some centers, several titles may be assigned to leaders who are assigned varying degrees of responsibility such as supervising senior leader, senior recreation leader, and recreation leader.

4. Recreation program aide. Workers in this subprofessional position assist the professional recreation staff in face-to-face leadership under constant supervision.

Specific Duties and Qualifications

Recommended standards have been widely adopted setting forth the duties, special qualifications, education, and experience considered essential for satisfactory performance in the various positions in community recreation. To a large extent they apply to positions in recreation programs for the handicapped. The duties of the center director, however, differ somewhat depending on whether the center is administered as an independent unit or as part of a municipal recreation department. The director of the former type of center, for example, is in complete charge, subject only to the governing body, whereas the director of a municipal recreation center is subordinate to the department executive and in some cases to a general supervisor as well.

The following pages contain a detailed statement of the duties, training, and experience of workers in typical leadership positions. They are based largely upon requirements established for these positions by the San Francisco Recreation Center for the Handicapped.

CENTER DIRECTOR. Among his specific administrative duties the director handles major correspondence; supervises intake of participants; directs the maintenance of the building and grounds, repairs, renewal of equipment, and control of building uses; supervises the keeping of personnel, property, financial, and statistical records, and prepares reports on staff, program, resources, needs, and progress. He also prepares and justifies to the board estimates of the center's budget needs; directs and controls the receipt and disbursement of the center funds in accordance with the approved budget and supervises fund raising activities, including the recruitment and direction of volunteer workers.

In his work with the board of directors he evaluates the effectiveness of the center services and makes recommendations for the advancement of program and facilities; studies community conditions and needs affecting the center for the purpose of developing or encouraging the development of immediate and long-range plans, including community-wide plans, for meeting new or changing needs; and works closely with the board and its subcommittees to assure their awareness of the needs of the handicapped and agreement and understanding of the center program, policies, activities, and practices.

In performing his responsibilities, he recruits, selects, and employs all workers; makes work assignments to staff members, directly or through their supervisors; develops and maintains good working relationships among the staff; trains and indoctrinates staff members through preservice and in-service training programs, including staff meetings, conferences, and interviews; recruits volunteers and develops a program for continuing their use. Among his duties, he develops a program of individual and group activities consistent with objectives and resources of the center, adapted to the needs of the handicapped, and supervises the planning, organizing, and adapting of a diversified program of individual and group activities.

The center director also develops community interest in and support of the center program through talks and use of visual aids before service clubs, parent associations, colleges, voluntary agencies, and related groups. He prepares and releases publicity regarding specific center activities or events; establishes and maintains cordial working relations with recreation, group work, and other related agencies in the community; coordinates the assistance of participating agencies, represents the center at official or public affairs; and attends recreation and group work meetings as directed by the board.

The director is expected to maintain an active interest in professional recreation organizations, publications, and local and national conferences; to contribute to recreation research and programs of professional associations when called upon; and to further his personal professional growth through appropriate reading, training courses, attendance at workshops, and other means.

Training and experience requirements are:

1. Graduation from a college or university of recognized standing with specialization in recreation, group work or allied fields; graduate study resulting in a Master's degree.

2. Five years of professional recreation and/or group work experience, including at least one year in a supervisory or administrative capacity. Two or three years' experience shall have been with nonhandicapped groups or individuals.

3. At least one year of the nonsupervisory experience should be in face-to-face leadership of handicapped or nonhandicapped groups at playgrounds, recreation buildings, camps, or similar centers.

PROGRAM DIRECTOR. Among the specific duties of the program director are to work closely with the center director on all matters pertaining to program; determine transportation needs of participants; suggest financial needs of the program; assist with budget preparation; substitute in absence of center director, assist in interpreting program needs to the board, and work with board subcommittees upon request of the center director.

In working with program personnel, the program director assists the center director in interviewing and hiring staff; prepares agenda for and conducts staff meetings; discusses over-all program with staff; arranges for in-service training; assists staff in planning programs for its groups; designs staff bulletins; and keeps staff informed of all activities desired and planned by members. He arranges for special events and coordinates transportation and planning between staff and participants. He also carries on research concerning new materials, literature, and program ideas for staff use, and he conducts individual interviews with the staff to evaluate programs and to discuss problems which he then reviews with the center director.

The program director also interviews prospective volunteers, supervises the keeping of volunteer service records, acquaints volunteers with the philosophy, aims, and objectives of the center, delegates their responsibilities, and evaluates their work in the program.

Important duties relating to the program include the supervision and coordination of regular activities and special events, program evaluation, direction of summer camps, the development of new program activities in consultation with the center director, and the preparation of reports pertaining to the program. He also has responsibility for arranging and coordinating all transportation of members to and from the center, for the care and use of all program equipment and supplies, and for keeping informed about essential membership records. He attends meetings, serves as host to groups or individuals visiting the center, and performs other tasks at the request of the center director.

Requirements as to training and experience are:

1. Graduation from a college or university of recognized standing with a major in recreation or a minor in recreation combined with a major in an allied field.

2. Two years of paid experience in recreation program leadership or its equivalent in allied fields.

3. Working knowledge of, and skills in, a variety of recreation techniques. Knowledge of the theory, planning, practice, and leadership of specialized recreation activities.

4. Ability to organize, conduct, and supervise group and individual recreation activities; ability to develop and maintain interest in social and recreation activities.

SENIOR RECREATION LEADER. This worker supervises the paid and volunteer staff assigned to him, maintains suitable records and reports as required, assists in carrying out the over-all program, including seasonal and special events, attends meetings and training courses, and performs necessary tasks to assure the enjoyment and comfort of participants.

To qualify for this position a person should meet the following requirements:

1. Graduation from a four-year college or university of recognized standing, with major course work in recreation, education, group work, or allied fields, or an equivalent combination of education and experience.

2. One year's successful experience working with individuals and groups in a recreational setting or the equivalent of one year's full-time successful recreation leadership experience working with individuals and groups.

Volunteers

Volunteers have played an extremely important role in the development of services for the handicapped. Recreation programs for the handicapped are frequently conducted with a minimum of professional staff and with a great deal of assistance from volunteers. This practice is particularly common where pilot programs are initiated to demonstrate a need in the community and until sufficient funds are made available to employ additional professional staff.

Volunteers can play an important role in all recreation programs but the need for them is especially great in recreation for the handicapped, where the ratio of staff to participants is exceptionally high. Groups initiating such programs, however, must be aware that there are many well-meaning but incompetent individuals who are eager to volunteer their services. Their efforts can usually be channeled, but the program must not become a haven for the maladjusted, whose motive is primarily to satisfy their own needs.

Types of Volunteers

In general, the types of volunteers needed in recreation programs for the handicapped are like those used in other recreation programs in both leadership and other positions. They are:

1. Individuals with administrative, promotional, or advisory experience, to serve as members on boards or committees. Persons skilled in publicity, advertising, law, and community organization are among the laymen who can assist in these capacities.

2. Skilled leaders who can instruct in activities such as arts and crafts, drama, and other special areas, act in an advisory capacity to hobby clubs, for example, or organize and conduct games and sports tournaments, as in checkers or bowling.

3. Persons who are willing and able to assist with transportation of the handicapped, or who have technical skills in carpentry, for example, for building adapted games or other equipment needed in the program. Persons who can do clerical work such as typing and mimeographing are always needed and welcome in recreation programs, as well as those who can perform maintenance work such as repairing and painting. Nonleadership service of this kind is invaluable and limitless.

Nonleadership Personnel

Professional and volunteer recreation leaders are not the only types of workers needed in the operation of a comprehensive recreation program or center for the handicapped. Essential duties are also performed by such workers as administrative assistant or business manager, office secretary, bookkeeper, driver, janitor, and kitchen aid. In performing their tasks these workers have frequent relationships with the handicapped children and adults and members of their family. Therefore they must not only be qualified to perform their duties in a satisfactory manner but they must have character and the ability to deal with people in a sympathetic but efficient manner. Job descriptions setting forth the duties, skills, and experience as well as the personal qualifications required for each position help in employing workers for these nonprofessional tasks.

CHAPTER 6

Personnel Procedures

Official adoption of job titles and of the requirements for the various positions in a recreation program for the handicapped does not assure the selection and maintenance of a qualified staff. Other factors must be taken into consideration and sound procedures must be put into effect in order to secure and hold competent workers. Policies must be instituted governing recruitment, compensation, advancement, in-service training, job security, and working conditions. In a program under an independent agency, these procedures and policies are determined by the managing group; in a municipally sponsored program they may need to conform to those established for all municipal agencies.

Recruitment of Leaders

Public departments initiating and conducting recreation programs for the handicapped should assign leadership personnel from their regular staff, insofar as persons who are qualified and interested in undertaking such work are available. All agencies will find state recreation associations and colleges and universities offering recreation curricula valuable sources for recruiting full-time recreation leaders. The National Recreation Association in New York City maintains a roster of recreation personnel and offers a placement service to individuals and agencies. To facilitate the recruitment process, statements describing the positions open, the essential requirements, and the conditions of work have proved useful.

Part-time and seasonal workers are usually obtained from local colleges, schools, and universities and from local agencies conducting recreation programs. Schoolteachers and supervisors or specialists in music, art, physical education, and other fields are usually available for employment in summer programs and camps and, in many cases, in the evening and weekend programs.

Sources of Volunteers

1. Colleges and universities offer one of the finest sources for volunteers to work in recreation programs for the handicapped. Students majoring in recreation, education, special education, social welfare, and related fields are anxious to have opportunities to work with a variety of groups including the handicapped. Some courses require students to spend a certain number of hours working in community programs for field work

experiences. Fraternities, sororities, and student associations are frequently willing to undertake projects which can be completed during a semester.

2. High schools are excellent sources for obtaining volunteers, especially for work as program aides on group projects. Experience has indicated that as a general rule only those who are seventeen and over should be considered for such service.

3. Youth groups such as the Boy and Girl Scouts, C.Y.O. clubs, B'nai Brith boys and girls, and many others are excellent sources for volunteers. In addition to providing program aides, such groups are good sources for exploring and developing integrated activities with the handicapped.

4. Community volunteer bureaus or agencies where persons may register who are interested in undertaking some form of volunteer work are an invaluable source for obtaining leaders as well as nonleadership types of volunteers for recreation programs for the handicapped.

5. Service clubs, fraternal and religious organizations, and men's and women's clubs are good sources for obtaining volunteers to help by providing transportation, financing aspects of the program, and in other ways.

6. Public and private health and welfare agencies, medical associations, and schools and colleges are some of the finer sources for obtaining volunteers to work in administrative promotional and advisory capacities.

7. Former recreation workers, specialists in music, the arts, games and sports, and other types of recreation, hobbyists, and school teachers are commonly recruited as volunteers to assist with various aspects of the recreation program.

Compensation

Workers employed in recreation programs for the handicapped are entitled to the same level of compensation as workers performing comparable tasks in community recreation or other fields. The salaries of leadership personnel should be commensurate with the nature of the duties to be performed and the high standards for personal qualities, professional education, and experience established for employment. Individuals who choose to serve as recreation leaders do not expect to receive a monetary return as high as if they worked in some other fields, but they cannot be expected to continue to serve unless they are adequately compensated. The salary scale should be based upon the nature of the position, not on the fact that work with the handicapped frequently entails the expenditure of greater-than-average physical energy and effort.

The following salary range has been adopted by the Board of the Recreation Center, the specific amount to depend upon the experience and qualifications of the individual employed.

Center Director	$8,000 to $12,000 per year
Program Director	$425 to $550 per month, with potential increases over a 5-year period
Supervising Senior Leader	$342 to $442 per month, with potential increases over a 5-year period
Senior Recreation Leader	$1.50 to $2.50 per hour
Recreation Leader*	$1.25 to $1.50 per hour
Recreation Program Aide*	$ .75 to $1.00 per hour

Persons employed for nonleadership service must usually be paid at rates comparable to those they would receive if they worked elsewhere in the locality. For example, the salary scale for the position of Administrative Assistant at the Recreation Center is from $5,000 to $7,000 per year. Other workers, such as the bookkeeper, driver, janitor, and kitchen aide are paid at prevailing rates on a monthly or hourly basis.

In-Service Training

Even though individuals employed in leadership positions have a college degree in recreation, continuous in-service training is essential in all recreation programs. It is of particular importance in recreation programs for the handicapped. In-service training for leaders in recreation programs for the handicapped must include the orientation of handicapped persons, demonstrations of adapted activities, methods of integration, and many other activities peculiar to recreation for special groups. Regardless of previous training or experience, all personnel, both professional and volunteer, should participate in a continuing program of instruction designed to help them increase their effectiveness as leaders.

Suggested Methods and Topics

Conferences, group and panel discussions, and lectures followed by question and answer periods should be an important part of in-service staff training.

* This position is not on the professional level.

Demonstrations which suggest means of adapting certain activities are also useful. They should include the techniques of physical handling of persons in wheel chairs and on crutches, special feeding, and related procedures.

Observations of techniques used in other programs for various types of handicapped assist in providing a better understanding of the methods of dealing with problems of a recreation program designed for these persons—for example, visits to special schools for the handicapped, integrated schools, or other programs where the recreation staff may observe, broaden their understanding, and often reaffirm and strengthen their belief in their own cause.

Recreation for the handicapped is a comparatively new field, and therefore methods and techniques developed by the staff should be shared with others who are interested. Recreation leaders who have had training and experience in such work should welcome opportunities to conduct institutes or seminars which will benefit a large number of interested persons. Such an institute was conducted for one week at the Recreation Center for the Handicapped in San Francisco. The Center was utilized as a laboratory for training twenty-five professional and lay persons in the methods and techniques of organizing and conducting recreation programs for the physically handicapped. The institute included discussions of philosophy and objectives, enrollment policies and procedures, recruiting and selecting professional staff and volunteers, principles of programming and adaptations, utilizing facilities, transportation, public relations, financing, and records and reports.

Training Volunteers

The importance of adequate training of professional recreation leaders, previously discussed, applies also to volunteer leaders, who should possess many of the same qualities expected of the paid staff. It is highly important that prior to working in the program the volunteer understands the aims and objectives of the agency and the philosophy and principles of recreation. He needs to know his relationship with and responsibility to the employed personnel and to the handicapped participants he is to serve. Persons working in nonleadership capacities also need similar orientation, as well as specific instructions as to the duties they are expected to perform. Training of volunteers, as well as paid staff, should be considered a process which is continued throughout their service by means of conferences, institutes, staff meetings, guidance and evaluation of their supervisors, observation of the work of others, and directed reading.

One-day institutes designed to train large numbers of volunteers to work in recreation programs for the handicapped have been very successful. Handbooks for volunteers are extremely helpful, provided the right type of information is included and explained briefly, and they can be used as the basis for an institute.

In one recreation program for the handicapped a handbook for volunteers was prepared by the staff with recommendations from volunteers who had previously worked in the program. The handbook consisted of eight sections and contained simple sketches, some of them humorous, which were used to emphasize and illustrate the various points stressed in the text. The sections were as follows:

Section I. *Welcome to Volunteers.* This contained a brief statement of reasons why the agency needed volunteers, such as: WE NEED your interest, enthusiasm, and skills in order to continue to provide enriching experiences for the handicapped participants of the program.

Section II. *What You Should Know About the Recreation Program for the Handicapped.* This dealt with philosophy, organization, facilities, and program.

Section III. *What You Should Know About the Handicapped.* This contained a definition of the handicapped, with brief explanations of various types of handicapping conditions and the need for accepting them as one would accept others.

Section IV. *What Volunteers Are Doing in the Program.* This described the ways in which volunteers help, such as serving as board members or as members of auxiliaries, as specialists, program aides, student observers, and in other ways.

Section V. *Getting Started as a Volunteer.* This explained specific procedures for volunteers, i.e., filling out applications, attending orientation sessions, and so on.

Section VI. *Responsibilities of a Volunteer.* This outlined what was expected of a volunteer, such as being punctual, knowing the philosophy and aims of the program, attending meetings, conference, and training sessions, and wearing proper dress.

Section VII. *Thank You, Volunteer.* This described the benefits to the volunteer and to agency; i.e., the experience is valuable training for volunteers.

Section VIII. *Volunteer's Code of Ethics.* This included a pledge which is particularly applicable to teen-age volunteers. It serves as a reminder of their responsibilities to the agency, such as the willingness to learn and grow on the job, dependability, and punctuality.

Employment Procedures and Conditions

Adoption of policies governing employment and working conditions helps to avoid misunderstandings and to assure satisfactory relationships with employed personnel. Policies and procedures naturally vary, but any agency establishing a recreation program for the handicapped should find useful the following policies adopted by the Recreation Center Board.

Selection Procedures

1. Allocation of Responsibility

   The Personnel Committee, which consists of three to five members of the Board of Directors, is responsible with the advice and assistance of the Director for recruitment and selection of all paid personnel.

2. The Selection Process

   Qualified applicants for full-time leadership positions are interviewed by the Personnel Committee, the Center Director, and the Program Director. The final selection is determined by joint agreement on the part of the Board Committee and the two staff members.

   Part-time leadership personnel are selected by the Personnel Committee on recommendation of the Center Director and the Program Director.

   Other full-time and part-time personnel are selected by the Personnel Committee on recommendation of the Center Director.

Conditions of Employment

1. Contracts

   In cases where it seems desirable, workers upon employment may be required to sign a contract covering their expected period of service.

2. Probationary Period

   Every person employed by the Center on a year-round basis must serve a six-month probationary period. Each employee will be evaluated three times during this period, and the results will be explained and discussed with the employee. The purpose of the evaluations is to inform the employee of the quality of his work and to offer suggestions that will help him do a better job. The third or final rating determines whether an individual is to be considered as meriting continuous employment by the Center.

3. Periodic Evaluation

   Service ratings of all year-round employees are made every six months on the basis of evaluations of the workers' performance. A standard rating form is used by the supervisor in recording his evaluation of the workers who are responsible to him. Effective use of ratings helps the employee realize his strengths as well as weaknesses, suggests ways in which services may be improved, and strengthens relationships between the supervisor and his workers.

   The services of summer leaders and other seasonal personnel are also subjected to periodic evaluation.

4. Health Examination

   Those employees entitled to sick leave are required to submit a physician's statement testifying to the general condition of their health. This statement must be presented to the Director during the probationary period.

5. Family Employment

   It is the policy of the Center not to employ more than one member of a family.

Working Conditions

1. Working Hours

   The work week of the Center for full-time employees is forty hours, consisting of an eight-hour day, five days per week. In case the work at the Center requires an employee to serve more than eight hours on a particular day, he is entitled to take off an equal number of working hours at such time as meets the approval of his supervisor. The working hours of part-time employees are fixed at the discretion of the Center Director.

2. Pay Days

   Center employees are paid on the first and fifteenth of every month.

3. Pay Increases and Promotions

   Salary increases are not automatic but are dependent upon how well the worker is doing his job. The Center has a definite plan for increasing the pay rate of workers who are rendering satisfactory service. The plan provides for such annual increases over a five-year period.

   Where feasible and warranted, job openings at the Center are filled by the promotion of qualified employees on a competitive basis.

4. Separation

   In case the services of an employee are no longer needed, because of changes in the program or for other reasons, the Center Director is authorized to dismiss the worker after due notice to the worker. It is the policy of the Center to give two weeks' notice on dismissal. It is also expected that employees give two weeks' notice before terminating employment at the Center.

5. Dismissal

   Full-time professional personnel employed at the Center may be dismissed for cause by the Personnel Committee on recommendation of the Center Director. Part-time leadership personnel may be dismissed by the Center Director, usually on recommendation of the Program Director. Other workers may be dismissed by the Center Director for cause. Any worker who believes he has been unjustly dismissed may appeal directly to the Personnel Committee.

Benefits

1. Sick Leave

   Full-time workers and others employed half time or more on a year-round basis are entitled to twelve sick days off per year, but may not use them during the first six months of employment. Absence in excess of two days resulting from accident or illness must be certified by a physician. Other part-time and seasonal workers are not entitled to pay for time lost because of illness or accident unless it is made up by the worker with the approval of the Center Director.

Sick leave is a privilege to be utilized only if necessary, should not be abused, and cannot be carried over into the succeeding year.

2. Vacation

Every full-time employee, and others employed half time or more on a year-round basis, are entitled to vacation at the rate of ten working days per year, but may not use his vacation credits during the first six months of employment. Vacation time not taken during the year in which it is earned cannot be carried over into the following year. Vacation schedules are arranged with the approval of the Center Director.

3. Holidays

The following are approved holidays for Center personnel:
New Year's Day—January 1
Washington's Birthday—February 22
Memorial Day—May 30
Independence Day—July 4
Labor Day—First Monday in September
Veterans' Day—November 11
Thanksgiving Day—Fourth Thursday in November
Christmas Day—December 25

In case his duties require an employee to work on one of these holidays, he is entitled to compensating time off in an amount equal to the hours worked on holidays.

4. Disability Compensation

Every employee at the Center is covered by workmen's compensation during his working hours. Every injury, however slight, should be reported immediately to the Center office in order to protect any claim for treatment.

5. Social Security

Employees are covered by Social Security benefits.

6. Car Allowance

A car allowance of eight cents per mile will be paid staff persons using their own automobiles to transport the children.

7. Others

In special cases, individuals who have demonstrated unusual merit or who have rendered exceptional service to the Center have been recommended for special awards or have been assisted in securing opportunities for advancement in their professional career.

Where the program permits and benefits to the Center are expected, workers may be authorized to attend local, state, and national conferences.

CHAPTER 7

Program Planning

Program planning for the physically handicapped is basically no different from planning for the nonhandicapped. As with all recreation programs, "the primary objective should be to provide more and better recreation opportunities for the satisfaction, enjoyment and benefit of the people they are intended to serve."[1] Guiding principles for program planning and evaluation as established for community recreation programs apply generally to recreation programs for the physically handicapped. Certain factors need to be emphasized, however, when applying these principles to the planning of recreation programs for this specific group.

Planning Principles

The pages that follow list the program planning principles that appear in *The Recreation Program* and suggest briefly their special application to programs for the physically handicapped.

1. Program planning should involve consideration of the diversified recreation interests and desires of the people to be served.

Many of the handicapped, particularly the severely physically handicapped, have had little if any opportunity to participate in organized recreation activities. Moreover, the lack of opportunities for formal education for some of these persons is an additional factor to consider. One seldom finds such individuals and groups with "diversified recreation interests and desires." Experience has demonstrated that these handicapped persons can rarely determine their interests, and so it becomes necessary for the leader to describe activities in detail, to furnish background information, and actually demonstrate them in order to encourage these individuals to participate. Leaders should be prepared to expand the interests of the handicapped in order that they may take advantage of a rich and diversified program.

2. Program planning should take into account the age, sex, racial background and economic status of all the people to be served.

The physically handicapped include individuals of all ages and racial backgrounds, of both sexes and of a diversity of economic status. In planning programs consideration should be given to the needs of the various groups. Care should be taken that no one is barred from participation because of limited financial resources.

[1] *The Recreation Program,* The Athletic Institute, Chicago, 1954, p. 6.

3. Program participants, paid and volunteer leaders, and governing bodies of the public or private agency sponsoring the program, should share in the process of program planning.

The success of a recreation program for the handicapped depends in large measure upon the degree to which all who are concerned with it participate in the planning process. Much of the value of the program is lost unless the handicapped persons share in determining the nature of the program. All too often well-meaning individuals tend to plan for them rather than with them.

4. Program planning should be related to the physical, mental, social and emotional characteristics of the people to be served.

On the whole, handicapped persons have needs, interests, and desires more like those of others than different from them. There are exceptional cases, however, especially where an individual has had unusually limited social and educational experiences. Furthermore, individuals differ from one another in their recreational interests. It is unfortunate that many persons who are severely physically handicapped are treated as children even after they have become adults. Even though they may be lacking in recreation experiences, activities presented to them should be based in most cases upon the usual interests and desires of persons of their age, sex, and background. Needs, interests, and desires as they relate to physical, mental, social, and emotional characteristics are discussed in detail in Chapter 2.

5. Program planning should provide an opportunity for participants at varying levels of proficiency and for instruction in recreation skills.

This planning principle is one of the most challenging to implement in recreation programs for the physically handicapped. Recreation leaders have the obligation to the handicapped to provide opportunities for the individual at whatever level he desires, to the extent of his ability to participate. The challenge to the leader is not only to develop ways and means that will enable the handicapped to participate actively from wheel chairs, beds, crutches, and the like, but at the same time to encourage and inspire them to attain a higher level of interest, desire, and achievement.

6. In program planning, use should be made of standards developed by national agencies, with such modifications as may be expedient to meet the needs of the group or community.

Although few standards have been developed for recreation programs for the handicapped, leaders working with these groups can benefit from the experience of many national agencies that have developed official rules, safety standards, or approved procedures for conducting specific activities. This is true even though adaptations may need to be made when the activities are included in programs for handicapped groups.

7. Long-range planning for program is a prerequisite to planning for organization, finance, leadership, areas and facilities.

Establishing the need for a recreation program for the physically handicapped in a community and determining the types of activities that should be provided are two first steps in establishing recreation services. They serve as the basis on which to determine such essential factors as type of organization, facilities, leadership, finance, and other provisions necessary for recreation services. Long-range planning for programs may have to begin several months earlier than would be necessary in a recreation program for the nonhandicapped. This is particularly true when the handicapped are utilizing facilities available to other community groups and when they must be transported to and from these places. It is always necessary for leaders to explore facilities well in advance to check entrances, exits, and all other features in order to assure the comfort and safety of individuals who must use wheel chairs, crutches, portable beds and the like while participating in the program.

8. Planning should provide for the use of all available resources that can provide variety and enrich the program.

Experience has indicated that the enlistment of all available community resources is not only essential to the development of programs for the physically handicapped, but is also necessary for the actual continuance and expansion of these programs. Invaluable assistance can be obtained from numerous groups as well as from interested individuals within the community. Public and private health and welfare agencies can be helpful, especially in referring individuals in need of recreation services. Fraternal, patriotic, religious and civic organizations are often able to supply not only leadership, facilities, and finance, but also transportation, which is a necessary consideration in operating programs for the physically handicapped. Recreation resources in the community that should be used by the physically handicapped include theaters, restaurants, museums, parks, recreation centers, indoor and outdoor facilities, the zoo, libraries, beaches, swimming pools, camps, bowling alleys, and all other appropriate recreation areas and facilities of the community. Use of these facilities makes possible a more varied, richer program.

9. Continuous evaluation, measurement and modification, where advisable, should be recognized as essential in program planning.

Evaluation of program content and quality is especially important in recreation programs for the physically handicapped because they are still largely experimental in nature. Whenever the appraisal indicates the desirability of a change in the activities offered, the scheduling of activities, the type of leadership, the form of group organization or the method of conducting specific events, and modifications in program planning are in order. Evaluation should be a continuous and cooperative process. Handicapped participants in particular, as well as recreation leaders, members of boards, and committees, must have a part in the evaluation process if it is to be effective.

The following are some of the bases for evaluation:

1. How much satisfaction and enjoyment do participants receive from their recreation experiences?
2. To what extent does the program serve the varied interests of the participants?
3. Does it give evidence of contributing to their personal development?

Implementation of Planning Principles

The application of the planning principles previously outlined necessitates the initiation, organization and conduct of a program. A few of the procedures that have proved successful in implementing the principles in a recreation program are described briefly.

Enrollment and Referrals

The desire to take part in a recreation program must be evidenced by a group of handicapped persons before activities can actually be started. It is therefore necessary for the sponsoring agency to make its plans known to the potential participants. It is aided in doing this by using the data gathered in the community survey, if one has been carried on in the locality. It should make available the names and addresses of handicapped persons in the locality and their disabilities and of the agencies rendering service of various types to the handicapped. Information concerning the proposed plans for the recreation program is sent to these groups and is widely publicized through the press and by radio and television. If no formal survey has been made, the operating group can secure names from agencies serving the handicapped, as described in Chapter 3, and through announcements in media reaching the general public. A number of programs have been successfully established in this manner, by starting with small groups of participants and by expanding the program gradually. When sufficient names have been secured, these individuals are invited to get in touch with the agency and to make known their recreation interests and their desire to take part in the proposed program. In some cities institutions serving the handicapped make arrangements for groups of persons to enroll in one or more phases of the recreation program and transport them to and from the place where the activities are carried on.

Before persons can be enrolled, the agency must establish criteria and procedures for admission to the program. All physically handicapped persons as described in Chapter 1, including the severely handicapped such as the bedfast, should be eligible for enrollment. The consent of parent or guardian must be secured before handicapped persons can be enrolled and permitted to take part in the activities. A statement by the individual's physician approving his participation in the program is also considered an essential prerequisite to admission. Both the parent and the handicapped person must agree to meet the announced schedule, especially as it relates to the transportation of the participants. Forms used in applying for membership in the Recreation Center are reproduced in Chapter 13.

Classification of Participants

At the end of a designated period for the filing and acceptance of applications, the agency has information about the number of individuals to be served by the program. It knows their age, sex, and education, the nature of their handicaps, and in some instances their recreation interests. It therefore has a basis for classifying them into groups so they may have a most beneficial and satisfying experience. Since some recreation interests tend to be common to large numbers of children, youth, or adults at various age levels, the ages of the handicapped influence the activities to be carried on. Persons are consequently grouped by age for some activities; yet young and old have a place in special events such as holiday celebrations. In general, children and young people take part in activities regardless of their sex, although only boys participate in some forms of sport and participants in such activities as make-up and hair styling appeal only to members of the fair sex. Insofar as possible, the nature and extent of the participants' handicaps should be considered a negligible factor in forming groups to take part in specific activities. On the other hand, if several members of a group have such serious disabilities that they slow down the activity greatly, this may restrict the enjoyment and benefit which more active members gain from taking part in it. Under such circumstances division of the group may be desirable.

Organization Factors

The optimum size of group required for carrying on an activity must also be taken into account in planning the program. A few individuals interested in a hobby can form a successful club, but most special events cannot be carried on unless a considerable number of individuals take part. Naturally the availability of areas and facilities also influences the types of activities that can be included in the program. Some activities such as table games can be carried on informally and more or less continuously by one or more individuals, whereas most forms of arts and crafts and drama, for example, must be conducted as regularly scheduled group activities. The time span and frequency of participation needed to assure satisfactory conduct of an activity also influence the feasibility of including it in the program. For example, instruction in swimming is unlikely to be effective unless the group meets at frequent intervals and for a sufficient number of sessions.

Schedules

The preceding factors must also be taken into consideration in setting up daily, weekly, and seasonal schedules. The amount of time required to transport participants from their homes and back, for example, affects the hours during which a program can be scheduled. Some activities that require much assistance from volunteers are carried on at such times as this help is available. A greater interest in an activity may be maintained when the group knows that it is to be offered at regular, specified periods, yet the schedule should be somewhat flexible and should take into account the fact that severely handicapped individuals, especially, require more time than other people to accomplish the same results.

The schedules that follow indicate the range of activities at the Recreation Center and are based on a typical weekly program which is conducted year-round. Over three hundred children and adults, aged three years to sixty, are enrolled. The majority are under twenty-one years of age.

MONDAY

No Scheduled program. Office hours 8:00 A.M.—5:00 P.M.

TUESDAY

All-day Program—Children Released from School

Time and Place:	10:00 A.M.—4:00 P.M. Recreation Center
Enrollment:	45
Activities:	Creative Writing, Literature, Writing, History, Spelling, Grammar, Arts and Crafts, Games and Sports, Drama, Music. Weekly afternoon trips are taken to various places of interest, and Integrated Activities with Nonhandicapped Groups are also included.

Evening Program—Adults

Time and Place:	3:30—9:30 P.M. Recreation Center
Enrollment:	75
Activities:	Art and Theater Techniques, Basic Grammar, Spelling, Reading, Creative Writing, Cooking and Meal Planning, Music Appreciation, Trips and Outings, and Parties and Dances with Nonhandicapped Groups.

WEDNESDAY

Teen-age Program

Time and Place:	3:00—9:00 P.M. Recreation Center
Enrollment:	70
Activities:	Social Dance, Hobbies, Play Production, Outings and Trips to Restaurants, Theaters, and many other places of interest in the community. Integration with Nonhandicapped Teen-age Clubs. Social Games and Sports.

THURSDAY

All Age Groups

Time and Place:	3:00—7:00 P.M. Recreation Center and Balboa Swimming Pool
Enrollment:	85
Activities:	*3:00—5:00* P.M. Activities at the Center (after school). Arts and Crafts, Games and Sports, Cooking, Music and Dance, Social Activities with Nonhandicapped Groups. *5:00—7:00* P.M. Recreation Swimming and Instruction at Balboa Pool.

FRIDAY

All-day Program—Adults

Time and Place:	10:00 A.M.—3:30 P.M. Recreation Center
Enrollment:	35

Activities:	Arts and Crafts, Cooking and Meal Planning, Indoor Gardening, Music Appreciation, Hobby Exploration, Social Activities, Trips and Outings.

Evening Program—Adults

Time and Place:	3:30—9:30 P.M. Recreation Center
Enrollment:	50
Activities:	Club Groups, Art and Theater Techniques, Basic Grammar, Spelling, Reading, Creative Writing, Literature, Cooking and Meal Planning, Music Appreciation, Trips and Outings, and Social Activities with Nonhandicapped Groups.

SATURDAY

All Ages (Nine different age groups, ranging from three to twenty-one years of age)

Time and Place:	10:00 A.M.—4:00 P.M. Recreation Center
Enrollment:	275
Activities:	Adaptive Sports and Games, Boating, Fishing, Camping, Horseback Riding, Bowling, Music Appreciation, Social Dance, Arts and Crafts, Theater Techniques, Advisory Council, Parties, Journalism, Trips and Outings, and Integration with Nonhandicapped Groups.

Added Factors

In addition to the preceding factors, leaders need to be aware of certain other elements affecting program planning. They are time, patience, and imagination. A great deal of time is required to enable handicapped persons, particularly those who have severe physical handicaps, to share in the planning and carrying out of their own activities. For example, time must be allowed for participants to express their ideas, even though they may have severe speech impairments—for various individuals to experiment with ways in which they might participate. Limited physical ability slows down the program and restricts the number of activities that can be conducted in a given period of time. Even when a program is conducted in a building, moving physically handicapped persons from one activity to another is a time-consuming process. The size of the group, as well as the physical limitations of individuals, necessarily determine the type and scope of activities offered within a given period.

The available free time of the handicapped is a major consideration in the scheduling of recreation activities especially for children. It is difficult for some children who attend school to participate in afterschool recreation programs due primarily to time limitations created by transportation problems, but efforts should be made to enable them to engage in recreation after school as far as possible. Weekends and vacations are the periods when recreation programs are most frequently scheduled, but the handicapped need opportunities to take part in recreation regularly at frequent intervals throughout the year.

Leaders should also be aware that they must have a great deal of patience to allow a severely handicapped person to participate at his own speed. If leaders are impatient this is obvious to handicapped persons such as the cerebral palsied. The latter become very tense and are consequently unable to function well.

Adapting activities to persons who have severe physical limitations requires also a great deal of imagination and ingenuity on the part of the leaders. It is no simple task, for example, to devise activities in which persons who are bedfast can participate with others who are in wheel chairs and even with those who are ambulatory. The success of such activities will be determined by the imagination and creative ability of the leader as well as the response of participants.

Guides for Adapting Recreation Activities

In addition to patience, imagination, ingenuity, initiative, and creative ability, leaders must also demonstrate a permissiveness which allows participants to develop at their own speed and within their limitations. Individuals should always be encouraged to participate, regardless of their disability. Persons who have been recently handicapped may need special encouragement, since they have had previous experience as participants, and are likely to compare their performance with their ability to participate before their handicap. Persons who have been handicapped since birth, on the other hand, may not have developed any notions of their inability to participate; consequently, they may be more willing to try.

In adapting activities, leaders need to be aware not only of real limitations, but also of imagined shortcomings caused by such conditioning as treatment by parents, fear of new experiences, and embarrassment because of speech defects. They must also take into account lack of incentive and lack of motivation that are often apparent, particularly in severely handicapped individuals. It has been stated that "all too frequently, the physically handicapped child is faced with rejection and withdrawal of affection at home and its counterpart, overprotection.

A crutch was used as a bat in the adaptation of baseball.

Either type of handicap is damaging, tending to increase the child's dependence, his fear of new experiences, his insecurity, and his exaggerated quest for affectional response."[2]

Leaders should always remember that participation is a matter of degree, which one should not judge by his own standard of participation.

[2] *Education of Exceptional Children,* 49th Year Book, University of Chicago Press, Chicago, 1950, p. 207.

In a dance program, for example, a boy with heavy braces and crutches "danced," as far as he was concerned, although he was able only to move his whole body slowly from side to side in rhythm to the music.

Specific Procedures

The following are a few suggestions for implementing the points stated in the preceding paragraphs.

1. Usually activities must be slowed down.
2. Trial and error, exploration methods are necessary.
   a. Leaders should not be afraid to experiment.
   b. Adaptations should be continuous and changing; one idea should not be overworked. Some leaders have a tendency, when they work out a successful adaptation, to offer it again and again, rather than to attempt new ones.
3. Several ways to adapt activities for groups are:
   a. Use the "assembly line" process, when working on group projects, by encouraging each individual to contribute according to his particular physical ability. In a sewing club, for example, only one person was physically capable of using a sewing machine; two persons were able to use scissors, while others pinned, measured, and so on.
   b. Suggest types of activities that can include every one, i.e., pantomime plays, puppetry, primitive dance, pottery, and so on.
   c. Structure activities in such a manner that individuals may participate by using their toes, one hand, one arm, and so on.
   d. Encourage groups and individuals to work out their own adaptations. Some handicapped individuals and groups can adapt activities for themselves. For example, in one program the recreation leader demonstrated the game of deck tennis as it is normally played to a group of severely handicapped children, and then suggested that the group work out their own adaptations. The fact that some were in wheel chairs, and some were on crutches presented a problem. However, they were able to adapt the game to their satisfaction and were all able to play successfully.

Selected activities that are successfully and easily adapted for severely physically handicapped children and adults are described in Part III.

CHAPTER 8

Program Integration

It is generally agreed that whenever and wherever possible, all handicapped persons should be integrated into our society. Groups interested in recreation for the handicapped should first explore the possibilities of integrating such persons into community recreation programs that are already established. Even the most severely handicapped person should be encouraged and assisted to participate in recreation programs in his own neighborhood along with the nonhandicapped.

It has been stated that "there must always be four active participants in the proper integration of the crippled child into society. The HOME (including relatives and close friends); the SCHOOL; the CHILD himself; and the individual members of SOCIETY with whom the child will increasingly be making contact as he moves toward adulthood."[1]

The handicapped people in a community generally fall into three categories: (1) those who are capable of integrating immediately into regular recreation programs but may lack opportunities for doing so; (2) those who are potentially capable but who may need guidance, encouragement, additional experiences, transportation facilities, or a combination of these to help them take this step into the community; (3) those who are so severely disabled that they may attain only partial integration at the most, and in some cases, none.

The recreation leader has a unique opportunity and a responsibility for helping all three handicapped groups: to integrate successfully, to attain partial integration, or to enjoy recreation activities even though integration is not feasible. The resourcefulness of the recreation leader in adapting activities so they can be enjoyed together by the handicapped and the nonhandicapped is a primary factor in assuring the success of an integrated program. The following quotation testifies to the feasibility of accomplishing this.

> Handicapped children with great courage and will power might not be able to "keep up" with "normal" children in the field of education or everyday accomplishments, but they can, with expert and understanding leadership, "keep up" by their participation in recreation and camping activities. In these environments, the deaf, the blind, the crippled, the cardiac, or the mentally retarded child can participate with "normal" children. Recreation and camping personnel are able to lead activities which are geared for all children; children who can participate in arts and crafts, in music, in drama, in swimming and other appropriate programs. These programs can give handicapped and non-handicapped children the opportunity to play, to learn to live and have fun together.[2]

[1] V. Mallinson, *None Can be Called Deformed* (London: Heinemann, 1956), p. 171.

[2] Baltimore Hearing Society, Third Annual Report, *Handicapped Children in Community Recreation and Camping Programs,* Baltimore, Maryland, April 1958, pp. 1–2. (Mimeographed.)

Examples of Integrated Programs

The following pages describe how integrated recreation programs have been achieved in several cities under different auspices.

Public Recreation Departments

The Santa Rosa, California, Recreation and Park Department, following the trend of most municipal agencies, began its recreation program for the handicapped on a very limited basis. The first organized activity for them, initiated in 1958, was a one-week session of day camping in the city park, conducted by the department's camp staff. Six handicapped children participated. The success of this activity met with such enthusiasm and interest from parents and school authorities that a weekly afterschool program was established in the park. The Board of Education cooperated by transporting the children to the playground in school-supplied taxicabs. Additional staff was provided to help the handicapped to participate more readily in the activities with the nonhandicapped. Summer camps for the handicapped were at first increased to two-week sessions and later combined with regular camp sessions for all children. During the school year and the summer months, enrollment of the handicapped increased considerably, and it was found that the neighborhood children integrated themselves into handicapped group activities. The nonhandicapped children were careful to help their handicapped friends, who participated in many more activities than the staff had thought possible.

A staff supervisor commented on the experience as follows:

> We are having difficulty in planning organized programs now because each child has different interests and is expressing what he wants to do and they are taking off to different parts of the park. This had been a transition from where a program was planned for them to one where they plan for themselves. It is not uncommon now for two wheel-chaired persons and four or five boys to be trudging up a hill to look for frogs or toads . . . for another person in a wheel chair to be rattling down to the ball diamond, surrounded by bats and balls. The team members are happy to have an umpire and score-keeper and our polio boy is so thrilled to be in the group. . . . Some girls like to play dolls and house in the club house . . . while the merry-go-round and equipment appeal to others. . . . The leaders are concerned that we are not offering a program, but we feel that this integration is the greatest possible thing for both groups. . . . The parents feel that this opportunity for the children to participate in municipal activities has given them additional prestige and a feeling of belonging. We are integrating the children into other activities also. Both the blind and cerebral palsied are encouraged to take ballet. One cerebral

A handicapped child becomes a regular camper in a city day camp.

palsied child has taken her physical therapy in a new light now that it is a part of ballet leg exercise. All city-wide events include the handicapped children. The special trips to the Giants' game, kite contests, Halloween parade, and many other activities. The city-wide yo-yo contest is also open to them, with their trick being limited.

Since 1953, the San Francisco, California, Recreation and Park Department has provided one week of day camping for mentally retarded children in the city's regular camp. Children with an I.Q. of approximately 40 to 60 participate with the nonhandicapped in a ratio of five retarded to approximately one hundred and twenty-five normal. The retarded children are transported to and from the camp site as a group, and their activities within the camp are closely supervised. Leaders have reported that the retarded are accepted by the other children and that of the twenty-nine who attended sessions in one summer, seven showed physical improvement during their week's stay. Thirteen improved in talking understandably, playing with others, and generally taking a more active part. Transportation and additional staff costs are sponsored by a local health agency dedicated to helping retarded children and other interested civic groups.

In addition to the camping program conducted for mentally retarded children, the San Francisco Recreation and Park Department in 1962, for the first time, included some children with severe physical handicaps in the regular day camp with the nonhandicapped. Twelve children, ages seven to twelve, who were members of the Recreation Center for the Handicapped, were able to participate for one week as a unit of the camp with approximately one hundred fifty nonhandicapped children. Most of the twelve children had multiple handicaps, which included cerebral palsy, postpolio, congenital malformations, and blindness. Some were in wheel chairs, some on crutches, and some were ambulatory.

Plans for integrating the two groups were actually started the year before, when some of the children of the Center visited the camp for one day to test the feasibility of such an undertaking. Even though the terrain was hilly and the area quite wooded, persons in wheel chairs, on crutches, and those who were blind found that, with some assistance, they were able to move about quite easily. Recreation leaders from the Center accompanied the children each day to and from the camp site in a bus provided by the Center, and leaders served as camp counselors for the unit. Integration took place quite rapidly, particularly after the first day, and most of the handicapped campers made many friends. An evaluation by the Center's staff stated that the greatest benefit to the handicapped was the motivation and stimulation that developed as a result of their participation with children who were more active, more experienced, and who had greater skills. The handicapped campers seemed more eager to participate and to learn skills with the nonhandicapped than they had previously shown in activities where all the participants were handicapped.

Private Recreation Agencies

The Recreation Center for the Handicapped, in San Francisco, primarily serves severely physically handicapped children and adults in need of a special program. However, the staff of the Center has developed several methods and techniques for integrating the handicapped into established community recreation programs throughout the year. One method which has proved most successful is that of cooperative planning with other recreation groups in both public and private agencies to insure opportunities for handicapped participants. For example, the Center staff plans with the directors of playgrounds, community centers, day camps, boys' and girls' clubs, and various other youth groups, ways in which they can include the handicapped in their programs. On

Saturday, for example, when over one hundred children are in attendance at the Center, it is not unusual for nine or ten groups of handicapped children of different ages to be participating in integrated activities throughout the city. On a typical Saturday, some of the children may attend a May Day festival conducted by the municipal recreation department, while others go boating with a local boys' club or ride horseback with a Junior Horsemen's Association. Still others go bowling, fishing, swimming, or camping with members of various local youth groups.

Another method of integration is attempted throughout the year when nonhandicapped children from playgrounds and various youth organizations come to the Center to participate in activities with the handicapped. Nonhandicapped teen-age clubs, in particular, together with the Center's Teen-age Club, enjoy planning and conducting parties and dances. Transportation and an adequate staff are two of the essential requirements for the success of such integrated programs. In a very interesting report entitled "Integrating the Orthopedically Handicapped Child into the Community Center,"[3] Arthur Schwartz and Marvin Lieberman tell of their experiences in integrating unserved orthopedically handicapped children into the ongoing program at the Mosholu Montefiore Community Center in New York City. The program, which was established in the Fall of 1961, was co-sponsored by the New York Service for the Orthopedically Handicapped. Twenty children in the neighborhood, aged six to twelve, were accepted and integrated into groups of nonhandicapped.

Most of the children needed transportation as few families had the use of automobiles during the day and public transportation was too difficult for them. Children were transported to and from programs by taxicabs, which were hired on a contract basis at an average round trip cost of $2.00 per day.

The ratio of handicapped to nonhandicapped was kept to one or two in each group. In one instance, a group of three handicapped to twelve nonhandicapped proved to be too difficult for the leader. The handicapped children were eager for social experiences as evidenced by the fact that they came to the Center in bad weather when attendance of the nonhandicapped was greatly reduced. They enjoyed the program very much and were accepted with comparative ease by the nonhandicapped children.

[3] Arthur Schwartz and Marvin Lieberman, "Integrating the Orthopedically Handicapped Child into the Community Center," Associated YM-YWHA's of Greater New York, New York, 1962. (Mimeographed.)

The project demonstrated that proper orientation and supervision of leaders was of primary importance; "the leadership offered these groups is one of the main elements contributing to success or failure."[4] These authors further state:

> Serving these children is not an impossible or overwhelming task. It does require additional resources and effort. However, all new programs require additional effort, especially in interpretation and involvement of parents, supervision and orientation of staff, and referrals and contacts with other agencies. Such a program does not change the basic purpose of the agency. It enhances it and adds impetus and support of group service goals and the value inherent in the social group work method. Introduction of this program has heightened staff awareness of differences and increased staff sensitivity to individuals. The program has had a positive effect on the membership of the Center; like their children, the adults originally reacted with pity, then with admiration, and in many cases with casual acceptance of these youngsters.[5]

The Baltimore Hearing Society conducted a three-year demonstration project from 1955 to 1958 for integrating hearing-impaired children with normal children in community recreation and camping programs. As a result of the project, over one hundred children having hearing problems were successfully integrated with children having normal hearing. The success of the project stimulated such interest among other social and recreation agencies that its purpose was expanded and it is now concerned with providing year-round recreation for all children with handicaps. The step-by-step method used for integrating children with hearing problems is highly applicable to integrating children with other handicaps and has been included later in this chapter in the discussion of suggested techniques for achieving integration.

Techniques for Achieving Integration

As previously stated, integrating handicapped persons with the nonhandicapped should be one of the major goals of recreation programs. Groups working with the handicapped, however, must recognize that integration is not possible for all persons and that under the most favorable circumstances many factors are involved which will determine the degree of success of any given program. The criterion for actual integration as established by some of the schools for the handicapped is highly applicable here. True belonging is the test for successful integration. This

[4] *Ibid*, p. 5.
[5] *Ibid*, p. 10.

means that "the child must be happy with his friends, feel accepted, be able to contribute, be treated as one of the class rather than as a china doll or as an oddity, and have a part in the group's plans and adventures in school and out."[6] Integration does not take place automatically, and physical placement of a child in a group does not necessarily insure acceptance. Usually it can be accomplished only through a great deal of organized effort on the part of many persons and through the careful observance of certain basic principles. The experiences of a variety of groups attempting to integrate the handicapped into established community recreation programs afford some common procedures that have proved to be successful.

Educational Program

The need for an educational program has been recognized by all agencies and groups concerned with recreation for the handicapped. It is considered an essential first step toward all attempts to integrate the handicapped into established programs. Many persons capable of participating in community recreation programs are not aware of the fact that these programs are available to them. Although some handicapped persons are using public recreation facilities, departments have reported numerous requests from parents who either did not know that their children were entitled to be included in recreation programs offered to the general public or were fearful of letting their children participate with others. One community center, attempting to integrate orthopedically handicapped children into group recreation with nonhandicapped children, found that parents were hesitant for various reasons, some of which had a very realistic basis. Some handicapped children are more susceptible to injury, and accidents may delay recuperation or rehabilitation. The reluctance of some parents is understandable as they want to make sure that the agency is capable of caring for their children properly, that it observes the rules of health and safety and that it is keenly aware of the physical limitations of their children.

An educational program should be designed for public information and should also be geared to alerting parents of the handicapped. The resources of the school system, parent-teacher associations, health and welfare agencies, public and private recreation agencies, churches, and all other related groups should be utilized for community education. The

[6] William M. Cruickshank and G. Orville Johnson, *Education of Exceptional Children and Youth* (Englewood Cliffs, N. J.: Prentice-Hall, 1959), p. 486.

educational program should not only inform parents and the general public of present services available, but it should interpret the importance of recreation for the handicapped and attempt to promote understanding and acceptance of them by others. The climate of acceptance, both for the handicapped and the nonhandicapped, is extremely important, as the lack of tolerance by others affects both emotional and social acceptance. Prejudices do exist and they are harmful to the process of integrating the handicapped into normal situations. Harold W. Robbins, Director of group services for the New York Service for the Orthopedically Handicapped, states: "Most normal children shun the disabled. This appears to be partly because of an aversion to people who are 'different' and partly because disabled children cannot keep up with normal children. Some normal children taunt disabled youths . . . and others adopt them as 'mascots.' Few approach them as equals."[7]

Attempts to provide opportunities for the severely handicapped to utilize public recreation and other community facilities have been met with open rejection and intolerance, particularly in instances where educational programs had not been conducted. In one community, in 1947, a group of severely handicapped cerebral palsied children was taken frequently to the city park playground. Neighborhood parents of the nonhandicapped children formed a committee to complain to city officials. They feared the disabilities might be contagious and that children of expectant mothers might be marked if the pregnant women saw such handicapped persons. Some restaurants, theaters, and other public places are fearful of accommodating groups of severely handicapped persons because they wish to avoid what they think may be an unpleasant situation for their clientele. The lack of community understanding can be one of the greatest hindrances to the success of a total program for the handicapped. The combined efforts of many groups and individuals, however, can help people to understand that the handicapped should be a part of the community.

ADVISORY COMMITTEE. The establishment of an advisory board or committee is probably a prerequisite to the development of a successful educational program for integrating the handicapped into established recreation programs. Such a committee should include representatives from all types of handicapped groups. In addition to assisting with the educational program, orientation of staff, and so on, an advisory committee

[7] "Normal Play Held Benefit to Disabled," *New York Times,* Western Edition, May 27, 1963, p. L11.

can act as a clearing house for youth-serving agencies and private camps willing to include the handicapped in their programs. This committee can also assist with "readiness" programs described later in this chapter.

In-Service Training Program

An in-service training program for the recreation staff can not only prepare them for working more successfully with handicapped persons, but it can also specifically train them in the methods and techniques of integrating the handicapped into established programs. Such training and orientation courses should be continuous and should be conducted with the cooperation of the advisory committee or of representatives from community agencies. Such courses should include discussions of specific types of handicapped and their particular needs in recreation. Training programs for those working with the severely physically handicapped, for example, should include demonstrations of methods and techniques of physical handling, adapting activities, and other specific areas discussed in Chapter 5, "Leadership Personnel."

Interim and Readiness Programs

Experience has indicated that the establishment of readiness recreation programs for the handicapped can help tremendously in the process of integration. Handicapped children, as well as adults, who have had little or no previous experience with recreation need some type of preparation before actual integration can take place. They need to learn some of the basic recreation and social skills individually and in groups, which will help them to feel comfortable and confident when they attempt to participate in regular programs with the nonhandicapped.

The importance of such preparation is illustrated by the experience of a cerebral palsied girl of twelve who failed to gain acceptance when she tried to participate with children in her own neighborhood recreation program. She had been previously sheltered in her home and had few, if any, recreation or social skills which would help her to participate successsfully with normal groups. In addition, she had a severe speech impediment, and it was difficult to communicate with her. When she tried to become a part of the group, she was completely rejected by the neighborhood children, and her family eventually referred her to a special recreation program for the severely handicapped. She attended this program for approximately three years and learned to dance and to swim and became quite proficient in many of the games and sports, in arts and crafts and in music. In particular, she learned how to get along in groups, how to behave in public; she learned consideration for others and developed a sense of fair play. Her skills enabled her to become a volunteer helper for the recreation program staff, and in this assignment she gained a great deal of confidence and self-assurance. Finally, she was able to return to her neighborhood group and to stand up against any rebuffs or criticism. She was able to prove herself with others because she could compete and participate on many levels, and in some areas she actually excelled. She no longer needed to participate in the special program; the fact that she had been able to prepare herself in a readiness program resulted in her successful integration.

Readiness programs have been deliberately designed to prepare specific types of handicapped for integration with the nonhandicapped. In 1955–58, the Baltimore Hearing Society established such programs for children with impaired hearing. A recreation therapist employed by the Society developed one to teach basic recreation and related communication skills. Specific activities conducted included a rhythmic class, a modified day camp, a ballet class, and an athletic club.

Some of the activities were conducted at the health agency setting by the Y.W.C.A. staff. The purpose of this program was to prepare the children to move from special classes in rhythms, ballet, and athletics into regular classes for the nonhandicapped at the Y.W.C.A. The demonstration project was very successful and enabled the children to move into new situations with little or no apprehension.

A modified summer day camp was conducted for eight weeks for eighteen children, ages 5–7, who had severe auditory and speech disorders and were not ready to participate with hearing children. "The lack of previous group experience, the lack of recreational and social skills, and the lack of adequate vocabulary development, placed these children in an isolated position."[8] A particular unit was stressed each week during the eight weeks of camp. It included nature lore, identification of animals, health, the farm, manners, travel, public servants, and the store. The recreation and speech therapists worked together to stress certain aspects of the unit. For example, hikes, arts and crafts, and films were used for nature lore and identification of animals. Parents were asked to help give the children as many nature experiences as possible during this time so that they would be repeatedly exposed to the subject. In order to assure the maximum benefit, the children were divided into groups of six each. The more severely handicapped attended two three-

[8] Baltimore Hearing Society, *loc. cit.*

hour sessions weekly and the less impaired attended one three-hour session weekly. Each child in the three-hour session received one half hour of individual speech therapy, one half hour of group speech therapy, and two hours of recreation, with emphasis on social activities.

At the end of the eight-week period, the staff, parents, and members of the Society noticed considerable progress. Each child progressed at his own rate and in different ways. Some improved in speech; others in group participation. With firsthand information on each youngster, the staff was able more effectively to advise recreation leaders in neighborhood programs where to place each child.

Neighborhood Acceptance and Participation

Integrating handicapped children into their own neighborhood programs is usually achieved on an individual basis, particularly when they are able to make their own way to the playground or indoor center or when parents or others transport them.

When conditions are favorable, integrating on an individual basis is not too difficult to accomplish. However, parents as well as handicapped children have stated frequently that attempts to participate with the nonhandicapped in public recreation programs have not been successful when an unfavorable atmosphere prevailed. Integration is difficult on unsupervised areas or on supervised areas where the recreation leaders are too busy to give the individual attention that is needed. One way to solve this problem is to provide additional leadership with the understanding and ingenuity necessary to include the handicapped with others. This is particularly true in the case of the severely disabled. (See Part III, "Activities and Programs.")

Using a "buddy" or "pal" system has been successful and is commonly used in schools and on some playgrounds where the handicapped are integrated with the nonhandicapped. In this event, nonhandicapped children volunteer to help the handicapped in moving about, in relating specific or emergency needs to the leader, in helping with feeding, and so on. Junior volunteer leaders, who are frequently used in recreation programs, can also assume this responsibility.

Children participating in readiness programs, or even in special programs, should at the same time be encouraged to participate in their own neighborhood activities, and parents should be informed of their responsibility to help. In one special program for the severely handicapped, the staff actually made arrangements for individuals to participate in their own neighborhood recreation programs. This was attempted only after a period of readiness and preparation. In most instances, the staff accompanied the individual on his first visit to the neighborhood center, in order to help make the transition more easily. One instance involved a young cerebral palsied teen-age boy, who, because of the severity of his handicap, was released from a special school. Although he was provided with a home teacher, he had a great deal of time to brood and became very depressed and lonely. He participated regularly in the special recreation program, but the leader felt that he was potentially capable of integrating with the nonhandicapped. The leader, with his parents, made arrangements for him to visit a boys' club in his own neighborhood, where he was ultimately accepted and became very active. He was eventually able to go to the club on his own and, through his own initiative, enter other programs, including playgrounds and the indoor recreation center. Even though the staff of public and private agencies may be able to refer handicapped children to neighborhood programs, parents must be educated to their responsibility for helping their children participate in various activities within the community.

USE OF NATURAL SETTING FOR INTEGRATION. One of the primary values of conducting special recreation programs for the handicapped in public recreation facilities is the opportunity for integration. Departments and groups conducting such programs have reported that nonhandicapped children participate quite readily even with the severely handicapped, particularly as they are exposed more and more to them, and that imaginative and understanding leaders can provide numerous opportunities for the children to have fun together.

Conclusion

One of the greatest benefits of extended service as conducted cooperatively by public recreation departments, welfare organizations, and youth-serving agencies is that while fulfilling the recreational needs of the handicapped, they can simultaneously work toward integrating these persons with the nonhandicapped. Scheduling activities in typical facilities with the regular leadership staff does not isolate the handicapped or set them apart nearly so much as when special facilities are designed for their use. Meeting in facilities used also by the nonhandicapped creates opportunities for the handicapped to be included with others, which is one of the most desirable methods of integration. Special programs are sometimes needed, but wherever possible, the handicapped should be integrated into established programs.

A few words of caution are offered to those who would attempt to place all handicapped children in established recreation programs with the nonhandicapped. Care must be taken that the handicapped child moves gradually and at his own pace. Some children may need to move back and forth for a long period of time between special programs and integrated programs before they are able to make a complete transition and participate entirely with the nonhandicapped. Some may never make the transition. Nonhandicapped children taking part in integrated programs must be guided and closely supervised, as their usual tendency is to help the handicapped too much. Handicapped children should not be allowed to be the center of attenion because they happen to be using crutches or wheel chairs.

Leaders must not over-protect handicapped or show different treatment of them that could be interpreted as favoritism by the nonhandicapped. The presence of a handicapped child frequently slows down a group and prevents a more active program. In some instances, it might be appropriate to slow down an activity, but it should not be done at the expense of the nonhandicapped. Leaders must understand how to fit handicapped persons into regular programs rather than to avoid those activities which are difficult for them.

The successful integration of handicapped persons is determined by many elements; however, of primary importance is the attitude and understanding of leaders.

CHAPTER 9

Financing Programs

Recommendations regarding fund raising for all programs for the physically handicapped, made at the 1960 White House Conference on Children and Youth, have particular application for recreation programs for these persons. In part, these recommendations state that fund raising appeals "should be based, not primarily upon differences between handicapped and normal children, but upon the aim of restoring handicapped children to fully functioning members of the community."[1]

Historically, community recreation programs for the handicapped have been financed primarily by voluntary health and welfare agencies, private agencies, service clubs, foundations and other groups, and by individuals. The ways and means of financing a recreation program for the handicapped, however, vary in different localities. When groups, individuals and agencies rally to raise money, the course they take and the methods they use depend upon many varying factors. However, experience affords examples of common procedures that have been successful in various localities. It indicates that in a large percentage of cases, several agencies, public and private, share in meeting the various expenses incurred in providing recreation programs for the handicapped. Wherever there are municipal departments, the major cost of the program should be financed by tax funds, collected to serve all the people. In planning their budgets, these departments should give as careful consideration to the funds as necessary for the operation of a program for the handicapped. One of the factors justifying the provision of proportionately greater funds is the higher ratio of leadership to participants which is essential in a recreation program for handicapped persons.

One public recreation department official stated that "financing a summer day camp for the handicapped costs three to five times that for other day camps operated by the department. Costs are higher because the required ratio of leaders per handicapped campers has proven to be one leader to four campers; and reliable and certain transportation service which can adjust readily to last minute demands is best secured by using taxis and drivers."[2] The need for transportation of the severely handicapped is perhaps the most serious problem confronting recreators in establishing and conducting recreation programs for the handicapped. (See Chapter 11, "Transportation.") Since all public recreation agencies are not authorized to spend funds for transportation of such persons, private and voluntary agencies frequently provide this service.

[1] *Conference Proceedings,* Golden Anniversary White House Conference on Children and Youth, Washington, D.C., 1960, p. 264.

[2] *Recreation for Handicapped People in California,* State of California Recreation Commission, Sacramento, May 1958, p. 47.

Financing Publicly Sponsored Programs

The following selected examples show how some public recreation departments are financing their recreation programs for the handicapped.

Santa Rosa, California, operates a year-round program for physically handicapped children, with weekly afterschool programs in the Community Center. The Recreation and Park Department provides leadership and some supplies. The school sends the children to the Community Center in taxicabs paid for by school funds, and parents furnish transportation home after the program. Other operating costs are paid by the Parent Guild. Summer day camps, which are also conducted in Recreation and Park Department facilities, are financed in the same manner.

In *Berkeley, California,* the Recreation and Park Department employs the staff that conducts weekly recreation programs for handicapped adults at the Live Oak Community Center. Transportation is provided by the American Red Cross; other basic operating costs are furnished by local voluntary agencies and groups.

In *Kansas City, Missouri,* a private foundation donated a grant to the Public Recreation Division to finance a pilot recreation program for the handicapped. The city authorities now provide a special recreation supervisor, but the basic operating costs of the program are financed by a Greater Kansas City Council for Recreation for the Ill and Handicapped, which includes all of the local health and welfare agencies.

San Mateo County, California, conducts two weeks of summer day camping for mentally and physically handicapped. Public authorities and private groups share equally in meeting the cost of operating the camp. The following figures are taken from the 1959 financial report for the camp, in which forty-seven children and youth, aged eight to twenty, participated for two weeks.[3]

Income		
Balance from 1958 camp	$ 78.53	
San Mateo County Parks and Recreation	500.00	
City of San Mateo Recreation Department	150.00	
Parents' Assn. for Mentally Retarded Children of San Mateo County	400.00	
Special schools for handicapped		
El Portal P.T.A.	50.00	
Sierra Morena P.T.A.	50.00	
Registration fees: 45 @ $2.50	117.50	
Total income		$1,346.03

[3] *Report of the Day Camp for the Handicapped—1959,* San Mateo, California (undated). (Mimeographed.)

Expenditures

Salaries:			$1,033.16	
Director	@ $2.50 hr.	$250.00		
2 Asst. directors	@ $2.00 hr.	250.00		
Bus driver, north	@ $2.14 hr.	96.30		
Bus driver, south	@ $2.14 hr.	176.24		
Matron, north	@ $1.54 hr.	148.20		
Matron, south	@ $1.54 hr.	112.42		
Craft supplies			14.35	
Transportation			82.53	
Insurance			79.90	
Cookout supplies			31.32	
Miscellaneous			19.06	
Total expenses			$1,260.32	
Balance on hand			85.71	$1,346.03

Financing Privately Sponsored Programs

In addition to appropriations from tax funds there are many sources from which money is secured for financing recreation programs for the handicapped in a community. Groups interested in fund raising should be familiar with the professional standards, principles, and procedures of raising funds, which generally apply in most communities, also with the regulations governing fund raising that have been adopted in many cities. Among the most common sources of funds are:

VOLUNTARY GROUPS: Health and welfare agencies and other fund raising groups for the handicapped, the United Crusade, service clubs, handicapped clubs, Parent Auxiliaries, and Parent-Teacher Associations are all sources for obtaining funds to operate recreation programs for the handicapped. The support of such agencies is especially needed for programs initiated on a demonstration basis before public acceptance of spending tax money for them has been achieved. Special schools for the handicapped are frequently able to furnish facilities, equipment, and supplies.

FOUNDATIONS: A foundation may provide the initial cost of establishing a recreation program for the handicapped in a community, as in Kansas City, where foundation funds were supplied to a public recreation division to explore a program for handicapped persons. Once the program was in operation, other private and voluntary agencies assisted in meeting the total cost. A number of programs have been assisted greatly through bequests, legacies, and gifts.

SUBSCRIPTIONS AND FEES: If the operating agency or responsible group is organized as a nonprofit corporation, membership fees in the corporation may be established that will help considerably in meeting the cost of the program. These fees commonly vary according to the types of membership, such as: student, active, affiliate, contributing, sustaining, and agency-affiliate. The fees can be determined according to the expected interest and response of a specific locality.

PARTICIPANT FEES: Fees charged handicapped participants are additional sources for financing recreation programs for the handicapped. In public recreation, "the objectives sought and the relationship of the charges to the people's ability to pay are major considerations in determining the results of any policy relative to fees."[4] This statement may serve as a guiding principle in determining fees for recreation programs for the handicapped. However, there are certain factors to be considered that were heretofore unknown to public recreation agencies or that apply only to programs for the handicapped.

The provision of transportation, a necessary consideration, affects the total operation of the program in terms of extent, scope, and frequency of service; this, in turn, affects the per capita costs and program fees and charges.

The necessary high ratio of personnel participants is another cost factor that must be considered. Special equipment and facilities also add to the cost. Therefore, the handicapped cannot be expected to meet as large a share of the cost of their recreation services as might generally be expected.

There is a wide difference of opinion on many questions relating to charges for public recreation services. Many persons believe that recreation is an essential public service and should be provided free of charge on the same basis of financial support as education. Groups providing recreation programs for the handicapped must also consider the pros and cons of charging fees to handicapped participants. The agency or responsible body for operating the programs usually determines the policy with respect to charges and fees, and their amount, in the light of financial need and the extent and cost of services offered. The cooperation of the Parent Auxiliary has often been enlisted in establishing the rate of fees.

One argument in favor of charging fees that is normally accepted by all agencies and groups is that if persons are required to pay something for what they receive, they appreciate it more. Experience indicates that

[4] George D. Butler, *Introduction to Community Recreation* (New York: McGraw, 1959), p. 499.

this concept most certainly applies to the handicapped; and if fees are necessary and an accepted practice, handicapped persons should pay for them the same as would the nonhandicapped. This attitude helps to promote the idea that recreation is being provided for them because they are *persons* entitled to these opportunities, not because they are handicapped and should have special consideration. Even if fees are not needed for the actual financial operation of the program, a small charge may help to increase the service rendered or make possible the enrichment of the program. In one recreation program for the handicapped, the members themselves, through the work of their member-advisory council, chose to charge monthly fees which would enable them to conduct special parties and events, and to purchase certain pieces of equipment which were not included in the regular budget.

It should be understood, however, that many persons are unable to pay fees at all, and they should be given certain consideration. No handicapped person should be deprived of recreational opportunities because he is unable to pay, and care should be taken so that parents of the handicapped fully understand the terms and policies related to the charging of fees.

In one community the establishment of participant fees and charges actually increased enrollment and attendance in an existing recreation program for the handicapped. The fees were established by the Parent Auxiliary, which also interpreted their need to parents. Many parents who are unable to pay are able to assist in some other way, which still gives them the feeling that they are doing their share. Further reference is made to this concept in another chapter relating to work with parents. A good way to make sure that participant fees and charges will be feasible and acceptable is to work closely with parents in establishing them.

As previously indicated, service clubs and other voluntary agencies will often assume the cost of fees incurred by one or more handicapped persons attending recreation programs. In one community, a great deal of monthly income for a recreation program for the handicapped is paid for by voluntary agencies, groups, and individuals that pay a monthly per capita cost fee. Inasmuch as per capita cost might be $15.00 to $25.00 per month, enlistment of a great many agencies and individuals to pay such fees helps appreciably in financing the over-all program.

The following selected examples show how some private recreation agencies finance recreation programs for the handicapped. They indicate not only money raising methods and sources of funds but also the types of expenditures incurred in operating such programs.

The San Francisco Recreation Center for the Handicapped was established in 1952 with grants-in-aid from a private foundation, amounting to $15,000 for a two-year period. Community support was obtained after two years, and the Center has continued to be financed entirely through voluntary contributions raised by the Board of Directors, primarily through the following methods:

1. A letter of solicitation is mailed annually to approximately 20,000 private individuals and business firms in the San Francisco Bay Area. The letter is signed by the President of the Board, the Finance Chairman, or individual Board members. It is part of an annual report, which contains photographs of some of the Center's accomplishments and an audited financial statement.

2. "Fund for Fun" is conducted annually at Christmas time and is directed to the general public through radio, television, and newspapers. A request is made that individuals send a Christmas card with a dollar enclosed to the Recreation Center for the Handicapped. Donations have increased yearly, and thousands of cards are received which are used to decorate the Christmas tree. (See Chapter 10, "Public Relations.")

3. Local foundations set up by corporations, by individuals, and by groups with a common interest contribute yearly grants to the Center. Such grants are obtained usually through personal contacts made by the staff and by members of the Board of Directors.

4. Voluntary groups, such as health and welfare agencies and others, make annual contributions. Most of these grants are in the form of camperships for a specific group of handicapped children or they are donated on a yearly per capita cost basis for specific groups. For example, the Muscular Dystrophy Association pays an amount sufficient to enable all muscular dystrophied children in the area to attend regular year-round recreation programs. This contribution is based on actual attendance of individual children.

5. Service clubs such as the Kiwanis, Lions, and Rotary Clubs, and fraternal and religious organizations, contribute yearly grants to the Center. Some of these are earmarked for specific purposes such as transportation, building improvements, and equipment and supplies.

6. Auxiliaries have been organized to help the Center in many ways, one of which is financing. Members of the Parent Auxiliary—one of these groups—raise funds, primarily through candy sales, rummage sales, bazaars, and raffles. (See Chapter 14.) The Women's Auxiliary, which consists of interested women of the community, is organized primarily to raise funds for the Center. The Auxiliary sponsors benefit teas, luncheons, flower shows, concerts, and horse shows and assists the Board of Directors in all of its fund raising events. (See illustrations in Chapter 10.)

7. Handicapped children and adults pay part or all of the nominal

program and camp fees and charges if they are financially able to do so. These fees were established by the Parent Auxiliary and are handled on a voluntary basis. Eligibility for attending the program is *not* based on ability to pay fees and charges. Additional costs incurred through group trips to restaurants, theaters, concerts, and operas, for example, are also paid for by the participants on the basis described above.

8. In addition to the actual funds obtained, which are essential in financing the basic operating costs of the Center, certain services are donated by public and private agencies and groups on a yearly basis. These contributed services are so essential to the over-all operation of the Center that without them it could not function, and their cash value has been estimated to be approximately equal to the amount actually expended by the Center. The following agencies and groups provide appreciable services.

The San Francisco Recreation and Park Department donates the use of the entire facility which was formerly a restaurant section of the Fleishhacker Pool Building on the Great Highway. It consists of 9,250 square feet of floor space, for which at a minimum rate of 17¢ per square foot the annual rental would be $18,970. Approximately $10,000 has been spent by the city on building changes and repairs over a period of years. Staff is also provided for the Center, particularly in the swim program. The total estimated cost to the Department per year is as follows:

Rental donated	$18,970
Building repairs	1,000
Utilities	6,432
Staff leadership	2,000
Material and supplies	150
	$28,552

The Adult Education Division of the San Francisco Unified School District supplies adult education instructors and furnishes the majority of office supplies, such as mimeograph paper, stencils, inks, chalk, and some program supplies. The district also furnishes some transportation in school-supplied taxis.

The American Red Cross and other voluntary agencies and groups furnish considerable transportation for the Center, at an estimated total cost of $15,000 per year. *The State Educational Agency for Surplus Property* furnishes surplus food such as dried beans, rice, flour, corn meal, canned meat, cheese, butter, powdered milk, and eggs at an estimated value of $3,000 per year.

Following is the statement of cash receipts and disbursements of the Recreation Center for the fiscal year ending August 31, 1961.

STATEMENT OF CASH RECEIPTS AND DISBURSEMENTS FOR THE FISCAL YEAR ENDED AUGUST 31, 1961 of the RECREATION CENTER FOR THE HANDICAPPED, INC. San Francisco, California*

Cash Receipts			
Contributions received		$24,363.65	
Membership drive		9,117.83	
Service fees—participants		3,034.28	
Day camp		4,410.00	
Loan received		1,100.00	
Sale of automobile		1,900.00	
Miscellaneous		276.98	$44,202.74
Cash Disbursements			
Salaries†			
Recreation leaders	$11,098.60		
Program director	5,200.00		
Office	3,750.00		
Kitchen aide and janitor	2,126.26		
Drivers	861.86	$23,036.72	
Day camp supplies and expense		307.92	
Program supplies and expense		1,066.76	
Transportation		7,879.95	
Office supplies		652.30	
Telephone		612.27	
Payroll taxes		809.63	
Field and travel		1,021.14	
Fund drive expense‡		1,883.53	
Automobile expense		722.94	
Repairs and maintenance		566.30	
Insurance		996.82	
Photograph and art		293.56	
Promotional		111.81	
Miscellaneous		725.56	
Purchase of furniture and equipment		2,043.00	
Loan Payment		1,100.00	43,830.21
Excess of Receipts over Disbursements			$ 372.53

* Prepared by Cecchi and Scheibner, Certified Public Accountants

† The Founder and Director of the Center is unsalaried.

‡ Fund Drive Expenses include payments for printing, stationery, postage, and so on.

The *Tulsa, Oklahoma, "Recreation Center for the Physically Limited"* was established in 1957 for children and adults by the Tulsa Section of the National Council of Jewish Women and is financed almost entirely by this group. Some local health and welfare agencies pay on a per capita cost basis. Use of the facilities in which the Center is located is donated by a local hospital.

Following is a statement of the Center's 1962 budget.

TULSA RECREATION CENTER FOR THE PHYSICALLY LIMITED
BUDGET FOR 1962
(Served 160 People)

Salaries		7,830
Transportation		
Salary	1,000	
Taxi service	600	
Gas & oil	700	
Upkeep	100	
Total		2,400
Convention		100
Program (including day camp)		1,500
Telephone		275
Postage		250
Stationery & office supply		375
Publicity		50
Insurance		375
Equipment		750
Repair and maintenance other than vehicle		100
Janitorial supplies		100
Gift shop		375
Miscellaneous		375
Sinking fund		1,000
Physical plant & utilities		4,000
Total		$19,855

The Seattle Handicapped Center was organized in 1957 by the Seattle section of the Indoor Sports Club. It is affiliated with the National Indoor Sports Club, a social club for handicapped adults, and serves adults only. The Center is financed by club members, primarily through club dues and funds obtained from advertising in the club's monthly publication *The Good Samaritan.* Use of its facilities is donated by the Seattle Recreation and Park Department.

Some General Conclusions and Recommendations

Every community, agency, or individual interested in initiating a program for the handicapped will do well to keep in mind the following:

1. The utilization of total community resources is essential in conducting successful recreation programs for the handicapped. While the ways and means of financing programs may vary somewhat in each community, joint sponsorship is the most common method and appears to be the most practical.
2. The financing of recreation services for the handicapped usually costs more than for the nonhandicapped. Factors that contribute to the higher cost of programs, particularly for the severely handicapped, include the following:
   a. The necessarily high ratio of trained personnel to participants.
   b. Special transportation requirements.
   c. Specialized or adapted building facilities such as ramps or rails required to accommodate persons in wheel chairs, beds, and so on.
   d. Special equipment, certain types of furniture, adapted games, sports supplies, and so on.
3. No particular agency or group has been recognized as being essentially responsible for financing recreation programs for the handicapped, but the public recreation agency, with its philosophy of recreation for all, has a large and primary responsibility toward these persons. One public recreation authority has stated its policy with reference to programs for the handicapped as follows:
   a. Educational programs must be directed toward developing a community awareness of the problem; parents of the handicapped must also be educated to the new horizons available through recreation.
   b. Community resources that are related to and concerned with the handicapped must be mobilized.
   c. Each agency, the public, and those concerned with the handicapped must be willing to accept a heavier load.
   d. The transportation problem must be solved.[5]

A report of a three-year study on the recreation needs of the handicapped in San Francisco included recommendations for the financing of recreation programs for the severely handicapped, as follows:

[5] 41st National Recreation Congress, *Proceedings,* "Role of Recreation Agencies in Providing for the Handicapped in the Community Recreation Programs," New York, 1959, p. 175.

The sub-committee in the review of its findings, reaffirms that the public recreation agency provides the basic floor of services and facilities for all people. It is agreed, however, that there will be the need for specialized programs especially for the severely handicapped. Such programs are not the responsibility of the public recreation agency *alone*, but should also be initiated or continued by the voluntary agencies in cooperation with the Advisory Committee named above. The necessary financing for such recreation services is the recognized responsibility of the governing boards of these public and private agencies, and of the community-at-large. A board may choose to meet this responsibility for service in either of two ways.

1. They can have their own qualified staff conduct the recreation programs for the severely handicapped.
2. They can include in their operating budget sufficient funds to provide recreational programs on a contractual service basis from public or private recreation agencies qualified to furnish such services.[6]

Evidence indicates an increasing interest in recreation programs for the handicapped, and the methods of financing them should be of special concern to the public recreation departments, as well as to the community at large. Groups and individuals willing to put forth the time and effort required to establish need will also find the ways and means of financing these programs.

[6] *Study Committee Report and Recommendations on Recreation for the Handicapped in San Francisco,* San Francisco Recreation and Park Department, February 10, 1961, p. 5. [Mimeographed.]

Recreation Center

By WILLIAM McPHILLIPS

'PRISONERS IN FREEDOM'

Recreation Center Proffers New Life to Handicapped

By CLAIRE LEEDS

Unique Program at Center for Handicapped

DIRECTOR JANET POMEROY OF RECREATION CENTER AND YOUNG DINA
Dina works potter's wheel with toes, molds with heel and toes

MARILYN GLAZES A CERAMIC PIECE
She steadies one hand with other; paints well also

INSTITUTE
Recreation
for the
Physically Handicapped
under the auspices of
Recreation Center for the Handicapped, Inc.
(A project of the San Francisco Guild for Crippled Children)
ADULT EDUCATION DIVISION
San Francisco Unified School District
THE SAN FRANCISCO RECRE[ATION]
AND PARK DEPARTME[NT]
THE STATE OF CAL[IFORNIA]
RECREATION COM[MISSION]
MARCH 1

Crippled Children Have Time Of Lives At Camp

By DOLORES WALDORF

Little Ricky is shown here as he sews an Indian costume for himself at the day camp of the Recreation Center for Handicapped Children on Fleishhacker Pool grounds.

18—San Francisco News —Thursday, Jan. 31, 1957

A GALLOPING PONY at a carnival at Recreation for the Handicapped, Inc., is 12-year-old Cassandra Hutchinson, whose wheelchair was easily rigged for her part in the production. This is the kind of fun open to children and adults at the Fleishhacker Pool Bldg., a Crippled Children's Guild project.

THEMSELVES

'New World' For The Handicapped

By DOLORES WALDORF

Helping Handicapped to Have Fun

BY JANET H. CLEAR

San Francisco Recreation Center Provides Activities for Physically Handicapped

San Francisco Progress ● Wed.-Thurs., Aug. 14-15, 1957

'Armchair Travel' Tour At Handicapped Center

Sec. I—S. F. Examiner Thursday, Dec. 22, 1960

Now the Handicapped Can Have Some Fun

By LARRY SCHNEIDER

Mon., May 15, 1961 S. F. News-Call Bulletin

Volunteers Help Handicapped

By ELOISE DUNGAN

People and Places:

A New Kind of Help for The Handicapped

By Marion McEniry
Women's Editor, The Examiner

Recreation for Handicapped

Children Are Camping Out

By Joan McKinney
Club Editor

CHAPTER 10

Public Relations

Public opinion is of the utmost importance in the development of recreation services for the handicapped because the future course of the recreation program will be determined by the degree of understanding, good will, and support of the people within the community. Public relations is the process by which favorable opinion may be created and maintained with the public. A continuous program of public education is essential to the development of recreation programs for the handicapped, not only for the purpose of assuring adequate financial and other support, but also to inform the public of the existence of handicapped persons and to interpret their recreation needs.

Important Factors

Several factors that must be considered in establishing and maintaining a public relations program will be discussed briefly.

Need for Interpretation

Persons attempting to promote recreation for the handicapped must have a thorough knowledge and understanding of recreation and enthusiasm for its benefits for individuals, the family, and the community at large. They must also be aware of the prevailing attitudes and general concepts, not only of recreation but of the handicapped, that are apparent in most communities. Many persons do not understand the need for organized recreation; some people think of it as a frill, while others still have the old Puritan belief that fun or recreation is sinful. The many services provided by public recreation departments are often misinterpreted as exclusively for children and/or the underprivileged.

The same misconceptions, with some additions, must be overcome in promoting recreation for the handicapped. The average person is usually convinced of the need for research, medical treatment, education, and similar services for handicapped people. However, because the need for recreation is a relatively new concept, many persons are not aware of its importance or of the difference between recreation and some of the other services already provided for the handicapped. Experience in working in recreation in general indicates that a great many individuals need an interpretation of recreation as a universal need and benefit as well as an understanding of its significance for handicapped persons. The mere establishment of a recreation program for the handicapped does not assure automatic or continuous support. As with any other new and worthwhile enterprise, it takes time and much effort on the part of a group to build good relations in a community and thereby assure its support. A program must be properly interpreted and understood before it is accepted; it must "prove" its worth before it can expect to receive substantial support.

Need for a Plan

Public relations consists of much more than mere publicity, and without a carefully thought out plan, publicity can overnight give a wrong impression that may take years to correct. G. Edward Pendray, a public relations authority, has said:

> Public relations . . . depends on the development of a sound program which must grow out of a complete understanding of the objectives, problems, needs and opportunities of the organization. . . . The basic idea that underlies all public relations is . . . WHAT PEOPLE THINK MAKES ALL THE DIFFERENCE. In the last analysis it is the public that decides whether any given business, institution or department shall live or die; whether it shall prosper or wither; whether it shall carry out its program and reach its objectives, or dry up and disappear through lack of support. The public decides all of these things for the most part unconsciously. The decisions are usually based on what people think they know, about the operation under consideration.[1]

Determining the Publics

The agency or group attempting to promote recreation for the handicapped must first decide what it wishes to accomplish through publicity, then to whom the publicity should be directed. The community is not one large public but is made up of many subpublics, most of which require a separate and specific type of communication. At the onset, publicity should not attempt to reach the *whole* public, but should be directed at groups of greatest importance. A way to determine these is to list each public in order of importance, together with what it could do if it were favorably inclined. This method not only helps to clarify what may be needed in attitude changing, but in attitude building as well. Some typical publics in recreation for the handicapped include handicapped participants and their families. Individuals who find satisfaction in participating in a program are its best advocates.

[1] National Recreation Association, *Communications and Public Relations,* The National Recreation Association, New York, 1959, p. 3.

Volunteer workers, private agencies, and potential donors are extremely important publics. Other organizations interested in the handicapped are publics that may be of great assistance. Of primary significance are the people who tell the story to the community: newspaper publishers, editors, writers, radio and television station managers, program directors, opinion leaders such as clergymen and educators, and all other disseminators of information in the community.

Establishing Objectives

The development of specific objectives not only helps to determine the most important publics for the program to reach, but it also assists in selecting procedures and media for implementing a public relations plan. The objectives of a program vary according to the specific needs of each group, but a typical example may be summarized as follows:

1. To interpret the need for and benefits of recreation for the handicapped.
2. To inform handicapped individuals concerning the program being offered and to enlist them as participants so that a greater number may benefit from the available services.
3. To enlist individuals to give volunteer services in some specific form.
4. To secure financial support necessary for the establishment and/or continuance of the program and to secure needed equipment and supplies.
5. To give the community an accounting of the work being accomplished in recreation for the handicapped.
6. To share information concerning recreation for the handicapped with related agencies, organizations, and groups interested in the handicapped.

Implementation of the above objectives into a public relations program requires the use of a variety of procedures and media. It consists of presenting and interpreting information about recreation for the handicapped to potential participants and their parents as well as to the general public. It requires a plan for the recruitment of volunteers and sponsors, and the development of acceptable methods of reporting to the public the accomplishments and benefits of the recreation program and of sharing information with related groups interested in the handicapped. Publicity must be thoroughly planned in advance and must consist of wisely selected materials designed to achieve specific objectives. To be most effective, a public relations program must be carried on continuously, but publicity releases and other aspects of the program need to be timed appropriately. In addition, publicity must be truthful, factual, informative, interesting, dramatic, direct, clear, and concise. Every suitable medium and available channel should be utilized in promoting recreation programs for the handicapped in any community.

Publicity Media

The variety of media of publicity can generally be classified in four areas. They are (1) visual methods such as demonstrations, motion pictures, and exhibits, (2) the human voice, as in speeches and broadcasts, (3) newspapers and magazines, and (4) other printed material.

Visual Methods

Demonstrations of program activities by handicapped persons themselves are the most effective of all methods of promoting recreation for the handicapped. Arranging occasions where the press and others have been able to see handicapped persons having fun and participating actively has proved to be the finest technique for interpreting the whole purpose of the program. Members of the press are frequently reluctant to visit programs especially for the severely handicapped, and they hesitate to photograph these persons. However, recreation programs offer rare opportunities for presenting handicapped persons in a happy and relaxed atmosphere which is appealing and acceptable to the average person, and in particular to the press photographers and reporters. In no way should handicapped persons ever be exploited, and demonstrations should be given only if they reflect the real enthusiasm and enjoyment of the participants. Handicapped persons can be helped to feel secure in meeting individuals and groups through a gradual process of inviting individuals and small groups to view the program. An example of how this confidence may be achieved is illustrated by the following experience.

A group of severely handicapped cerebral palsied young adults participating in a recreation program for the first time decided after three months that they would like to give some type of demonstration of their activities. They agreed, first of all, that they would invite only close friends and parents to this event. It was eventually decided that they would present a marionette play in order that they could be "behind the scenes" and not on the stage, where they would be seen. Although all of them had severe speech impairments, one person, whose ambition was to be an actress, read the narration over the microphone, but still behind the scenes. The play was presented in an informal setting, and both the participants and guests felt at ease with one another. As a result of this first experience, the group was encouraged to present other plays and various activities. Gradually its members gained sufficient confidence in themselves to present pageants and plays on the stage; to act as hosts and hostesses at an open house for the press and invited public; to plan and present a circus, a Mardi gras, and many other special events for friends, parents, interested individuals, and for the general public.

One of the greatest benefits derived from having handicapped persons participate in community activities is that more people are enabled to see them. Visits to the zoo, museums, plays, concerts, public restaurants, and other places of interest not only enrich the experiences of the handicapped, but serve as a form of demonstration which helps to educate the general public toward better understanding and acceptance of these individuals.

Television has proved to be one of the finest media for presenting activities visually to the greatest number of people within a community or region. Both radio and television stations are required by federal law to provide public service programs, and there are numerous opportunities for utilizing these media to promote recreation for the handicapped. Most large cities have local television stations with programs that can present some phase of such activities. Programs thirty minutes or longer are able to "tell the story" of an agency by telecasting its activities. Other programs including daily news broadcasts will take pictures of special activities for showing at a later date. They will also interview persons on these programs and use films, slides, photographs, exhibits, displays, and other visual aids for publicizing the recreation program.

A recreation program for the severely handicapped in San Francisco was televised live on a half-hour program called "Success Story." A script, prepared by the television writers with advice from the recreation staff, was developed specifically to interpret recreation as a need and a benefit for handicapped persons and to gain wider community support for the program. The public response was most favorable, and a kinescope which was made of the show proved of great value to the agency. The use of movies and colored slides of recreation activities for the handicapped has been most effective in interpreting and promoting the program, especially to potential sponsors. Such visual aids are invaluable to use with service clubs and many other groups, especially if the groups are unable to view the program in person.

Window displays and exhibits that include photographs of the recreation activities are excellent means of informing the general public of the program. Exhibits that show articles made by the handicapped are interesting and effective media for interpreting the type of activities conducted. For example, objects made in arts and crafts groups, such as pottery and paintings, and murals or items made in the sewing club or woodworking class, make interesting and informative exhibits for publicizing recreation for the handicapped (see pp. 260–287).

The Human Voice

The use of the human voice—one of the most effective methods for transmitting information—can be used to influence a large audience, to "sell" a particular group, or to enlist the support of key individuals. It can tell the many human interest stories that can be found in recreation programs for the handicapped—stories that have tremendous emotional appeal for an appropriate audience. The establishment of a speakers' bureau contributes to the greater development of recreation programs for the handicapped through talks given before Parent-Teachers Associations, civic clubs, religious, educational, fraternal, and patriotic organizations and groups, which are constantly looking for speakers who can talk on topics of vital community interest. Outstanding speakers are frequently willing to serve on a speakers' bureau, as a public service to the locality. Speakers must be thoroughly familiar with the program and its objectives in order to interpret them effectively and accurately to various groups. Films, slides, posters, exhibits, and other visual aids can be used to advantage to illustrate points made by the speakers. The audiences reached by the speeches are greatly increased when these are publicized through the newspapers, radio, and television.

The effectiveness of participants in recreation programs in promoting them was demonstrated by a group of twelve severely handicapped young adults. They served as members of a panel that discussed recreation and its benefits with college students, recreation leaders, and administrators. They created such a favorable impression that they were invited to discuss the need for recreation for the handicapped at the State Conference in Social Welfare. Appearances of handicapped persons on television and radio are one of the best means of interpreting a recreation program for their group. In particular, handicapped children who are articulate and appealing to an audience are invaluable in this phase of the over-all public relations program.

Newspapers

The newspapers are considered the most important medium for regularly publicizing community recreation programs. In order to establish and maintain good relationships with them, it is vitally important that personal contacts be made periodically with newspaper executives and their staff. Their confidence must be cultivated, and this can be best achieved through contacts over a long period and through the presentation of news honestly, factually, and impartially. Editorials commending the program, especially when unsolicited, afford evidence that the newspaper has confidence in its merit, and they help win public support, especially if they appear at the time of a financial campaign. The following editorial, that appeared in The San Francisco *News*, is an excellent illustration of the type that has great value.

THE BEST TONIC OF ALL

Recreation is a splendid medicine for everyone, but for the handicapped who are denied the outlet of everyday activities, it can be almost literally a life-saver.

This has been proved at a unique San Francisco institution which for seven years has been dispensing fun and diversion for young and old crippled by a multitude of afflictions.

The institution is the Recreation Center for the Handicapped, an internationally-copied pioneer in its field.

WHEE—Lloyd Riddle pitches his first snowball. (*Photograph and caption from a newspaper article appearing in the* San Mateo Times.)

Almost all its work is done by volunteers. Its modest cash needs are met by donations. If you would like to help keep the door to new lives open to those with heavy physical burdens, you can do so by sending your check to the Center at Fleishhacker Pool Bldg., San Francisco 16.

FUN IN THE SNOW—Cathy Southward and Lloyd Riddle, volunteer aides (behind her) pull Jerry Walsh along in visit to snow country. Jerry's wheel chair fitted the double toboggan very well. (*Photograph and caption from a newspaper article appearing in the* San Mateo Times.)

Recreation for the handicapped affords much material in the form of dramatic human interest stories, and illustrations are welcomed by the papers if presented in suitable form. As previously mentioned, handicapped persons must never be exploited, but stories about them can be effective and appealing without being morbid or pitiable. As a rule, this can be accomplished only if stories are written by trained writers. Photographic releases must always be obtained from parents of handicapped children and from handicapped adults. (See sample release in "Records and Reports," Chapter 13.) Other types of newspaper publicity which may be used to promote recreation for the handicapped are feature articles, announcements and reports of special events, and reports of interviews and speeches.

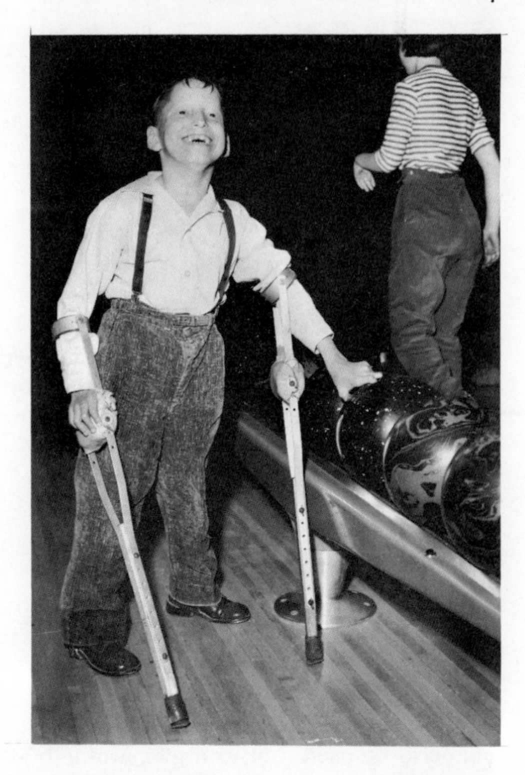

STRIKE SMILE — is just as good on the face of a physically handicapped youngster, as Johnny Romero of 1758 Dewey Avenue, San Mateo, illustrates. (*Photograph and caption from a newspaper article appearing in the* San Mateo Times.)

Magazine articles or stories of recreation programs for the handicapped not only publicize the programs reported but help educate the public to the need for similar action in every locality.

Other Printed Materials

Every agency providing a recreation program for the handicapped should have a variety of printed materials that tell its story in order adequately to interpret and promote the program. Materials should be attractive and tell their story simply and effectively. Excellent materials can be prepared inexpensively on colored paper with sketches and various types of illustration through the mimeograph and lithograph process. Offset lithography is the least expensive method of printing and reproducing photographs. Several other factors must be kept in mind in the preparation of materials. One is the public to whom they are all primarily addressed. Their content must be such as to induce people to read them, and the same copy may not appeal to all types of individuals. The method of distribution is another factor that may influence the size and

FIRST OUTING—Bruce Oka gets toboggan's eye view of his first snow experience, while volunteers Bob Draher and Mary Ferra act as his team. (*Photograph and caption from a newspaper article appearing in the* San Mateo Times.)

shape to be used. For example, a nine-by-twelve-inch sheet, folded twice, makes a brochure that can be mailed in a standard business envelope and that fits readily in a pocket. A simple sheet containing factual data may serve for wide distribution at meetings and conferences, whereas materials prepared for potential donors need to have eye appeal. All publicity materials should bear the name and address of the agency, and a listing of officers and directors is usually desirable.

Following are suggestions for types of printed materials that are most desirable and useful in recreation programs for the handicapped.

Brochures or folders range from a three- or four-page mimeographed leaflet to a beautifully illustrated booklet prepared in various colors. Photographs assist immeasurably in telling the story with a minimum of copy. Brochures should be concise, with plenty of white spaces and clear type in sizes large enough to read without difficulty. Most important, the copy should convey clearly the intended message. Brochures of the more elaborate type are commonly mailed to selected lists of people; the simpler forms are convenient for handing out to audiences, for display at exhibits, and so on.

Fact sheets should be exactly what the name implies. They should contain factual information about the program presented with a minimum of words. The who, what, where, and when question and answer type of format is popular and is particularly valuable if it answers the questions that are commonly asked about the program. Such a format may also include questions as "What is the Purpose of the Program?" "Whom Does It Serve?" "How are Persons Referred?" "How is it Organized?" "How is it Financed?" "Who are the Personnel?" "How are Handicapped Persons Transported?" "What are the Benefits to the Participants?" "What Does it Cost to Participate?" and other questions and answers which help to explain the particular program. Fact sheets need to be revised if marked changes occur in the nature of the program or in the operating policies. They are especially beneficial and useful in explaining a new program to the press and the public.

Appeal letters are used primarily for the purpose of raising funds. However, because most people today receive a great deal of mail, especially advertisements and requests for funds, mailing must have eye appeal, or they are likely to be a waste of time, effort, and expense. Appeal letters must be easy to read, so that they must be broken up into short paragraphs. In general, the introductory paragraphs must capture the reader's interest, and the entire letter must be brief, direct, and to the point. The type of stationery used in direct mailing has a bearing upon the success in getting across the message to the recipient. Use on the stationery of a symbol which identifies the agency or its program has proved an excellent means of publicity, especially if it conveys an idea of the nature of the program. At the Recreation Center, a photograph of a boy on crutches walking up a ramp into the Center with the words "Send us your lame . . . your chair-bound too!" is used as the symbol on letterheads, annual reports, buses, and other publicity media. The preparation or selection of the mailing list is a factor that determines to a considerable degree the response to an appeal letter, and should therefore be done with the greatest care.

Annual Reports of recreation programs for the handicapped can be an excellent publicity medium if they tell the story of the service rendered in a way that makes evident the value of the program. It is customary to mail copies of the annual report to sponsors and other persons who have evidenced interest in the handicapped. The format of annual reports must be attractive, readable, and interesting in order to derive the greatest benefit from their use.

Posters, handbills, flyers, announcing scheduled programs, and postcards are other types of printed materials that can be used effectively in publicity and in the promotion of recreation for the handicapped. A special form used to recognize the service rendered by volunteers, similar to the example reproduced on page 127, has also served a useful purpose.

SAN FRANCISCO RECREATION CENTER for the HANDICAPPED, Inc.

A non-profit corporation of the State of California

BEFORE THE GAME . . .
Out early to see their hero, this threesome from the Center spent a wonderful day at the Ball Park through the generosity of the San Francisco Giants.

FLEISHHACKER POOL BUILDING
GREAT HIGHWAY NEAR SLOAT BOULEVARD
SAN FRANCISCO 16, CALIFORNIA **OVERLAND 1-6534**

PURPOSE AND PLAN OF THE CENTER . . .

FAST FRIENDS
The love of a child for an animal is one of youth's inalienable rights. At the Center we have many pets—not all of them as unresponsive to friendly overtures as this tabby.

The purpose of the San Francisco Recreation Center for the Handicapped is to bring happiness and companionship to those who are deprived of normal group activities. This is a non-profit organization serving the San Francisco area only and is not affiliated with any state or national organization.

Year-round we provide planned recreational programs for children and adults of all races and creeds who share a common bond because of their physical limitations. Through their experience at the Center youngsters especially are helped to

WHO COMES TO THE CENTER?

Children and young adults who have been handicapped from infancy or whose physical activities are limited because of Arthritis, Cerebral Palsy, Multiple Sclerosis, Muscular Atrophy, Muscular Dystrophy, Poliomyelitis, Visual handicaps, and others. They come to us from San Francisco and the entire Bay Area.

WHAT DO WE DO AT THE CENTER?

Under the guidance of a professional recreational staff our young people participate in sports, hobbies, social, cultural and creative activities. We've pictured them here because seeing them at play tells the story better than any words of ours.

WHERE DO WE LEARN AND PLAY?

As the pictures show, throughout the year we have many outings, but, of course, we also have a "home base"—our Club House complete with social halls, library, music and game rooms, and kitchen, plus a real stage where we perform. Here we eat together and play together and have parties for our non-handicapped friends. We are proud of our Center and hope you will come and visit us.

CAN YOU REMEMBER YOUR FIRST HAYRIDE?
It was a tremendous thrill, we feel sure; so imagine, if you can, how doubly thrilling the Hayride is to these

We operate every weekday, including Saturdays, because the need is great. Call us for hours and an outline of programs.

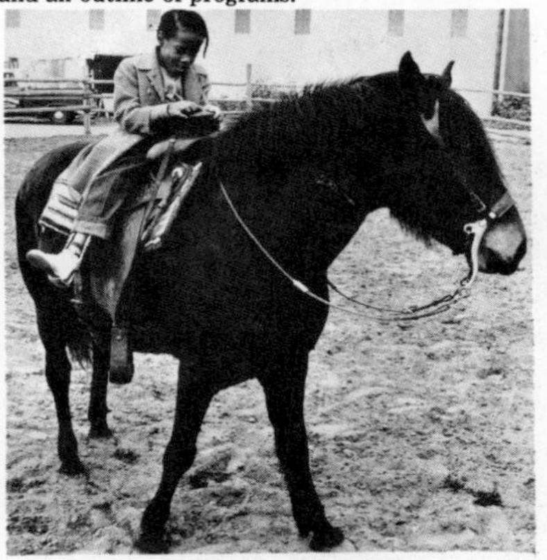

NEW EXPERIENCES!
JANICE, a post-polio youngster, takes her first horseback ride on MIDNIGHT, a patient pony.

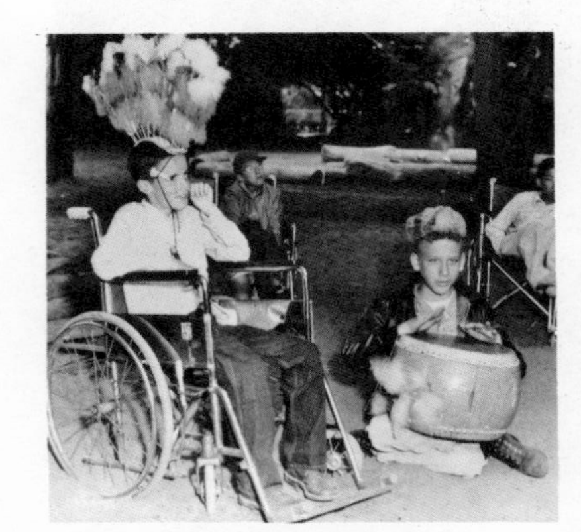

BIG CHIEF "BRAVE SPIRIT"
The Chief can't war dance, but he listens intently as drum number is rehearsed for evening ceremonies at Summer Camp.

Anyone who needs the services we offer! If possible, parents pay a small fee to aid in cost of transportation and program supplies. However, no one who needs us is ever turned away.

A PAIR OF SEVENS
Seven-year-old children prepare for an overnight campout during the regular Summer Day Camp.

HOW CAN YOU HELP US?

By making a donation to this work to celebrate a happy occasion, in memory of a friend or just to say you are with us in our program. Your contribution is tax deductible—you will forget tomorrow that you gave—but the children who benefit through your generosity will remember for a lifetime.

President . . . HONORABLE JOHN B. MOLINARI
First Vice President . . . . MRS. RICHARD GLYER
Second Vice President . . . . JOHN S. EHRLICH
Secretary . . . . . MRS. JACQUES PEDEUBOY
Treasurer . . . . JOSEPH FOGARTY
Past President . . . . MRS. JOHN M. DOUGLAS

DIRECTORS

DONALD E. ANDERSON	GEORGE JOHNS
LEONARD BERGER	TED KOHLER, Ed.D.
GEORGE CANRINUS	WALTER MAILS
GINO P. CECCHI	MRS. LAWRENCE S. MANA
JAMES A. CLARK, JR.	GEORGE MARDIKIAN
PETER COHEN, M. D.	HON. FRANCIS McCARTY
GEORGE S. DOLIM	PRIMO R. REPETTO
NICK GERACIMOS	ROY SCOLA
JOHN F. HENNING	MRS. DANIEL STONE
DALTON HOWATT	MRS. H. ALLEN THOMPSON

FOUNDER AND DIRECTOR

MRS. MORRIS POMEROY

SPONSORING COMMITTEE

Chairman: GEORGE CANRINUS

JOHNNIE ANTONELLI	JAMES B. MOFFET
FRED APOSTOLI	LEO NOMELLINI
IRA BLUE	JOE PERRY
ANNE CURTIS CUNEO	BILL RIGNEY
BOB FOUTS	BILL RUSSELL
CURLEY GRIEVE	BOB ST. CLAIR
RED HICKEY	CHARLES SAVA
DON KLEIN	DINK TEMPLETON
BILL LEISER	KEN VENTURI
HANK LUISETTI	HARVIE WARD
JACK McDONALD	ROGER WILLIAMS
WILLIE MAYS	PHIL WOOLPERT

Contributions Are Gratefully Accepted

RECREATION CENTER FOR THE HANDICAPPED, INC.

Great Highway, San Francisco 16, California

☐ Patron $100 or over ☐ Sustaining $10 to $49
☐ Donor $50 to $99 ☐ Active $2 to $9
☐ Enclosed is my check for $________
☐ Please send additional information

Name____________________

Address____________City________

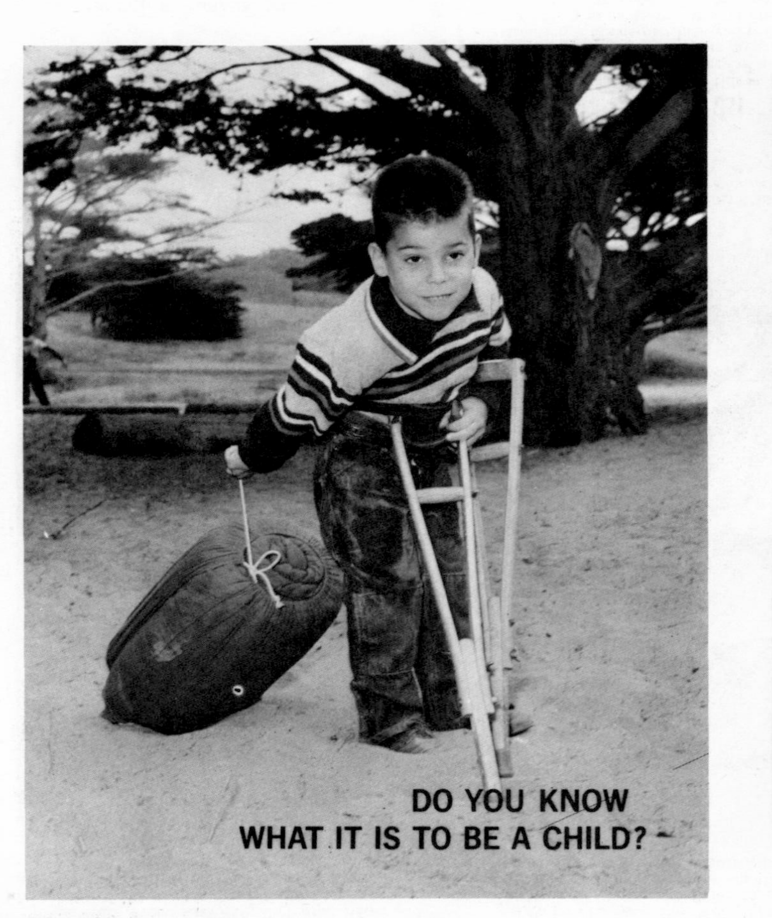
DO YOU KNOW
WHAT IT IS TO BE A CHILD?

IT IS TO BELIEVE IN LOVE . . .

Here Johnny, a victim of cerebral palsy, and David, a non-handicapped child weave together — and share together a bond of friendship.

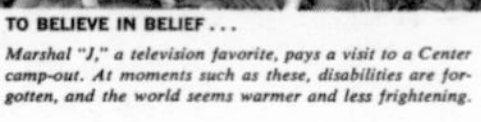

TO BELIEVE IN BELIEF . . .

Marshal "J," a television favorite, pays a visit to a Center camp-out. At moments such as these, disabilities are forgotten, and the world seems warmer and less frightening.

RECREATION CENTER FOR THE HANDICAPPED, INC.

WHAT WE DO

We try in every way possible to have children who are unable to attend school participate daily in educational and cultural activities. Without the Center these youngsters would spend lonely lives in the confines of their homes.

LEARN AND PLAY

The Center is both a clubhouse and home-away-from-home. Here in their own social hall, library, game room and kitchen the children learn to the extent that their capabilities allow. They are extremely proud of their Center where they eat together, play together and sometimes even have parties for their non-handicapped friends.

WHEN ARE WE OPEN?

Six days of every week—every day but Sunday. Programs are conducted each day and evenings. Office hours are 9:00 a.m. to 5:00 p.m.

WHO MAY COME?

The Center is open as far as possible to everyone who can use the services offered. The only restriction is the length to which our funds can be stretched. Parents, when possible, pay a small fee to aid in the cost of transportation and program supplies. The Center now has two buses and two full-time drivers, thus reducing the cost of regular transportation. Taxis are used only in emergencies.

1962 Accomplishments — and an Even Larger Program for 1963

★ Nine different age groups were formed, from three years of age and up. Some of these include Tiny Tots, Pre-Teens, Young Teens and Older Teens.

★ "Trip Camping," a progressive camping experience, was established for teen agers. Over-night campouts were held in various state parks in California.

★ Non-handicapped children from various city playgrounds participated in recreational activities at the Center with the handicapped.

★ A long-time dream was realized for a group of the Center's homebound boys when, for the first time in the nation, a Sea Scout unit was organized for them. The members, who were installed in December, will participate in many of the activities with non-handicapped Sea Scouts.

★ Totally deaf children were included in the Center's program for the first time.

★ Several snow trips were taken by pre-teens and teen agers.

★ Many of the children experienced their first trip to a farm where they visited with baby animals. They also slid down haystacks and rode ponies.

TO BELIEVE IN LOVELINESS . . .

Cathy, totally blind, finds beauty in the touch of clay. Her face radiates an inward light . . . although she cannot see her own creation.

Send us your lame ... your chair-bound too!

RECREATION CENTER *for* THE HANDICAPPED INC.

Fleishhacker Pool Building,
Great Highway near Sloat Boulevard · OVerland 1-6534
San Francisco 16, California · OVerland 1-5441

Hello—

I'm Gary Foss, and you might call me the original theme boy for The Recreation Center, as the little fellow on the letterhead was drawn from a photograph of me made when I was nine. That was ten years ago, and I'm still making it up the ramp on crutches, since cerebral palsy makes it impossible for me to walk without them.

How come I'm writing you? Well it happened this way. I was in Mrs. Pomeroy's office (she is our Director) when the Board members were talking about how they could tell the public about the fine work being done at the Center. They were reading a letter aloud, and I couldn't help interrupting. "How can that man tell people about what the Center does for us?" I asked. "He isn't handicapped!"

Everyone looked startled. Then Mrs. Pomeroy spoke up and said "Why don't you write the letter, Gary?"

Actually, I can't write well enough to tell you what the Center has meant to me. I've tried—I've even talked it over with some of the others—but we always end up at the same place—talking about how dreadful it would be without the Center. Maybe we're frightened that we'd go soft if we tried to spell out the warmth, the friendship, the special training in crafts and sports, even the feeling of security and achievement that the Center gives us.

Take me. My dad is a service man, away most of the time. I do have two brothers, but they are much older and married. My mom is a peach. She tried hard to keep me occupied, but she couldn't give me the kind of help I needed, because she is "unhandicapped" and couldn't understand what I needed was fun and activity rather than sympathy.

Today, at 19, thanks to the Center, I can do a lot of things that no one thought I'd ever do. Understand, I'm not going out for track, but I can make it on a bus on my own. I'm also taking two special courses at Samuel Gompers School. Also — and most important—I have friends—people who like me and want to be with me—people with whom I have much in common.

That is my story—and much too long too. The real purpose of this letter is to ask you to make a generous donation to The Recreation Center for the Handicapped. There are 300 more like me—and to all of us the Center means everything.

Please send a donation today.

Sincerely,

Gary Foss

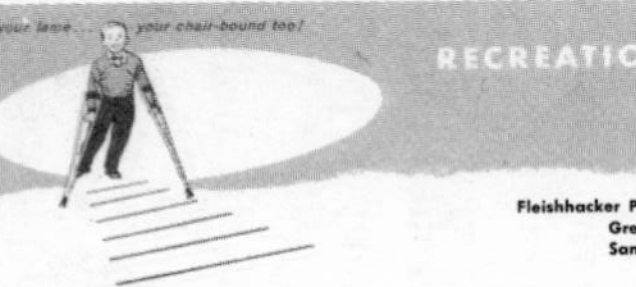

Now, at 19

CONTRIBUTIONS TO SUPPORT THIS VITALLY NEEDED WORK ARE TAX DEDUCTIBLE

HOW YOU CAN HELP US

The Recreation Center for the Handicapped relies on public support to continue its work of providing guided recreation for handicapped children.

This non-profit organization serves the entire San Francisco Bay Area, and is not affiliated with any state or national organization.

More than 325 severely handicapped persons are enrolled, and new applicants are interviewed almost every day.

The Center needs your support—this year more than ever. Mail your check today to:

Recreation Center for the Handicapped
Great Highway near Sloat Boulevard
San Francisco. California

STATEMENT OF CASH RECEIPTS AND DISBURSEMENTS FOR THE FISCAL YEAR ENDED AUGUST 31, 1962

CASH RECEIPTS			
Contributions received		$33,164.15	
Membership drive		8,363.60	
Service fees – participants		2,986.02	
Day camp		2,591.21	
Miscellaneous		1,952.13	$49,057.11
CASH DISBURSEMENTS			
Salaries and wages			
Recreation leaders	$12,266.14		
Program directors	7,923.00		
Office	4,584.95		
Kitchen Aide and janitor	3,330.25		
Drivers	2,762.88	$30,867.22	
Day camp supplies and expense		76.00	
Program supplies and expense		2,496.61	
Transportation		6,055.56	
Office supplies		1,328.20	
Telephone		997.33	
Payroll taxes		939.22	
Field and travel		1,242.46	
Fund drive expense – Note 2		1,500.41	
Letter drive expense		509.92	
Automobile expense		1,314.18	
Repairs and maintenance		416.87	
Insurance		353.04	
Photograph and art		805.28	
Purchase of automobile		2,662.03	
Miscellaneous		696.14	52,260.47
EXCESS OF DISBURSEMENTS OVER RECEIPTS			$(3,203.36)

Notes: (1) The founder and director of the Center is unsalaried.
(2) Fund drive expenses include payments for printing, stationery, postage, only.
(3) Many volunteers give of their time and skill to make our programs possible.

Prepared by
Cecchi and Scheibner, Certified Public Accountants

It is sometimes advantageous for an agency to issue a publication that serves the purpose of two or more of the types of printed materials previously mentioned. The Recreation Center, for example, has used successfully an illustrated folder containing an appeal letter, facts about the Center, an annual report, and a certified statement of cash receipts and disbursements for the year. The accompanying pages reproduce portions of one of these folders.

The Use of Committees

Publicity committees can be extremely valuable in assisting the staff to develop and maintain a public relations program. However, it is of the utmost importance that lay persons on such committees be familiar with the recreation program and be able to talk intelligently about it or write news releases for the press. Professional workers from public relations and advertising agencies often volunteer to assist on publicity committees as a community service. In one recreation program for the handicapped a group of professional public relations directors, advertising managers, and other promotional personnel served as a committee to handle most of the public relations matters for the agency. Their services included the development of brochures, appeal letters, posters, billboards, and the release of publicity to the press. This type of assistance is invaluable to the over-all promotion of the program.

Establishing Policies

Any type of program concerned with public relations must establish policies that will help in implementing the over-all plan. The policies needed will vary for each program or agency, but they are essential in clarifying the objectives of the public relations plan. Following are some typical policies.

1. All publicity must be honest, comprehensive, dignified, and in keeping with the philosophy of nonexploitation of handicapped participants.
2. All available publicity and promotional media will be utilized, such as letters, posters, streamers, banners, throwaways, local and program newspapers, bulletins, postcards, and word of mouth.
3. The publicity program shall be continuous and well planned.
4. All printed materials shall be attractive, interesting, colorful, neat, and current.

Sheriff's Posse

HELP OUR HANDICAPPED

HORSE SHOW
Sept. 15, 16
Polo Grounds Golden Gate Park
$1.00

PROCEEDS—RECREATION CENTER FOR THE HANDICAPPED

5. Publicity shall be especially prepared for the specific groups that it is intended to reach: teen-age readers, service groups, and so on.

6. The resources of the recreation program for the handicapped shall not be used in political issues of the city.

7. The publicity committee shall be kept informed of all scheduled activities, regardless of their importance.

8. Radio, television, filming, or any other outside promotion connected in any way with the program shall be cleared through the publicity committee.

9. Personal thank-you letters shall be written to acknowledge all gifts or assistance, regardless of how small.

10. All volunteers shall be appropriately recognized and their work acknowledged through letters of appreciation, certificate awards, teas, and so on.

11. All supporting agencies and groups will be recognized through suitable publicity for their assistance to the program.

Conclusions

There is no quick or magic way to build or maintain good public relations. "Only hard, careful, persistent, honest effort can change adverse opinions or reinforce and strengthen favorable ones . . . good opinion must be deserved and earned."[2] Public relations are much more than the competent use of mass communications. The conduct, manners, and behavior of all employees on and off the job, the manner in which assistance is acknowledged, and every other point at which the public comes in contact with the program are all phases of public relations. Creating and sustaining good will should be the goal of every person even remotely associated with the program or agency.

[2] National Recreation Association, *op. cit.*, p. 5.

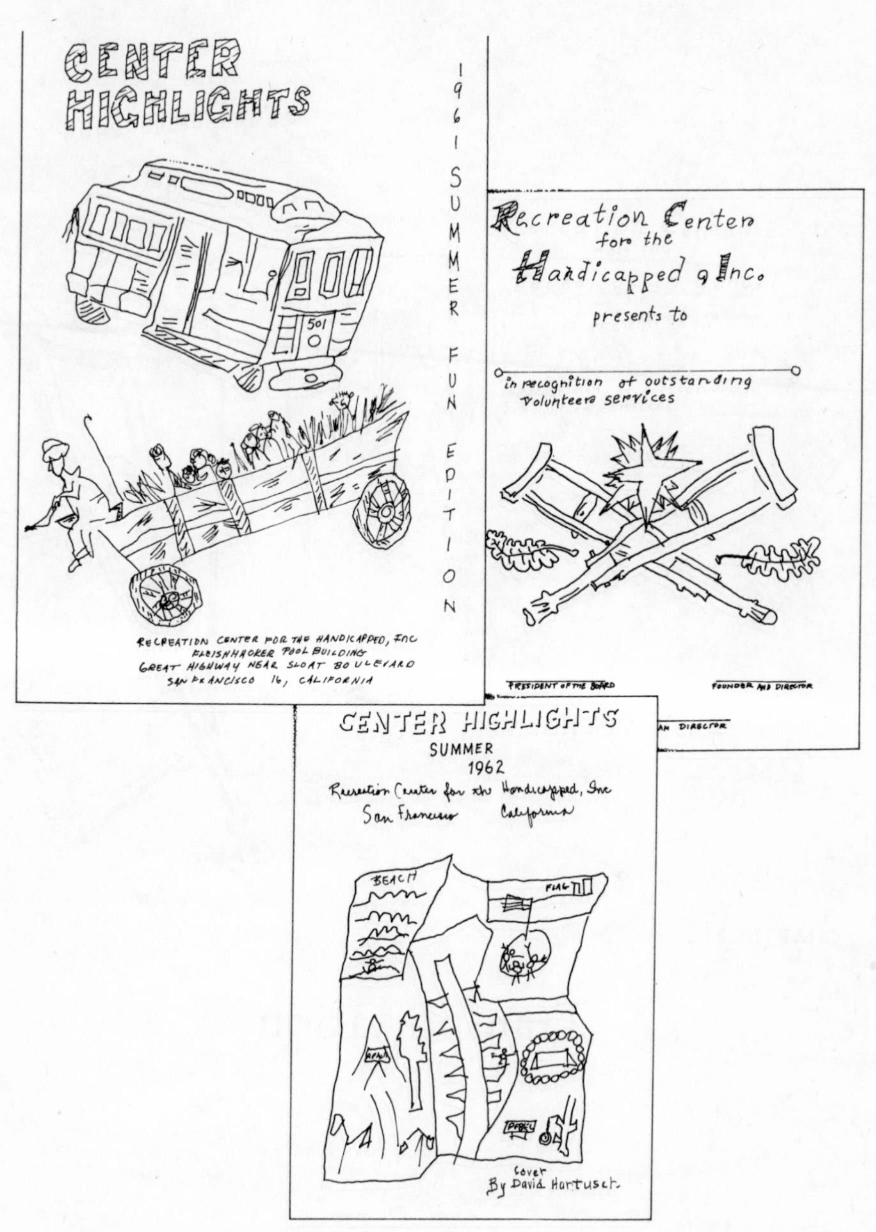

Typical program announcements and award certificate for volunteers.

CHAPTER 11

Transportation

The problem of transporting physically handicapped persons has for many years been a major concern of groups and individuals associated with them. It has been an important topic of discussion among health, education, and welfare agencies since services for the handicapped began, and many solutions have been attempted. Participants in an institute, after long deliberation, agreed that the provision of transportation is basic to the realistic planning of any type of program for the severely handicapped and that recreation leaders should solve the problem of transporting the handicapped before activities are offered to them. They further agreed that since transportation is a vital part of the program, it is imperative that the agency make ample provision for this service in its budget.[1] Major considerations include qualified drivers, safety and comfort, time en route, and economy.

Some recreation programs for the handicapped have been started only to be discontinued because transportation was not included in the initial planning. While the provision of transportation has not been of major concern in the average community recreation program, it is an important factor in planning programs for the handicapped. The mere provision of recreation activities for the handicapped does not assure attendance. It is understandable that persons in wheel chairs, in beds, and many on crutches are unable to use public conveyances and that some type of special transportation must be provided for them. It is especially important that this problem be solved when groups of handicapped persons are involved, even before developing plans for offering an activity.

Many factors to be considered in planning transportation for handicapped persons create difficult problems. However, experiences of special schools, health and welfare agencies, and recreation groups afford some methods and techniques that have been quite successful in solving them.

Types of Transportation

Special schools that have been established for the physically handicapped have developed transportation procedures that serve as an excellent guide in planning recreation programs for these persons. The number of handicapped persons in a given locality, the severity of their disabilities, the distance which they must travel, and the availability of qualified drivers are some of the varying factors that determine the types

[1] National Recreation Association Proceedings of the Third Hospital Recreation Institute, *Recreation for the Ill and Handicapped Homebound,* New York, 1958, p. 47.

of transportation needed. In general, three types of transportation have been used successfully: buses, taxis, and private automobiles. There are large differences in the expense involved between these types, and groups planning transportation must take this factor into account.

Buses

Some school districts purchase coaches which are especially constructed for transporting physically handicapped boys and girls. Such coaches have ramps for children in wheel chairs or hoists to lift them into the vehicle. Some have special seats with belts which hold children who need support to prevent them from falling. Some buses also have special "wells" in the floor of the vehicle into which the wheels of the wheel chair will fit and be braced securely. This arrangement permits a child to remain in his wheel chair during the trip.

There are several automobile coach manufacturers who build these special buses. Although the initial cost of such a bus is quite expensive, it has several advantages, particularly where daily transportation is required, as in a school program. One advantage is the fact that a great deal of time and effort is saved when a child does not have to be removed from his wheel chair into a vehicle. In addition, the necessity for lifting severely handicapped persons and for folding, unfolding, and transporting their chairs and other paraphernalia with them is a factor that must be considered in the employment of drivers. This type of duty usually eliminates the use of women bus drivers, who have been used very successfully with special-built buses where lifting of persons and special handling of wheel chairs are not required.

Frequently, the use of large chartered buses is a realistic solution to the problem of transporting large groups of handicapped persons, particularly in recreation and camping programs. Such buses have been used very successfully for trips and outings.

Bus drivers and all others who drive the handicapped should be carefully selected not only for their ability to drive, but also for special qualifications which are considered essential. These qualifications are discussed in detail later in this chapter, but their importance warrants mention here.

There are some disadvantages in using large buses to pick up groups of handicapped persons, regardless of whether they are specially built or whether they are regular type buses. One of these disadvantages concerns the time element. It is not likely that in a given community handicapped persons will be living in close proximity to one another; they will usually be scattered throughout the locality. If a program is being planned for large groups of handicapped persons, the provision of a special bus, even though it would accommodate most of them, is usually not the solution. The reason is that the amount of time it would take to pick them up and return them home might require some of the children to remain on the bus for an hour or more. This is much longer than the thirty or forty minutes designated by some schools as the maximum time a child may spend en route in order to avoid fatigue. Therefore routes must be arranged so as to keep at a minimum the time each person must spend in travel.

Another disadvantage of using a large bus is the fact that some residences are not accessible to such vehicles. The problem of maneuvering in and out of narrow streets, alleys, and on steep hills must be considered. In addition, the use of large buses frequently creates problems in loading and unloading of the handicapped. Some schools have built special ramps, loading decks, or pavillions for buses and other vehicles to minimize this problem. Where considerable time is required for loading and unloading, marquees or canopies have been built to protect children from inclement weather.

In case handicapped persons are scattered over a large area, it is better to use several smaller buses or automobiles to handle the transportation for segments of the area. Some communities have found it expedient to plan "feeder" routes, which pick up handicapped persons in various sections and bring them to a location where they can be transferred into a larger coach and taken to their final destination. Others use regular school buses or station wagons to transport the handicapped. Wheel chairs and reclining chairs are folded up and transported with the pupils, along with other special equipment used by the children.

Station wagons and smaller buses have been used successfully by the Recreation Center. Compact-type buses, which accommodate twelve to fifteen persons, have been adapted for use by the installation of seat belts and special racks to accommodate eight to ten wheel chairs. Such racks can be built by an experienced carpenter or fabricated by any good machine shop. The rack must be built long enough and high enough so that the folded wheel chairs can be safely stacked.

Taxicabs

Taxicabs have been used to transport handicapped persons to school, to rehabilitation programs and other health services, and for recreation and camping programs. Some groups have found the use of taxicabs under contract to be a reasonable solution, especially where the time element must be strictly observed for certain children. The use of taxicabs can be adjusted readily to last-minute demands; as compared to volunteer drivers, it is much more reliable. It is important that drivers be carefully selected for their driving ability and that they know how to assist the handicapped properly.

Taxicabs are expensive, but in some instances where other costs are considered, such as insurance, the employment of competent drivers, the maintenance of automobiles, and other expenses, it is cheaper for groups to use taxicabs than to own their own vehicles or to use other modes of transportation discussed in this chapter.

Private Automobiles

Private automobiles have been used with much success in some programs and have proved to be very unsuccessful in others. In some areas, particularly where there are small groups, parents have formed car pools to transport their children. However, experience indicates that in general this plan has not been very satisfactory for several reasons. It is especially difficult for mothers to transport severely handicapped persons because of the lifting involved. Furthermore, some parents do not have automobiles, or they do not know how to drive. Many parents have other children at home whom they cannot leave; others must work. These and other factors prevent their driving in car pools or even transporting their own children. For the same reasons, many women volunteers other than parents of handicapped children, who drive their own cars, are not completely satisfactory. Drivers of the American Red Cross Motor Corps and of other such organizations which provide vehicles and trained drivers are the exception to the rule that women volunteers do not transport the severely handicapped successfully. The problem of lifting and handling wheel chairs must be solved even with these drivers, as their duties do not require them to lift. Women drivers can be used very successfully to drive the blind and persons who are ambulatory and/or able to help themselves in and out of automobiles.

Men have generally proved more satisfactory volunteer drivers, especially members of fraternal and other organizations that undertake to drive the handicapped as a project. Such groups as Kiwanis, Lions, Elks, and many others have formed transportation committees for driving the handicapped to recreation programs, especially on weekends and evenings when they are not working. Individuals rotate at driving, and if the committee is large enough, each persons may have to drive only once every two or three months, depending on the number of handicapped persons and the frequency of the program.

In one community, used car dealers were organized and volunteered to transport severely handicapped children for the month the summer day camp was operated. Children were transported from their homes to the camp four days each week by the drivers. Parents and other volunteers were responsible for returning the children to their homes. Volunteer drivers are frequently willing to provide partial transportation, which helps considerably. Pickup trucks and other automobiles have been loaned by commercial firms, and in one city an undertaker donated the use of his ambulances.

Insurance is a factor which must be considered in the use of private automobiles. It is most essential to have adequate covering liability and property damage insurance when transporting any individual or a group. Some persons are reluctant to transport the handicapped, even if there is sufficient insurance coverage, because of the rare instances where suits have been filed when accidents occurred.

Regardless of the method used for transporting handicapped persons, several important factors that must be observed are "safety, comfort, time en route, economy, and the availability of specially qualified and insured drivers."[2]

Drivers of the Handicapped

The selection and orientation of drivers is of particular importance in the transportation of the handicapped. Character, personality, and resourcefulness must be considered along with their ability to drive safely. The relationship of the driver to the handicapped may have a far-reaching impact upon their mental attitude and adjustment. A driver of the severely handicapped, in particular, has close and intimate contacts with these persons. He may be the one who lifts them from their home into the bus and straps them in with a safety belt. He is probably also the person who carries them from the bus to the program site. The attitude of the driver and his remarks and comments during such times make a marked impression on the handicapped. The driver for recreation programs must accept a special responsibility for public relations, as he comes in contact with a large portion of the general public.

[2] *The Education of Exceptional Children,* 49th Year Book, Part 2 (Chicago: U. of Chicago, 1950), p. 214.

Job Description and Qualifications

The following job description for drivers at the Recreation Center was based on qualifications for school drivers of the handicapped.

DEFINITION. Under general supervision, the bus driver operates a bus in transporting handicapped children to and from their homes to the Recreation Center for the Handicapped.

EXAMPLES OF DUTIES. The driver operates the Center bus over a prescribed route; picks up children at designated stops, and assists children on and off the bus, lifting as necessary; adheres to a prescribed schedule to deliver children to the Center on time or to take them home; refuels the bus, adds oil and has tires checked when necessary; washes and cleans the inside of the bus and reports the need for mechanical repairs; makes special trips; fills out and turns in reports concerning number of children carried, miles traveled, and general condition of bus. During the part of the working day in which he does not drive the Center bus, the bus driver performs transportation duties as needed.

DESIRABLE QUALIFICATIONS. It is important that the driver, who comes in contact with the public, make a good appearance and conduct himself in a manner fitting an employee of the Center.
He should have:

1. *Knowledge of:*

   The California State Motor Vehicle Code and the Education Code, particularly as they relate to the operation of vehicles in transporting children.
   Geography of the local area.
   Safe driving practices.
   Basic preventive maintenance of automotive equipment.

2. *Ability to:*

   Operate a large and small bus with patience and skill.
   Make minor mechanical adjustments of automotive equipment.
   Understand and carry out oral directions.
   Get along well with children.
   Maintain a calm, even disposition.
   Exercise mature judgment in relation to driving and child care.
   Maintain a semblance of order on the bus.
   Handle large children and adults with heavy braces.

3. *License:*

   A valid Class "B" chauffeur's license.
   Red Cross first aid certificate.

4. *Experience:*

   Two years of successful full-time paid experience in driving commercial or heavy-duty vehicles. Experience with children. Safe driving record and current driver's license.

The Center's bus shows special-built racks for wheel chairs. The symbol on side of bus is also used on Center letter head and promotional materials.

Coordinator of Transportation

Some agencies providing or arranging transportation for the handicapped have found it necessary to have a coordinator or dispatcher who is responsible for the many phases of the transportation program. The time required to accomplish this task and related duties is determined by the number of persons in need of transportation, the frequency and type of programs, modes and variety of transportation, and many other factors. This job is frequently assigned to volunteers, but where daily recreation programs are conducted for large groups, it is almost certain that at least one person will be needed full time to coordinate the transportation. The coordinator should be encouraged to recommend policies and procedures that he believes would help in the over-all operation of the transportation program. He may be assigned other duties such as the supervision of the maintenance of buses and other automobiles. He must be able to work successfully with volunteer drivers as well as with the paid staff and drivers of taxicabs and chartered buses.

The Recreation Center provides or arranges transportation for most of its three hundred and twenty-five members. Daytime and evening programs at the Center are conducted daily for various age groups, who are scattered over large areas. The Center, as well as other agencies, has found it expedient to use a combination of buses, taxicabs, and private automobiles. As mentioned previously, factors considered in planning the routes are the time element, economy, and the desirability of transporting groups from small segments of the total area. The person responsible for transportation at the Center also serves as janitor, but the increasing demands on his time by duties as transportation coordinator indicate the desirability of making this a full-time position.

Suggested Transportation Policies

The type of policies or rules needed varies with each transportation program, but some are common enough to be considered here. Policies should be established or some type of ruling made regarding the following:

Lifting

The responsibility for lifting handicapped persons into and out of conveyances, buildings, and so on, must be defined. Volunteer drivers and taxicab and chartered bus drivers are usually not required to lift these persons, although many of them do so willingly. Parents, paid staff, or others must be designated as responsible for lifting, and this should be clearly understood by all concerned.

Participants

Parents should be told the approximate time that the driver is expected to call for and deliver their children. They should also be expected to have their children ready, and a maximum time limit should be established for waiting. Some type of policy should also be established concerning cancellations. It should not be necessary for drivers to stop for participants only to learn that they failed to telephone that they could not attend. A written or verbal request by a parent is required in order that a child be called for or left at a place other than his home. Schools and some other agencies require special permits before the children are released to the Center's driver.

Use of Staff Cars

Policies should be made concerning the use of staff cars in the transportation program. If they are used, and this is often a necessity and a great help, adequate insurance must be required and renumeration be established on a mileage basis.

Special Arrangements for Vehicles

In the discussion of program planning principles in Chapter 7, a brief mention is made of the need for advanced planning as it relates to safety, comfort, and transportation of the handicapped participants. Where large groups of handicapped persons are to be transported to places of interest and on trips and outings, it is wise to check the areas to make sure there are suitable facilities for taking participants in and out of vehicles. Sometimes it is necessary to secure police assistance or special permission for parking, loading, and unloading in certain areas. Such special arrangements are not difficult to make as most individuals and agencies understand these particular needs of the handicapped and cooperate readily.

CHAPTER 12

Facilities, Equipment, and Supplies

In general, the basic areas, facilities, equipment, and supplies needed for recreation programs for the handicapped are the same as those required for comparable programs for the nonhandicapped. The specific types needed depend upon the scope of the program and the kinds of activities offered. The handicapped are entitled to use public recreation areas and facilities, and fortunately these are usually suitable for programs for this group. Because this is true, public parks, recreation centers, playgrounds, and day camp areas are used by the handicapped in many cities. Other public facilities serving the handicapped include art museums, libraries, school buildings, and zoos. Privately owned recreation facilities such as camps, lodge halls, churches, estates, libraries, and school buildings, which are designed primarily for use by nonhandicapped people, are also made available for recreation programs serving the handicapped. One advantage of using such public and private facilities is that they afford handicapped persons the opportunity of associating with the nonhandicapped.

Suggested Modifications

Facilities used for recreation programs for the handicapped, as for other groups, vary from a basement room to a large recreation building with a gymnasium, auditorium, and club and activity rooms. Whatever is used, the over-all facility should be such that the handicapped will be able to help themselves and require a minimum of assistance. Modifications are sometimes necessary in existing buildings and facilities such as swimming pools to encourage self-help and enable persons on crutches and in wheel chairs to move about with ease and confidence. Many public recreation facilities are being built with a consideration of the needs of special groups such as the handicapped and older citizens. Some common modifications are:

1. In order to accommodate persons in wheel chairs, on guerneys, and so on, permanent ramps may need to be installed at entrances, exits, and wherever steps would otherwise be needed, or temporary ramps may be used at steps that will permit safe ramping.
2. Handrails may also be needed where there are steps to help persons on crutches or otherwise ambulatory. The installation of handrails or parallel bars in rest rooms also encourages self-help and independence on the part of the participants.
3. All doors must be safe enough to accommodate persons in wheel

chairs, on beds, and so on, and paraphernalia that might be used in the program.

4. Floors and paved areas should be of nonslip material.

Most public playgrounds and day camp areas require no modification at all, while others may need minor adaptations. For example, in sandy or heavily wooded areas, paths with a comparatively smooth, firm surface may need to be built to accommodate wheel chairs, as well as for persons using crutches.

Some individuals and agencies hold to a theory that special facilities are needed for the handicapped, but this could have far-reaching effects if widely adopted, since it would tend to deter their integration in community programs, including recreation. Elaborate playgrounds and camp sites with specially built-in features have been built by some health and welfare agencies serving the severely physically handicapped. One such agency developed an area with a fishing pond, water play area, a playground with specially built slides but without climbing devices or swings. Also installed were special standing tables with safety belts, which are now considered outdated in schools for the handicapped. All of these special items were designed and built to give these children experiences in a "structured, protected setting."

The concept behind this type of area implies that the severely handicapped should grow up in a special world which isolates and protects them from the realities of everyday living. This theory is not only at odds with modern-day philosophy of the handicapped, but its implications that special facilities are needed would certainly tend to discourage community recreation leaders from establishing programs for the handicapped. A sound procedure is to encourage the handicapped to use the same facilities as other people whenever and wherever feasible, rather than to build special facilities for them. In a report by Arthur Schwartz and Marvin Lieberman, where orthopedically handicapped were integrated with nonhandicapped they state:

> We feel that the need for special equipment has been overemphasized and has often prevented community centers from starting programs that could have been beneficial to handicapped children. A previous study found that demands for special equipment are often directly related to the amount of experience that the person has had with handicapped children. Those most experienced with handicapped children stated that what was needed was an increase in more traditional group work services such as additional supervisory time, recording time, and more leaders; those least experienced asked for special equipment and different types of personnel, such as nurses. This was borne out in our experience. We did not need special service or equipment but there were additional demands made of staff such as more paper work and referrals.

The intake interviewing was time consuming as was the planning of parent meetings. Most important was the burden of additional supervision of the part-time staff who did most of the actual leadership.[1]

Selected Examples

The facility used for the Recreation Center is an example of a public building that has been remodeled to serve the needs of the handicapped. It is part of a public swimming pool building, which was originally a restaurant. The use of the facility is donated by the San Francisco Recreation and Park Department, which also furnishes heat, gas, lights, and maintenance.

Because it was formerly a large restaurant, it has many advantages and was easily converted into a recreation center. A stage was installed in one of the large main halls, and other areas were converted to club rooms, a music room, library, craft room, and offices. The kitchen, which is ideal for cooking, is large enough to prepare food for over three hundred persons. Some of the original counters in the restaurant were left intact for various uses. One counter is used as a marionette stage, for planters, for serving food or drinks, for nature or arts and crafts displays, and for many other purposes. Old built-in refrigerators were converted to linen and game closets. Display cases, which were used originally for cakes and pies, have been used for exhibits of arts and craft items made by the children. Ramps and rails were installed at entrances and in rest rooms.

At the day camp site, which is in the park and adjacent to the pool building, the only adaptations needed for the handicapped were smooth paths for wheel chairs. This improvement was necessary because the area, which is across from the beach, is quite sandy, which makes it difficult to push or propel wheel chairs. Because rest room facilities are quite distant from the camp site, chemical toilets have been used quite successfully, even for the severely handicapped.

The Zoological Gardens, in which the building and camp grounds are located, is a site offering excellent opportunities for nature study and camping. In addition to the swimming pool, the center is within walking distance of the Zoo, Children's Story Land, a lake for boating and fishing,

[1] Arthur Schwartz and Marvin Lieberman, "Integrating the Orthopedically Handicapped Child into the Community Center," Associated YM-YWHA's of Greater New York, New York, 1962, p. 8. (Mimeographed.)

and the beach. Riding stables are close by, as are several playgrounds, parks, and public transportation.

A center for handicapped adults was established in one city in two buildings which were formerly a part of a government housing project. The county deeded the land to the city, and the city purchased the buildings and made them available for use by the adult handicapped club. In another city, the wing of a local medical center was converted into a recreation center for physically limited children and adults. Although the space is donated by the medical center, it has no direct affiliation with it.

Equipment and Supplies

Chapters in Part III list certain equipment and supplies for many of the activities and describe how some of them may be made or obtained for programs.

In addition to the materials needed for use in connection with the program activities, there are certain items that, although not essential, are quite useful in the program. They are:

Wheel chairs help considerably in reducing transportation problems. Because wheel chairs require space, if some participants can leave their chairs at home and use those in the program, more room is made available in the vehicle for others.

Wheel chair trays that fit on the chairs are convenient for some persons participating in arts and crafts, games and sports, or other activities.

Heavy, sturdy furniture such as sofas and chairs is generally more comfortable for the handicapped. Individuals who are unsteady on their feet have some difficulty in sitting down in or arising from low, lounge-type furniture.

Sources of Equipment and Supplies

Frequently individuals and groups who are interested in the program prefer to give something tangible such as equipment and supplies so they will know that their money was spent for certain items. Service clubs, as well as foundations, have given station wagons, buses, wheel chairs, portable beds, movie projectors and screens, games and sports equipment, and many other useful items. Some groups in making a donation designate that it be used for a specific purpose such as arts and crafts supplies. Many useful items may be obtained for little or no cost at surplus stores, veterans' shops, and other such places. Hospitals and similar institutions will frequently donate used wheel chairs, portable beds, and other items to groups working with the handicapped.

In some areas, the state agency responsible for surplus property will include certain recreation and camping groups in their food program. Eligible groups are entitled to receive such commodities as dried beans, rice, flour, corn meal, milk, canned and frozen meats, butter, cheese, lard, and oil. Some groups are also eligible to purchase surplus property at a very nominal fee. Items available may range from jeeps or buses to photographic and art supplies, camping and kitchen equipment to a variety of furniture such as desks and file cabinets.

Another excellent source for obtaining certain equipment and supplies is through the newspapers, radio, or television. A plea for supplies or certain pieces of equipment needed for the handicapped, made through such media, usually produces positive results.

Insurance

The possibility of accidents to handicapped individuals using recreation facilities is sometimes less than in the case of the nonhandicapped because most of them cannot move as quickly or engage in activities in as strenuous a manner. However, because the possibility of an accident always exists, it is of the utmost importance that the agency conducting or sponsoring the program be protected from damage suits. This is especially true because of the tendency of juries to sympathize with the handicapped in accident cases. A private agency therefore needs to be covered adequately as a protection against damage suits in case of accidents occurring on its property or while individuals are taking part in its program. Public agencies providing facilities or programs for the handicapped, that need to carry liability insurance for their areas and facilities, should be covered through comprehensive policies. Fire insurance on building and structures is also essential.

CHAPTER 13

Records and Reports

The fact that recreation for the handicapped is still in the developmental stage and that programs must be conducted on an experimental basis makes the keeping of accurate and detailed records exceedingly important. Such records are invaluable not only to the agency administering the program, but as a reference source for other groups interested in establishing similar programs. Record keeping therefore merits even greater consideration than in community recreation programs.

Carefully kept records, as in every recreation agency, are essential for evaluating the program, for intelligent planning, and for financial accounting. They are indispensible to an agency in justifying an appeal for funds and are a valuable aid in the orientation of new paid and volunteer staff. Detailed information about program participants, especially the severely handicapped, is essential inasmuch as the staff must understand the nature of their experience and limitations in order to help and handle them correctly and effectively.

Types of Records

The number and types of records to be kept depend upon the scope of the program, the basis of financial support, and other factors. Several types of records and reports usually needed in recreation programs for the handicapped are:

Participants

Participant records should include all pertinent information about each handicapped individual. Completed application forms, shown later in this chapter, should include name, address, age, medical report, and other pertinent information and be signed by a parent and the family physician. Parents might also be asked to sign releases from legal responsibility and authorizing the use of photographs. All information concerning individuals, including referrals, case histories, photographs, and evaluations, should be kept in individual participant files.

Personnel

Personnel files should include current and accumulated records of paid and volunteer personnel, such as correspondence, personnel policies, completed applications, references, evaluations, and other pertinent information relating to the staff.

Business Transactions

Business and financial records, including copies of budget, payrolls, expenditures, agreements, insurance policies, accident reports, correspondence, minutes of all board and committee meetings, and so on, should be properly filed and maintained for ready reference.

Program

All materials relating to the program, such as attendance records, announcements, camp reports, reports of activities and programs, are essential to the over-all operation. It is imperative, as with all programs financed by public funds, that a detailed accounting be given of how the money was spent and what was accomplished. This type of information is most effective in annual reports. An annual report, including an interpretation of objectives and policies, a description of the program and its achievements or failures, together with an audit and recommendations, should be submitted to all contributors and interested individuals and groups.

Typical Forms

The following are typical forms used successfully at the Recreation Center.

1. Membership Application. This form must be filled out and signed by the parent or guardian of the individual applying for membership. One portion must be filled out by the applicant's physician.

2. Physician's Recommendation for Aquatic Participation. This form must be submitted by each individual wishing to enroll in the weekly swim program.

3. Application for Center Leadership. Persons seeking a leadership position are required to complete this form.

4. Volunteer Application. This form must be filled out by individuals offering their services as volunteers.

5. Recreation Director Evaluation Rating. The semiannual evaluation of employees is recorded on this form copies of which are filled out by the employee and by one or more supervisory personnel.

6. Activity Report. This form is used primarily for recording and appraising ongoing group activities.

7. Report of Individual Participant. The preferences, experiences, and needs of each participant in the summer day camp are recorded on this form. A somewhat similar form is used periodically for Center participants.

8. Summer Day Camp Evaluation. Each staff member of the camp submits a copy of this form at the conclusion of the four-week camp session.

9. High School Volunteer's Evaluation. This form is used about every three months to secure opinions of high school students serving as volunteers at the Center.

10. Outings. The leader of every trip or outing submits a copy of this form to the program director before leaving the Center.

Copies of these forms are duplicated on the pages that follow. The name, address, and telephone number of the Center appear at the top of most of the forms, although they have been omitted here. Such identification, however, is important.

MEMBERSHIP APPLICATION[1]

Date ______________________

Last name ______ First name ______ Middle name ______

Street address ______ City ______ Phone ______ Emergency phone ______

Age ______ Birth date (Incl. year) ______ Weight ______ Religion ______ Nationality ______ Language ______

Other children in home: Boys:______Ages:______ Girls:______Ages:______

Occupation: Father:____________________ Mother:____________________

School attended by participant________________No. of years____Grade____

What group experience has your son or daughter had, such as Scouts, etc.?

____

Does participant read and write?______________________________

What are participant's hobbies?______________________________

What activities does he like best?______________________________

How much time has participant spent in hospital?______________________

What experiences away from home has participant had?________________

____

Does participant associate with others in his neighborhood?______________

What does the family enjoy doing together?________________________

Approximately how many close friends does participant have?____________

Is your son/daughter inclined to be outgoing?________Shy & timid?________

Please tell us anything else about participant and his life at home that you think would help us in making him feel at ease and in helping him to have fun at the Center:______________________________

____

____

Does participant need rest during the day?__________________________

How did you hear about the Center? Friend______School______Other______

[1] Used with permission of California Society for Crippled Children and Adults, Inc.

Name of participant

What physical disability does participant have?______________________

(Note: Please tell us about any limitations in use of arm, legs, hearing, sight, and speech which he has and what disease or condition caused this limitation.)

Please circle YES or NO

Can participant walk? ...... YES NO
With assistance? .... YES NO
Without assistance? ..... YES NO
Use crutches? .... YES NO
Use Canadian crutches? .. YES NO
Use a walker? .... YES NO
Does he use mechanical aids? YES NO
Does he use wheelchair? .... YES NO
Does he wear helmet for protection against falls? .. YES NO
Does he wear day braces? ... YES NO
Does he wear night braces? .. YES NO
Can he climb stairs? .... YES NO
Does he need hand rail?.. YES NO
Can he dress himself? .... YES NO
Need assistance with buttons? .... YES NO
Need assistance with shoes? .... YES NO
About how long does it take him to dress self?.. ___Mins.
Can he feed self? .... YES NO
Does he need to be fed?.. YES NO
Does he need help in holding cups? .... YES NO
Does he need straws, special spoons, etc.?.... YES NO
Is he able to use regular eating utensils? .... YES NO
Approximately how long does it take him to eat a meal?.. ___Mins.
Does he need a tray for his wheelchair? .... YES NO
Does he need assistance in toileting? .... YES NO

Can he go to the bathroom alone? .... YES NO
Does he need to be lifted on or off the toilet? .... YES NO
Does he need a hand rail in the bathroom? .... YES NO
Can he use toilet paper? ..... YES NO
Can he adjust his clothing before and after toileting? YES NO
Does he have accidents with bladder and bowel control? YES NO
Does he tell adults when he has to go to the bathroom? YES NO
Has she started menstrual periods? .... YES NO
Does he require special diet? (If YES, attach list)...... YES NO
Does he have spells or blackouts? .... YES NO
Does he have any hearing difficulty? .... YES NO
Does he have any speech difficulty? .... YES NO
Is he taking medicine of any kind? .... YES NO
Does he have any allergies?.. YES NO
(If YES, specify)
Does he need a bed rail?..... YES NO
Who usually takes care of him at night?______________
Does he have any pressure sores from braces? ...... YES NO
(If YES, indicate)
Does he wear glasses? ...... YES NO
Does he wear hearing aid?... YES NO

On the line below, please tell us of any precautions you wish your son or daughter to observe while at the Center:______________________

Please give any directions for the proper use of braces, appliances, etc. (for example, hearing aid). For instance, if he wears long leg braces, may he stand with the braces locked and for how long at a time?______________________

Note: Member must be able to take all prescribed medicines by himself as the Staff is not permitted by law to administer medication to the participants.

____
Name of participant

PARENT'S CONSENT

I hereby request that ______________________ be permitted to attend the Recreation Center for the Handicapped and authorize the Director of the Center to act for me according to his best judgment and ability in any emergency requiring medical or surgical care that may arise.

Date______________ Signed______________________
(Parent or Legal Guardian)

PHOTOGRAPHIC RELEASE

I hereby give my consent to the Recreation Center for the Handicapped to photograph______________________, and without limitation, to use such pictures and/or stories in connection with any of the work of said Recreation Center for the Handicapped without consideration of any kind, and I do hereby release the Recreation Center for the Handicapped from any claims whatsoever which may arise in said regard.

Date______________ Signed______________________
(Parent or Legal Guardian)

(Note: It is not necessary for you to sign this photographic release in order for your son or daughter to attend the Center. It would be to our convenience if you would sign it, however.)

TRANSPORTATION

☐ I can furnish transportation for my son/daughter to_____and from_____the Center programs.

☐ I can furnish transportation for_______others.

NOTES TO PARENTS

1. If possible, parents are expected to pay a program fee of $1.00 per program. Please send your fee *each* time your child attends programs.
2. Parents are urged to attend regular parent group meetings held the third Thursday evening of February, May, August and November, from 8 to 10 P.M. and to take an active part in the activities of this group.
3. The Center will furnish hot chocolate, tea and coffee. However, participants are required to bring their lunch each day unless otherwise specified. *Be sure* to put your son's or daughter's name on the bag or lunch box.
4. Please read carefully all notes sent to your child, as pertinent information regarding Center activities are communicated in this way.
5. We will notify you when your son or daughter is accepted and will let you know when and where he should report.

____
(Signature of Recreation Leader after reviewing application, etc.)

MEDICAL REPORT FOR RECREATION CENTER FOR THE HANDICAPPED

(To be filled out by participant's PHYSICIAN and returned to the Center, Fleishhacker Pool Building, Great Highway, San Francisco 16.)

Name of participant________________________Date of birth_________

Address ____

Diagnosis: Medical term:________________Layman's term:_____________

Is participant under medication?.................................YES__NO__

Is he/she subject to seizures?....................................YES__NO__

Are there any precautions you wish him/her to observe?..........YES__NO__

____

____

May he participate in carefully supervised swimming activities?...YES__NO__

Is participant, to your knowledge, suffering from, or has he/she recently been exposed to, any contagious disease?............YES__NO__

Immunizations: (Date if available)

Diptheria ....
Whooping cough ....
Tetanus ....
Smallpox ....
Previous injections of horse serums ....
Typhoid ....
Chest X ray ....

I hereby give my consent for this person to attend the Recreation Center for the Handicapped, Inc.

________________________ M.D.
Name

____
Medical Agency

FOLLOWING QUESTIONS MUST BE ANSWERED BY ORTHOPEDIST, IF INDIVIDUAL IS UNDER SUCH CARE.

1. What braces, appliances, or prostheses does this person wear?
2. Please give specific instructions for their use—any precautions, etc.

________________________ M.D.
Name

____
Orthopedic Clinic

PHYSICIAN'S RECOMMENDATION FOR AQUATIC PARTICIPATION

The person named below is planning to enroll in the aquatic program of the Recreation Center for the Handicapped, in cooperation with the Aquatics Division of the S.F. Recreation and Park Department. The program includes recreational water games and sports in addition to the instructional program. This recommendation will assist in the proper group placement of the participant and in the selection of appropriate swimming strokes and body positions, if any. Your assistance in this matter will be greatly appreciated.

Name________________________________ Age________

Home address________________________ Telephone__________

Name of parent or guardian________________________

Organization referring participant______________________

1. Medical diagnosis __________________________
2. Diagnosis in laymen's terms______________________
3. Parts of the body involved (if any). Please indicate degree (slight, moderate, severe).

   Arm—right__________________ Leg—right__________________.

   Arm—left__________________ Leg—left__________________

   Neck__________________ Trunk__________________

   Other ____________________________________

4. Applicant (please check):

   Needs to wear a nose clip________ear plugs________should *not* dive________

   Should not put face under water________.

   Any other specific precautions which should be taken? List. ____________

   ____

5. Do you recommend any specific body position?

   Back__________________ Left side__________________

   Stomach__________________ Right side__________________

6. Do you recommend any specific movements or actions?

   ____

7. Other comments:________________________________
   I hereby give (do not give) my approval for the above-named person to engage in this recreational aquatic program.

Date____________ Name of physician____________________

Phone ________________________

APPLICATION FOR CENTER LEADERSHIP

Date________________

Name__________________________

Address________________________

City____________Phone__________

Age____Birthdate_______Place________

Sex____Married_____U.S. citizen: Yes__No__

Condition of health________________

Any physical handicaps?_____________

No. of children: ages:______________

Circle years of school completed:

8 9 10 11 12 13 14 15 16 17

If in school, give name, year, major and minor subjects:________________

____

____

Kind of Work Desired

Full time________________

Part time________________

Seasonal________________

Social Security No.__________

Do you have:

Driver's license?____________

Automobile?______________

First-aid certificate?_________

Lifesaving certificate?_______

If in school, are you earning your way in part or entirely?________________

What experience have you had, either paid or volunteer, that is related to the position being sought? When and where? Be specific.

List other jobs you have held:

List three references, including, if possible, a recent employer:

Name	*Address*	*Position*

APPLICATION FOR CENTER LEADERSHIP (*Continued*)

What are/were your chief interests in college/high school?

In what school activities are/were you active? Positions held?

What recreational activities can you conduct with each of these categories? Where possible, be specific.

Arts and crafts

Camping

Clubs and social activities

Drama (theater) and dance

Games and sports

Music

Outings and travel

What experience have you had in planning, presenting, and evaluating special events? Where were they held?

Give *your* definition of recreation.

What are your favorite leisure time activities?

(If more space is necessary to complete any of the above questions, please use back of this page.)

Signed______________________________

Interviewed by:______________________________ Date:_______________

VOLUNTEER APPLICATION

Name:______________________________ Date:____________
Last First

Address: ____
Number Street City Zone

Telephone number:____________________ Age:________

Occupation:______________ Where?______________________

Education: Elementary______ High______ College______ Major______

Do you drive?______Own a Car?______Be willing to use it occasionally?______

HAVE YOU HAD ANY PREVIOUS EXPERIENCE with a recreation or group work agency? If so, please list particulars.

____

____

List days and hours you are able to serve in the following programs:

Tuesday	—10:00 A.M.–3:30 P.M.	At-home Teens:______
	2:30–9:30 P.M.	Adults:______
Wednesday	— 3:00–9:00 P.M.	Teen Club:______
Thursday	— 3:00–5:00 P.M.	After School:______
	5:00–7:00 P.M.	Swim Program:______
Friday	—10:00 A.M.–3:00 P.M.	Adults:______
	2:30–9:30 P.M.	Adults:______
Saturday	—10:00 A.M.–4:30 P.M.	All Ages:______

From the following activities check those in which you have some skills or have had previous experience. *Give particulars.*

__Arts & crafts______________ __Camping______________

__Games______________ __Music______________

__Sports______________ __Singing______________

__Dramatics______________ __Storytelling______________

__Dancing______________ __Journalism______________

Please list three (3) references. Student observers need only give teachers name, class, and required number of hours.

NAME	ADDRESS	TELEPHONE
1.		
2.		
3.		

RECREATION DIRECTOR EVALUATION RATING*

INSTRUCTIONS: A copy of the rating sheet is to be given to the director or leader at the time of his orientation with the explanation that evaluations will be a regular part of the supervisory process. The rating sheet may be used as a self-evaluation, or it may be used at regular intervals with the supervisor.

Personal Characteristics	*Poor*	*Below Average*	*Average*	*Above Average*	*Outstanding*	*Comments*
1. Is my personal appearance as good as I can make it?						
a. Dress—Is it neat, clean, and appropriate?						
b. Grooming (hair, nails)—Can it be improved?						
2. Is my manner natural and sincere, rather than Affected?						
3. Am I able to communicate clearly and easily?						
4. Am I courteous and considerate of others?						
5. Are there traits in my disposition that I should hold in check?						
a. Is my attitude positive?						
b. Am I fair and impartial?						
c. Do I have a sense of humor?						
d. Am I able to control my emotions under all conditions?						
6. Have I established effective working relationships with my supervisor and fellow workers?						
7. Am I able to generate a feeling of confidence in the staff, the agency, and the program?						
8. Am I prompt and dependable?						
9. Do I show a general knowledge in other fields in a variety of subjects and in current events?						

Ability as a Recreation Leader	*Poor*	*Below Average*	*Average*	*Above Average*	*Outstanding*	*Comments*
1. Is my program developed with the assistance of those who participate in it; is it developed with the children and adults rather than for them?						
2. Am I able to adapt activities so that even the most severely handicapped person may participate?						
3. Do I formulate specific objectives for each day's activities—for each week's program—for special days—for different seasons?						
a. Are my aims specific?						
b. Are my objectives apparent in the organization of the activities at the center?						
c. Do each month and each year bring about vital progress and interesting changes in the activities? Do I show knowledge of each activity?						
4. Do my program objectives conform to the over-all agency philosophy and policies?						
5. Is the program mentally and physically stimulating and socially sound?						
6. Has the program been planned with concern for the maximum welfare and safety of the participants?						
7. Have I made use of all the available community resources?						
8. Do I, within necessary limits, provide activity for all age groups?						
9. What evidence is there that those who attend the recreation facility are improving their self-control and initiative? Are they learning to solve their own difficulties?						
10. Do they attack hard problems gladly, or do they want help in every problem? Do they evaluate the results?						

Management of Facilities	*Poor*	*Below Average*	*Average*	*Above Average*	*Outstanding*	*Comments*
1. Have I done all within my power to make the facility an attractive place?						
2. Is the room arrangement properly adjusted to the persons and program using them?						
3. Is the housekeeping in the facility as orderly as I can possibly make it?						
4. Do I have a routine procedure for securing the facility upon closing?						
5. Do I open and close as scheduled?						
6. Do I know where the controls to the utilities are in my facilities?						
7. Do I know how to use them properly?						
8. Do I have at my fingertips all of the information I need for routine procedures in case of emergencies—including Civil Defense procedures?						
9. Do the custodians and I have a mutual understanding of each other's responsibilities so that we can harmoniously and efficiently serve together?						

Professional Qualities	Poor	Below Average	Average	Above Average	Outstanding	Comments
1. Administrative Function:						
a. Reports and records—neat, on time, usable, accurate?						
2. Supervisory Responsibility:						
a. Have I been able to accept supervision?						
b. Have I accepted the responsibility of the supervision of staff?						
c. Have I assumed some responsibility for helping the growth and development of staff?						
d. Have I accepted responsibility for the total facility?						
e. Have I accepted the responsibility for the total program at my facility whether I am on duty or not?						
3. Program Responsibility.						
a. Have I made best use of staff?						
b. Have I used the best methods to publicize recreational activities at the center?						
4. What methods do I employ to have readily available appropriate and needed materials?						
5. Am I growing professionally?						
a. Do I keep up with current literature in the field of recreation?						
b. Do I take advantage of opportunities to attend classes, lectures, conferences, etc., related to recreation and closely allied fields?						
c. Do I take an active interest in professional organizations?						
d. What are my skills?						
1. Am I using them to the best of my ability?						
2. Am I striving to learn new ones all the time?						

ACTIVITY REPORT

Activity____________________ Leader____________________

No. of participants______________ Group____________________

Length of time for activity________ Date____________________

I. Materials:

II. Preparation:
Include resource materials and any contacts made as well as physical preparation.

III. Type of Group:
How many persons in wheel chairs, on crutches, in portable beds, etc.?

IV. Steps in Presentation of Activity:

V. Teaching Techniques and Adaptations:

VI. Difficulties or Problems:

VII. Age Group Relation to Activity:

VIII. Group Interest:
Did they enjoy the activity—would you recommend that it be continued?

IX. Individual Reactions:
Give the good or bad reactions you received from individual persons. Be specific.

X. Summary:
General conclusions plus any further plans that might be necessary in continuing the activity.

THE ABOVE IS A GUIDE FOR MAKING YOUR ACTIVITY REPORT. USE ALL THE SPACE YOU FEEL IS NECESSARY TO DO A COMPLETE JOB OF REPORTING ANY OR ALL OF THE ABOVE ITEMS.

REPORT ON INDIVIDUAL PARTICIPANT
(SUMMER DAY CAMP)

Date______________________

A report covering the following items is to be completed for each individual participant of each group by the Unit Senior Counselor by the end of the first week and another at the close of camp.

1. What are the recreational interests and needs of this individual?

2. What experiences can be provided to help this individual meet his recreational interests and needs?

3. What methods should be used in order to provide this individual with these recreational experiences?

4. What recreational experiences did I provide for this participant?

5. What success did I have with these recreational experiences? (See question 2)

6. What additional recreational methods and/or experiences may be necessary for this participant to assure social growth?

____________________________ ____________________________

Name of Participant Name of Counselor

SUMMER DAY CAMP EVALUATION

I. How do you feel regarding the over-all plan and organization of the Summer Day Camp?

Fair ( ) Average ( ) Good ( ) Excellent ( )

II. How successfully do you feel the following activities were conducted with your group?

	Fair	*Average*	*Good*	*Excellent*
a. Nature study	( )	( )	( )	( )
b. Pioneering	( )	( )	( )	( )
c. Arts and crafts	( )	( )	( )	( )
d. Camp music	( )	( )	( )	( )
e. Games and Sports	( )	( )	( )	( )
f. Dramatics	( )	( )	( )	( )
g. Outings and trips	( )	( )	( )	( )
h. Overnight campouts	( )	( )	( )	( )

III. What recommendations would you give to facilitate the success of any of the above, such as further knowledge and skills of staff, more interest of the staff, or more interest of members?

1.

2.

3.

4.

5.

6.

SUMMER DAY CAMP EVALUATION (Continued)

IV. What camping experiences do you feel should be added?

1. 4.

2. 5.

3. 6.

V. What do you feel were the most valuable experiences for your group?

1.

2.

3.

4.

5.

6.

VI. Was adequate time given for staff meetings and discussions?

Yes ( ) No ( )

VII. Was resource material adequate to your needs?

Yes ( ) No ( )

VIII. Do you feel that facilities, equipment, and supplies were adequate?

Yes ( ) No ( )

IX. Was the preseason in-service training program adequate?

Yes ( ) No ( )

X. If answer to any of the four questions above is No, please give particulars and recommendations.

____

Camp Staff Member

HIGH SCHOOL VOLUNTEER'S EVALUATION

Please give the following information about yourself:

Referred to Center by a friend_______adult_______school_______club______

Date started as volunteer_________________School grade now___________

Volunteer on Saturday_________ Tuesday_________ Wednesday__________

Group you usually volunteered with______________________________

Group you would like to be with________________________________

1. Did you feel oriented before actually working with a group?
   YES_____NO_____. If NO, state what you needed to know before starting.

2. Do you feel needed by the group leaders? YES_____NO_____.
   By the members? YES_____NO_____.

3. Why do you volunteer with this type of program?

4. Do you think program activities are fun for the members?
   YES_____NO_____. Which ones do they seem to enjoy the most?
   (Be specific.)

5. Do you think your group's senior leader is a poor____average____good____
   excellent_____ leader? Is the assistant leader poor____average____good____
   excellent_____? Make any comments about these people here:

6. If you were the group's leader what would you do differently?

7. Do you have fun at the Center? YES_____NO_____. Have you made any
   new friends since coming here? YES______NO______. Are they members
   __________or other teen-agers?__________

8. Do you find the Staff Bulletin useful?

9. Do you think the Saturday morning preprogram meetings are helpful?
   YES_____NO_____.

10. Remarks:

Sign if you wish.

OUTINGS

Leader ____

Group ____

Number in group ________________

Number of wheel chairs ___________

Number of crutches ______________

Number of walkers _______________

Kind of Transportation Needed:

Center bus ________________

Red Cross bus ________________

Red Cross station wagon ________

Private cars ________________

Destination ____

Time of departure ________________

Time returning ________________

Not returning to Center ____________

Lunch needed ________________

Money needed ________________

Information on destination:

Toilet facilities ____

Stair problem ____

Eating facilities ____

Needed Supplies:

Flex Straws

Food

Blankets

Towels

Fishing tackle

Life preservers

Drinks

Etc. ____

CHAPTER 14

Relationships with Parents and the Handicapped

Many factors involved in planning and conducting recreation programs for the handicapped require a closer working relationship between parents and recreation leaders than would be expected in the average recreation program. For example, many parents of the handicapped are among the citizens in a community to whom recreation must be interpreted as a universal need and a benefit to all persons. Most parents of the handicapped recognize the fact that their children need special services such as medical treatment, therapy, vocational training, and others, as they have had to fight many battles, often through legislation, to obtain some of them. Such services initiated by parent groups have occasionally included recreation, but many parents are still not aware of the importance of recreation or that their children are entitled to participate in such programs that are available to all others. Developing a community educational program as described in Chapter 4 is one of the best methods of stimulating interest among parents and enlisting their support to establish and maintain recreation services for their children.

Need for Active Participation

Recreation administrators and leaders need the cooperation of parents who are willing to participate actively in initiating, establishing, and maintaining recreation programs for the handicapped. Parents who believe in recreation as a vital need and a real benefit for their children are frequently the most effective promoters of the program.

There are numerous ways in which parents may assist, depending upon their skills, experience, interests, and the time they have to give. Parents have assisted recreation programs by serving on boards of directors, advisory boards, parent auxiliaries, transportation, fund raising, public relations committees, and in many other ways. While it is very important that recreation leaders know how a particular group of parents can help, it is equally important for them to know how they cannot help effectively in a recreation program. For example, it might defeat the primary purpose of the program to have parents working as recreation leaders or in any phase of the program where they would be with their own children. Parents themselves support this theory and believe that the child gains independence, learns how to get along with other children, and is afforded many other advantages by being away from his home and parents.

Parent Auxiliary

A parent auxiliary or council is one of the best ways in which parents can assist the recreation program. Such a group can be most effective, especially if it is organized and governed by the parents themselves. Most parents of the handicapped have been involved in a great many "parent education" programs which are designed to help them with various problems relating to their handicapped child. Many demands are made upon them; consequently they tend to resist additional efforts to "organize" or "educate" them. Parents may be encouraged to help a recreation program by working as a group in their own way, but they should not be coerced. They should be made to feel that their efforts are needed and wanted and, above all, that their opinions and suggestions are respected by the professional staff. It is very important that recreation leaders realize that each parent group is unique and that its ability to assist will be determined by the composition of the group. Experience has indicated that some parents will give little, if any, assistance and that they may not be willing to work with other parents. It has been pointed out that frequently the only interest some parents have in common is a handicapped child; this in itself does not assure compatibility among them. Working parents, a parent alone, and parents with several young children usually have very little time to give to programs. Some parents may be able to help only if the work can be done at home, such as telephoning, typing, and so on.

Selected Examples

Some recreation programs have been initiated with the help of individual parents rather than parent groups, and councils or auxiliaries were formed after the program was in operation. One such parent auxiliary was organized about a year after the program was established, when it appeared that the program would have to be discontinued for lack of funds and community support. Parents organized themselves specifically to assist the recreation program "in ways that it could," and the group requested assistance from the recreation staff in establishing its own by-laws and committees. The auxiliary started with realistic projects such as the building of cabinets and special games equipment and the making of costumes and properties for play productions. After they had worked together for some time and had become a unified group, they decided that they could undertake more difficult projects such as fund raising for the program. Their first attempt was a rummage sale, the success of which encouraged them to try other fund raising methods such as luncheons, flower shows, and candy sales, all of which were quite successful. This group increased the interest and participation of other parents through potluck suppers, parties, and square dance sessions.

Parents themselves have mentioned the fact that they, too, need recreation and that membership in an active parent group not only enables them to help the recreation program but affords advantages for themselves as well. Parents have pointed out the benefits of being able to talk with other parents who have similar problems. Frequently, this is effective therapy when parents realize that they are not alone and that there are others who may have even more difficult problems to cope with.

Some parent groups have given a great deal of assistance to summer day camp programs. Parents have helped with enrollment, transportation, financing, and obtaining equipment and supplies, to mention just a few forms of assistance. In all recreation programs for the handicapped, assistance from parents is needed and should be welcomed; where the severely handicapped are included, certain information and help from parents are essential.

The Parent and the Recreation Leader

Parents must provide the recreation staff with a great deal of information about their children, in particular, relating to the physical handling of them. Some of this information must of necessity be transmitted to the leader verbally through demonstrations. Such demonstrations and explanations are especially helpful in working with individuals who have severe speech impairments and are therefore unable to relate their physical needs or explain how they can be helped. Information is needed on locking and unlocking braces, feeding, seizures, specially built wheel chairs, and certain equipment needed for the comfort and security of individuals. Parents also need to give information on what not to do for their children. For example, if a child can walk independently but prefers the luxury of being assisted or carried, leaders should know this and insist that they walk. It is also helpful for recreation leaders to know something about the participants' previous recreation or camping experiences so that new opportunities may be offered and that they be encouraged to carry over certain activities into the home.

The recreation leader frequently needs to have conferences with parents in order to evaluate the progress of their child, but should avoid any clinical or negative comment concerning the child's handicap. Parents are often surprised to find that their children can do things away from home that they had previously thought were impossible for them. Therefore they should be encouraged to visit activities in which their children are taking part.

Occasionally, leaders also need to confer with the participant's social worker, teacher, or physician, to discuss personal problems relating to his conduct, in many cases due to his lack of sex education. As mentioned previously, many handicapped persons live very sheltered lives. Some have had little, if any, preparation for adulthood. Persons associated closely with them including parents, tend to overlook the fact that handicapped persons have the same physical drives and interests in the opposite sex, as the nonhandicapped. The lack of sex education among the handicapped frequently creates problems in social conduct and personal relationships that requires special counseling. However, in working with parents, their children, or others associated with the handicapped, a recreation leader should always bear in mind that his particular role with the handicapped is unique. He is not a social worker, a therapist, or a psychologist, and he is not shirking his responsibilities when he confines his efforts to the fulfillment of their recreational needs.

Physical Handling

In general, when handling a handicapped person, one should ask him in what specific ways he prefers to be helped. In most instances, the handicapped person is appreciative of one's efforts to assist him and willingly gives the best possible information as to what help he needs. Some handicapped persons are accustomed to well-meaning individuals who simply "take over," and unless the handicapped are made very uncomfortable physically, they hesitate to register a complaint. One should never "hover." Handicapped persons like to be treated according to their age.

Crutches and wheel chairs are necessary accessories for many handicapped persons, and one should never take them away unless the person indicates that he wishes them removed after he has been seated. Handicapped persons may feel "stranded" unless they are nearby. If communication with a handicappd person is difficult or impossible, the leader should request the assistance of persons more closely related to him. *One should never give help when it is not needed. BUT when help is given one should make sure that it is the right kind of help.*

A post-polio boy of seven, who had difficulty using his legs and feet, besides being unable to use his hands or arms, learned to get up after he had fallen down by standing on his head.

Essential Procedures

The suggested procedures for the physical handling of handicapped persons in various situations are based upon experience and merit careful study by all who are called upon to work with this group.

Wheel Chairs

1. Always remember that many handicapped individuals do not have a good sense of balance even when sitting. Be sure that all straps that are supposed to be fastened are fastened securely.
2. In pushing wheel-chaired participants *up* ramps, one should go forward, using arm and shoulder muscles.
3. In going *down* ramps, persons in wheel chairs should be wheeled backward. When wheel chairs are taken down forward, they are in danger of gaining too much momentum and thereby getting out of control. Chairs can, however, be tilted and taken down forward, but in all cases care should be taken that persons in the chairs do not slide out.
4. When assisting a wheel-chaired person to go up low curbs and other impediments, one should use the small foot bars to tilt the chair backward. A wheel chair should be taken up curbs forward and down backward.
5. It is always dangerous to push a wheel chair at a fast or running speed.
6. Individuals in wheel chairs and/or beds, who are unable to shift positions, frequently need assistance to make them more comfortable.

Crutches

1. Most persons who use crutches know how to use them properly, but if assistance is indicated, one should ask what help is needed. One must learn the proper way to hand crutches to a handicapped person.
2. When assisting a person up an incline, it is best to hold him at the back of the waistline or just below it or by the pelvic brace band (if such a brace is used).
3. In rainy weather or on wet terrain, it is more practical and safer for those persons who normally get about with crutches to use wheel chairs.

Braces

1. In assisting a person who uses braces, one should inquire what help is needed from him or from a person who is closely related to him.
2. Braces should be kept as clean as possible, i.e., protected against infiltration of sand into the ball-bearing joints, and should be oiled only under direction of the participant or parent.

Falls

1. If a person who is being assisted loses his balance, it is best to catch hold of his hips to try to help him regain his balance. If he is falling one should try to *break* the fall and prevent injury, but it is not necessary to prevent the fall if one would injure his back by doing so. It may be possible simply to let the person down to the floor gradually.
2. When a handicapped person falls, wait for him to give a cue as to whether or not he needs help in getting up. If he can get up by himself, he may prefer doing so; if he needs a lift, he can usually explain how one should help. As a precautionary measure it may be best to let the person rest for a few moments where he has fallen in order to decide whether he is hurt and to permit him to recover before trying to arise. One should also check for serious injury and give first aid if necessary.
3. *Always let handicapped persons help themselves as much as possible.* However, if a person has fallen *heavily,* sometimes it is wise to give more aid than he might otherwise require and to keep an unobtrusive eye on him for a few moments.

Feeding

1. It is often necessary to have some experience and relationships with certain individuals before one can assist in feeding them.
2. It is practical and beneficial to encourage the handicapped to assist each other in feeding.
3. Special care must be taken in using sharp cutlery around persons who have a great deal of involuntary motion.
4. Because many handicapped persons have difficulty in swallowing, they should be fed slowly to avoid choking.
5. Flex straws for drinking are practical and helpful.

Toilet Assistance

1. Participants usually need a wide variety of help in rest rooms, such as:
   a. In going to and from the bathroom.
   b. With clothing.
   c. In getting from wheel chair to stool and back to wheel chair or in being held in stalls.
2. Leaders should check with participants, administrative staff, or parents on how often noncommunicative participants need to be taken to bathroom facilities.

Lifting

1. One should always call another or even a third person to help lift a handicapped individual rather than risk injury to one's back. Again, let the individual tell you how to assist him and let him help as much as possible. Some need total help; some can support their own weight when stood upright, but cannot keep their balance, while others can help by holding onto furniture or another person's hips or shoulders. Some can shift their weight when held upright. Persons who do not need to be carried up or down stairs usually have their own unique methods for "making" them.
2. In lifting one should take a broad stance and face in the direction in which he will be moving the person, so that he is not caught off balance. It is impossible to do this while wearing a narrow skirt. One should keep the weight of the person he is lifting over his own base as much as possible.
3. As a protection to the back, one should:
   a. Bend and straighten the hips and knees instead of the back when lifting.
   b. Move feet around instead of twisting back.
   c. Take a deep breath and hold it while lifting.
   d. Help with the knee or thigh when possible. Sometimes one can brace one's elbow on his thigh or hip.
4. Props can be helpful in lifting, i.e., bracing legs or hips against a wall or table. When possible let part of the weight of the person rest on the floor, table, or bed, as a fulcrum.
5. Other positions in lifting require that one:
   a. Stay as *close* to the person he is helping as possible.
   b. Brace the person's feet if they tend to slide.
   c. Use his own body weight to the best advantage. (Also see 7b.)

6. Lifting into or out of a wheel chair:
   a. The wheel chair should be placed so that the distance the person is to be moved is as short as possible. One should then figure out the most efficient angle between the wheel chair and the spot where the person is to be placed.
   b. The brakes of the wheel chairs should be secured before transfers, unless it will be more efficient to be able to push the wheel chair away quickly. A wheel chair can be braced with the foot of the person doing the lifting.
   c. Sometimes locking or unlocking braces such as leg or hip braces at the proper time helps in lifting.
7. Moving a person from side to side in bed:
   a. Unless a person is very light, one should move his legs, hips, and shoulders in sequence, not all at once.
   b. When moving any weight horizontally, one should try to have the weight at about the height of the waist and bend one's knees if necessary.

PART THREE Activities and Programs

Participation in activities provides the means whereby individuals satisfy their recreation interests and desires. Agencies providing recreation programs for the physically handicapped therefore need to be familiar with the types of activities that can be used successfully in such a program. This section contains chapters describing recreation activities under each major category that can be included in a recreation program, suggests ways by which they may be adapted so individuals with various handicaps can take part in them, and records experiences of handicapped individuals and groups that have participated successfully in such activities.

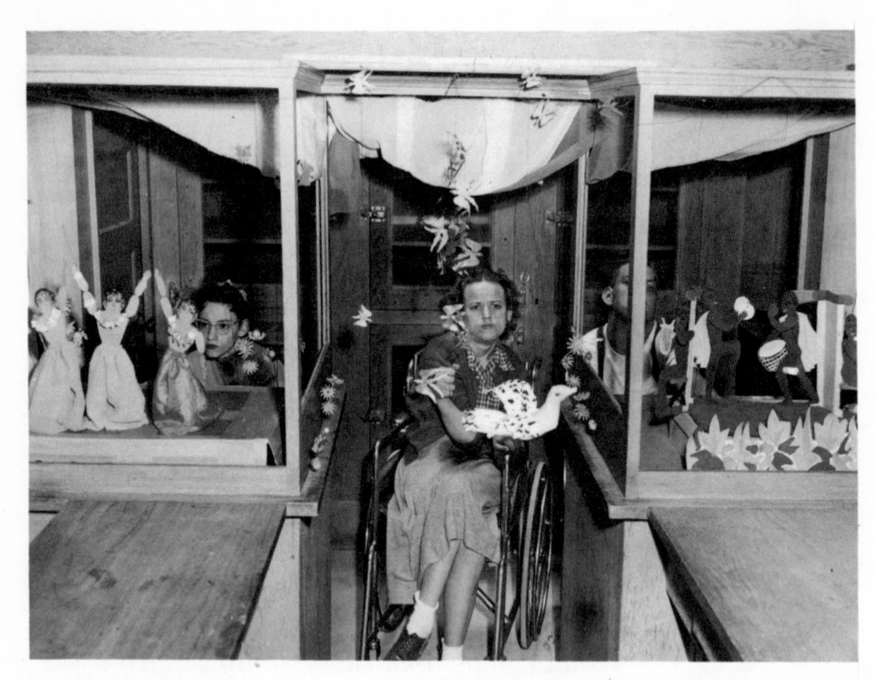

An old restaurant counter makes an excellent marionette stage.

CHAPTER 15

Drama

Dramatics has proved to be one of the most popular types of activity in which a group of physically handicapped people can participate. It has been interesting to note that each individual, regardless of his limitations, is eager to take an active part in dramatics. Fortunately the field of drama offers a number of activities which are readily adaptable to physically handicapped individuals. In many of these certain individuals appear before an audience, while other members of the group help in a variety of ways behind the scenes. Drama also affords groups an opportunity to express themselves creatively by writing and producing original plays and adapting others for their special use.

The value of dramatics as a means of bringing satisfaction and self-confidence to the handicapped is illustrated by the experience of a group of cerebral palsied individuals. As mentioned earlier, in their first attempt at dramatics the members of the group chose to produce an original marionette play in order that they could remain behind the scenes and not have to appear before an audience. Later on, they decided to write a play in which they played the parts themselves in the presence of an audience. After presenting several plays they had progressed to the production of talent shows which required much more individual participation.

Pantomime

Pantomime is one of the most successful activities for the physically handicapped. Because it requires no talking, a pantomime lends itself exceptionally well to the needs of a group that includes individuals with speech impairments. It offers a chance for those individuals who are embarrassed by their speech defects to forget themselves by interpreting their roles with gestures and action. Exaggerated gestures—the big, sweeping motions peculiar to some cerebral palsied individuals—actually assist the pantomime play.

A pantomime is an excellent group endeavor because it can be adapted to each handicap in such a way as to include each member. As an example, if the play used has a narrative, one of the group who is confined to bed but is able to speak clearly can read or recite the play while the more active participants interpret the action. Individuals in wheel chairs or on crutches can carry signs or have the signs tied about them as they walk or roll their chairs across the stage to portray the characters in the play. Pantomimes give an opportunity for the group to assume responsibilities for making the necessary signs, props, and scenery.

Because a pantomime needs only the minimum of props and can be done very simply, and since the actual time for complete presentation is usually a matter of only fifteen or twenty minutes, it is easy to rehearse and perform. Participants should be encouraged to write the plays themselves. The subjects chosen are unimportant if they are undertaken with zest and completed with enjoyment.

Pantomimes not only allow the most severely handicapped to participate in a recreation activity but encourage them to walk or to improve their coordination in other ways. When a play was first presented by a group of cerebral palsied children and young adults, a youth of twenty-one, with no desire to walk, who had spent most of his life in a wheel chair, was assigned a part. Because of his speech impairment he was given the part of "Hours." His role was simply to wheel himself across the stage, carrying a sign on his wheel chair labeled "Hours," to represent the passing of time. After several rehearsals, he decided he would like to walk across the stage. He practiced for months with heavy leg braces, walking on crutches, something which he had been afraid to attempt before. During rehearsals someone always had to walk with him, with a hand holding him by the back of his belt. When the play was presented before parents and friends, however, he walked across the stage alone for the first time, perspiration dripping from his face; but he had been inspired to accomplish this difficult task. Today he is able to walk slowly on crutches, by his own efforts. He subsequently achieved his ultimate aim; he learned to "dance," even with heavy braces and crutches.

The narration of a pantomime can act as a stimulus for speech improvement. A young woman of twenty-six, who has a speech defect and must speak very slowly, was most anxious to act as narrator. She practiced faithfully, reading the part until she could speak clearly enough in the tryout to convince the group that she could have the role of narrator. Since that time, she has acted as narrator in many plays, and likes particularly to read them over a microphone. Her speech, as well as her poise and confidence in herself, has improved noticeably, and she points out that is was her desire and ambition to act that made the difference. Since her speech has improvd, she has learned to sing and has sung several solos for groups—thus realizing another ambition.

Because pantomimes allow participation by the most severely handicapped, they offer a rare opportunity for individuals to develop their imaginations in creating and projecting their roles. Each individual should be encouraged to do his part in contributing to the total effort.

Development of a Pantomime

1. Actions. Emphasis should be placed on exaggerated movements, sweeping gestures, simple and easily recognized movements.

2. The Reader. The timing of the narrator is very important, and his pace must be adjusted to accommodate the slowness of handicapped movements. The reader should watch the performers in order to permit them to perform at their own tempo. If one of them fails to respond to a cue, it should be read again. Even in the final performance, this adds to the amusement with which the play is received.

3. Scenery. Little or no scenery is required for a pantomime. However, simple or even elaborate scenery can be added if the group is able to create it.

4. Properties. Simple props can be made of paper or cardboard, and these should be made by the group, if possible. In one play presented at the Recreation Center a girl who was unable to use her hands and arms painted the signs by holding the brush with her toes.

5. Costumes. The mere suggestion of an appropriate costume is usually enough for a production. For example, the addition of a Spanish hat or a bolero, a sash or a paper mustache, is sufficient for costuming a Spanish nobleman. The addition of a cap or apron, perhaps made of paper, adequately costumes a maid.

Because pantomimes do not necessarily require elaborate preparation, they can be produced successfully on the spur of the moment. At a party, for example, each person can pretend to be something he is not—an elephant, a trapeze artist, a window washer, and so on. Charades, an adaptation of pantomime, can also be used to advantage. Stunts of any sort enliven a party, and pantomime can serve to illustrate a comic speech. Songs played by a hidden phonograph record can be interpreted in pantomime or can be used as the basis of a play. Once a pantomime has been suggested, appropriate dialogue can be developed.

A Typical Pantomime

The following pantomime has been used with great success by several groups of individuals with cerebral palsy. A play of this sort can be adapted for individuals in any age group, eight to thirty in number, and has proved stimulating and inspiring to every member of the group, if only as a means of encouraging other activities of a similar nature.

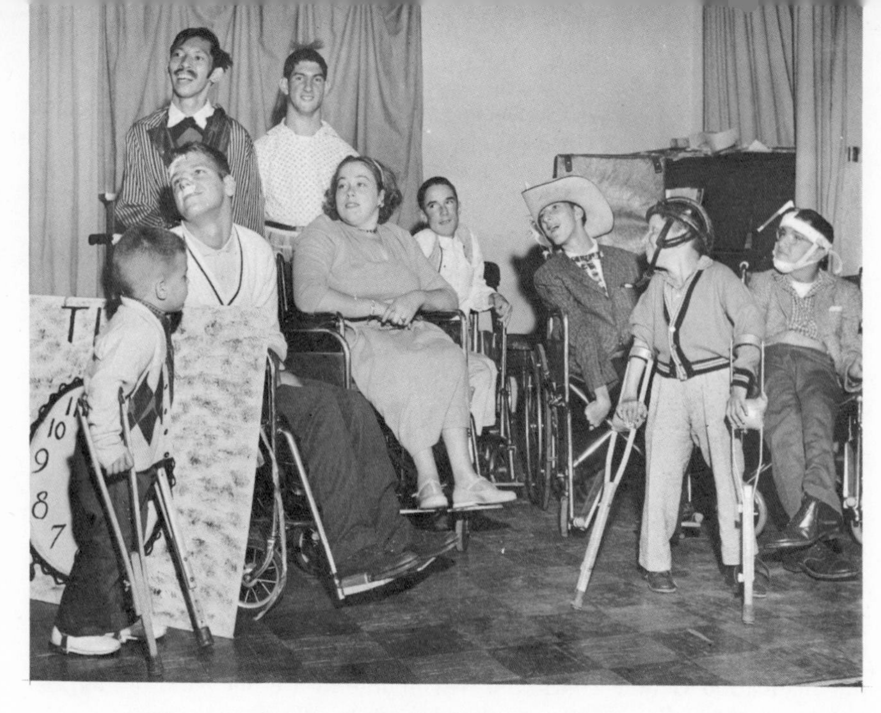

The cast rehearses "A Mellerdrammer," a pantomime play.

A MELLERDRAMMER[1]

A One-Act Play in Pantomime
by Oscar L. Gustafson

THE CAST

Manuel Del Popolo, *the Villian*	The Sun
Maggie O'Brien, *the Heroine*	Stairs
Patrick, *the Hero*	Darkness
Zingarella, *the Maid*	Shadows
Curtains, *one or two people*	Horizon
Hours, *one or two people*	Curtain

PROPERTIES

Pitcher; banana; whip; stamps; broom; rope; chalk; box of matches; flatiron; dark cloth; two salt shakers; handful of leaves.

When the play opens, the SUN is lying on the floor. The CURTAINS stand in the center of the stage with their backs to the audience. (In this case, the signs saying "Curtain" should be hung on actor's back or on wheel chair.) The STAIRS

[1] Lynn Rohrbough, Handy I–II (Delaware, Ohio: Cooperative Recreation Service, 1961).

stand at the back of the stage. MANUEL is seated at the table upon which are seen the pitcher, paper, whip, and stamps.

Players must keep their signs in plain sight, and while the story is read slowly and distinctly by the reader, the players carry out the actions indicated. Directions in parentheses are merely suggestions to the reader, who must *give time for each action* before reading the next.

READER

The CURTAINS are parted, and our play is on. (CURTAINS side-step slowly or wheel to opposite sides of stage.) It was early morning and the SUN *rose.* (SUN stands up.) MANUEL DEL POPOLO, son of a rich Spanish nobleman, sat in his father's castle. He was *pouring* over his notes (pours with pitcher), and so anxious was he to *whip* them into shape (whips them) that he simply *devoured* them (chews the notes).

Finally he arose, muttering curses. "Hither, Zingarella," he cried. ZINGARELLA came *tearing* down the stairs (tears sign marked STAIRS) and *tripped* into the room (trips over a rug).

"Did you call?" she asked. "Yes," answered he. "Where is Maggie O'Brien?" "She is in her room." "Then bring her to me at once," he commanded.

ZINGARELLA *flew* to do her master's bidding (makes motions of flying). While waiting for Maggie, MANUEL *crossed the floor* once—twice—thrice (makes chalk crosses on the floor). Then he sat down and *stamped his feet* (pastes stamps on soles of his shoes).

Soon MAGGIE came *sweeping* into the room (sweeps with broom.) "Maggie, for the last time, will you marry me?" cried Manuel. "Oh, no, no, no!" cried Maggie.

"Ah, curses—then I will lock you up in the tower until you will consent," he said.

"Oh, sire, I *appeal* to you," she cried. (She kneels and peels a banana before him.)

"Your *appeal* is *fruitless.*" (He takes the banana, eats the fruit, and hands the peel back to her.) Muttering curses he *leaves* the room. (He sprinkles a handful of leaves as he exits.)

MAGGIE *flew around* in an agony of fear. (She flies about with an expression of agony.) She knew Manuel would keep his word. Oh—if Patrick, her own true lover, would only come. He would save her.

Would he come?????

The HOURS *passed,* but oh, so slowly. (HOURS walk past very slowly.) Finally, she *took her stand* (moves stand to center of table) and *scanned* the HORIZON. (She looks at HORIZON, who moves back and forth.)

Suddenly a whistle sounded from below. "Oh, Patrick, my boy, is that you?" she cried.

"Yes, it is I. *Throw* me a line." (Maggie throws rope out to Patrick.) PATRICK gallops into the room. "Oh, Maggie!" he cried, and tenderly *pressed* her hand. (He presses her palm with the iron.)

At this moment, MANUEL entered the room, and maddened at the sight of the two lovers together, challenged Patrick to a duel.

They *assaulted* each other (go through a lively duel by shaking salt at each other), and after a few moments, MANUEL gave up the *match* (takes a match

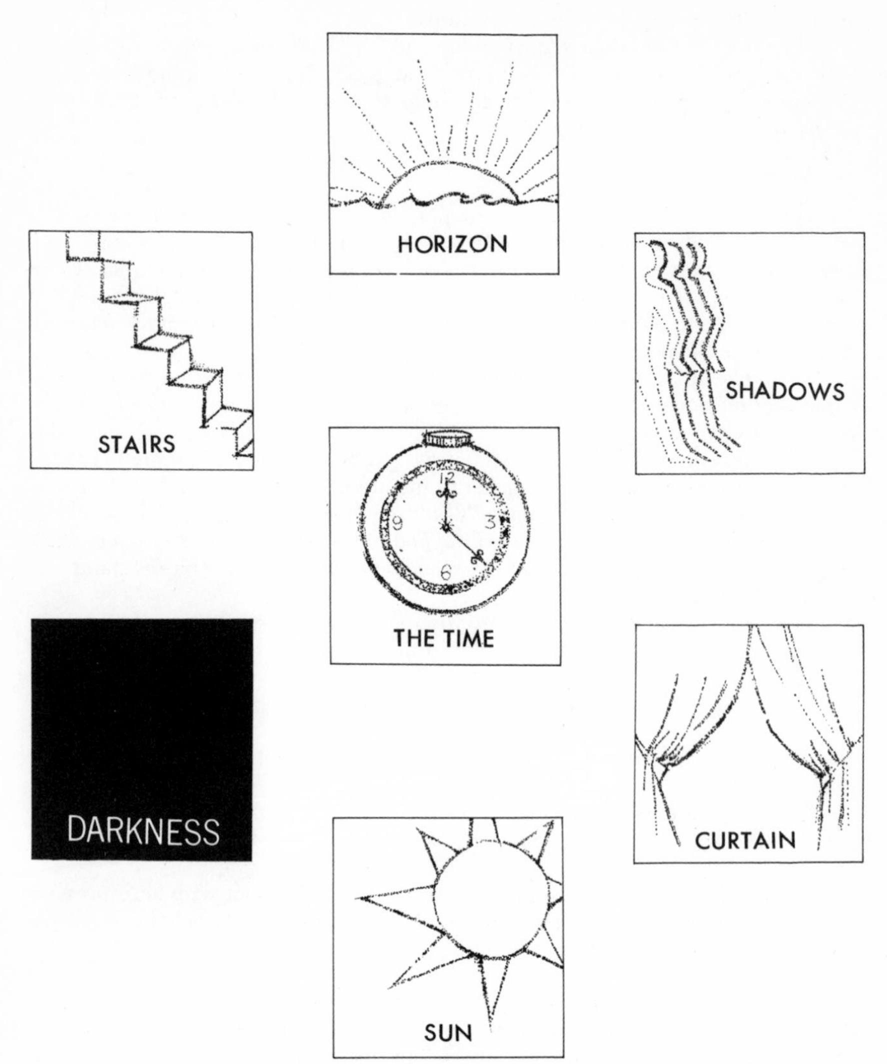

An example of signs used in "A Mellerdrammer."

from box and gives it to Patrick), acknowledged that he was defeated, and sorrowfully left the room.

"Come, Maggie, my love! Now there is none *to stand* between us. You are mine!" And Patrick led her from the room. (He passes rope around her neck and leads her from the room.)

The HOURS *pass* (hours cross stage), the SUN *sets* (sits down), DARKNESS and the SHADOWS of the night *come on* (player with dark cloth over his head, or with sign reading "Darkness," and player with "Shadows" sign come on stage). The CURTAINS *close* (CURTAINS step slowly to center)—and our play is ended.

THE END

Adaptation of Character Parts

To illustrate how character parts can be adapted for a group of individuals with cerebral palsy, the following suggestions are offered, together with examples from a performance of "A Mellerdrammer" as it was presented at the Recreation Center.

Usually there is at least one person in the group who can act as narrator and read the play. If not, the instructor or leader should read it. All parts can be portrayed by individuals in wheel chairs or on crutches. Manuel can "pour over his notes," "stamp his feet," and fight his duel from a wheel chair. Manuel, in one production, was played by a paraplegic who had the use of only one hand and arm. He managed his props by carrying the salt shaker in his pants pocket and the leaves and matches tucked in his sash. Maggie O'Brien managed to "sweep" from a wheel chair as she was being pushed on the stage. The maid was able to "tear down the stairs" from a chair; the stairs consisted of a cardboard sign within reach, held by another person in a chair.

The curtain, or curtains, can be played by one or two people, depending on the size of the group. One girl, who has a severe speech difficulty, loss of hearing, tonic neck reflexes, and extreme involuntary motions of her arms and hands, was given the role of the curtain. She could walk unaided, and her balance was maintained by arm braces and by a band worn around her chest and arms which held her arms close to her sides. A "Curtain" sign was placed around her neck, and she side-stepped slowly away from the center of the stage to indicate a curtain parting. The "Hours" were portrayed by one or two people carrying signs in wheel chairs or on crutches; the slow, unsteady gait of a young boy was most effective. The "Sun," in the same production, was a young boy who was just learning to walk on crutches and to stand up again after many falls. His part in the play proved an excellent incentive to learn to sit down and get up with crutches.

"Darkness," "Shadows," "Stairs," and the "Horizon" can be easily portrayed by individuals on crutches or in wheel chairs or even by those who cannot sit up. For example, the "Horizon" can wiggle back and forth on a cot, bed, or chair. "Darkness" and "Shadows" in one presentation were pushed on the stage in their chairs because they were unable to wheel themselves.

Other Pantomimes

Two additional pantomimes suitable for use by the handicapped are described in the pages that follow. Others can be written for a particular occasion. The number of characters can usually be increased or decreased in accordance with the number of individuals in the group. Not all parts need to be portrayed by individuals; signs may be placed about the stage to represent them. It is well to remember that wheel chairs take up space, and there is a danger in getting too many actors on the stage at one time. The participants themselves often suggest actions or punning gestures which can be added to the play, and one pantomime may suggest a number of others. Additional plays are listed in the bibliography, and other possible sources of material suitable for pantomimes are indicated.

LAVA—OR LOVE

A One-Act Play in Pantomime

THE CAST

Leawahnie
Kahuna
*Moon, *shimmers*
*Stars, *twinkle*
*Blue ocean
*Beach, *lies on floor*
*Tide, *a character who rolls on floor or holds box of "Tide" Detergent*
Tradition, *a sign*
Winds, *a person who catches sign "tradition"*
Hours, *two actors who pass each other*
Palm Trees, *two actors who wave arms*
Volcano, *actor rumbles*

(The starred actors could use cardboard signs to signify their parts in the play.)

PROPERTIES

Hair brush; kitchen mop; rocks or marbles; three carrots; beet; household iron; whiskey bottle; broom; tape measure.

ACTION

The following play is read slowly and distinctly. The narrator allows time for each action before reading the next line. The players carry out, with much exaggeration and enthusiasm, the action indicated. Each capitalized word represents the character in action at the time, and the underlined words indicate the action.

When the play opens, Leawahnie, the Moon, Stars, Ocean, Beach, Tide, Palm Trees, and the Volcano could already be on the stage, ready for action. Properties used in the play, such as the mop, broom, and so on, need to be conveniently placed for immediate use.

MUSIC

Hawaiian music for background.

NARRATION

Many, many moons ago,
On a little island in Hawaii
Lived a beautiful, dusky maiden,
Whose name was Leawahnie.

One evening, when the STARS *were twinkling*
And the MOON *was shimmering* in the sky,
LEAWAHNIE started for a stroll beside
The blue OCEAN. (She strolls by person on floor who is OCEAN.)
The HOURS passed slowly (HOURS walk past very slowly),
And LEAWAHNIE, feeling tired,
Sat down on the BEACH to rest (sits on BEACH).

She *drank in the sweet perfume* (picks up whisky bottle
and drinks)
Of the night-blooming cereus,
As she watched the TIDE *roll* and (TIDE rolls)
Splash upon the white sand . . .
And the tall PALM TREES *wave*
Their slender branches in the
Soft night's breeze.

Suddenly from behind the shadows
Stepped Kahuna, her own true lover.
"Leawahnie," he said excitedly, "we must
Leave this island at once. Mauna Loa,
The angry VOLCANO, has started to *rumble*.

"Oh, no, no," said Leawahnie, "I cannot . . .
I must stay and sacrifice myself
To Mauna Loa . . . for my people."

"But, Leawahnie," said KAHUNA, "I *press*
My suit. . . . (He presses suit with iron.)
Come with me, and I will save you. . . ."

"No, I cannot. . . . It is the tradition
Of our ancestors. . . . I must give
Myself to the angry volcano
To save my people."
"Let us *throw* TRADITION to the winds," (throws sign away)
Said Kahuna.
"No, the tie between us must be broken,"
LEAWAHNIE said sadly as she *brushed*
The tears from her eyes. (She brushes with hair brush.)

"Then I must go without you . . . 'Aloha,' "
He said sadly as he *swept past her* (sweeps with broom).

The HOURS *passed by* and the MOON rose (HOURS cross stage
and MOON stands up)
Higher and higher.
All was still save the loud *rumbling*
Of Mauna Loa, the angry VOLCANO.

Then, at last, the pent-up emotion sought
An outlet, and the *tears* of LEAWAHNIE
Fell like raindrops. . . . (Rocks or marbles are dropped.)
After several hours, she suddenly
Felt a strange *beat in her heart* (pulls beet out of dress),
"Something has happened to the volcano,"
She said aloud.

At this moment, KAHUNA came *running over the* BEACH.
"Leawahnie, you are free! *Mop up your tears* (mops with mop).

"Mauna Loa has ceased its rumbling."
"Yes," said LEAWAHNIE, facing him,
"Our *love has been measured*" (measures with tape measure).
And as they pledged their troth
With a *three-carat ring* (puts carrot ring on finger)
The STARS *twinkled* down upon them.
The MOON *shimmered* in the sky,
The TIDE rolled and splashed over the BEACH (splashes "Tide"
over BEACH).
And our play is ended!

THE END

Production Suggestions

Lava—or Love can be presented simply, with mere suggestions to indicate each character, or it can bring in a variety of arts and crafts. Simple or elaborate signs and properties can be created. For example, such objects as the beet or carrots can be made from papier-mâché; Hawaiian leis and a grass skirt for the leading lady, from crepe paper. In one use of this play, Hawaiian type masks were made from papier-mâché. The sound effects for the "Tide" rolling and splashing and the "Volcano" rumbling can be achieved backstage or by the actors on stage. For example, the rumble of the "Volcano" was played by a boy who had great difficulty in speaking but was able to achieve a wonderfully effective type of gurgling, rumbling sound as the "Volcano" erupted.

POKEY HUNTUS[2]

A Pantomime

Cardboard signs with long strings attached for hanging around the neck must be prepared in advance for the following characters:

THE CAST

Curtain	Maple	Pokey Huntus
Scene	Sun	Danger
North Wind	Brook	Chief Powder Can
Pine Tree	Squirrels	Holy Father
Elm	Situation	Birds
Plum	Captain John Smith	

PROPERTIES

Broom; bucket; nuts; flashlight or matches; ladder; hatchet; rope; block or box; large heart cut from red cardboard; pair of cut-out goggle eyes; a "warrant" and a "manifesto"; two scrolls which may be rolled up, one containing the words "Not on your life" and the other "If he goes, I go."

ACTION

The play is read slowly and distinctly by the narrator. The characters, holding the cardboard signs in plain sight, act out the words literally, with much exaggeration and enthusiasm. Each capitalized word represents the character in action at the time, and the underlined words indicate the action.

[2] "Handy Stunts," Cooperative Recreation Service, Inc., Delaware, Ohio, 1932. Revised, 1961, p. 8.

MUSIC

Indian music for background.

NARRATOR

Young folks, have you heard the story,
Heard the great and thrilling story
Of the Princess of Virginia,
Of the noble Pokey Huntus,
How she saved the captive white man?
Listen now, and I'll unfold it.
John Smith was the captive white man;
Pokey Huntus, Indian maiden.
And Virginia owned as chieftain
Powder Can, whose savage people
Ruled with might and ruled with power.

Softly now the CURTAIN *rises.*
See the SCENE *laid* in the forest.
Where for many moons I'm thinking
That fair scene will keep on lying.
Through the forest *comes* the NORTH WIND
Shakes the trees and makes them wiggle.
Wiggles now the stately PINE TREE,
Wiggles, too, ELM, PLUM, and MAPLE.

Lo, where in the highest heaven
Mounts the SUN (SUN climbs a ladder)
And *casts* its bright ray (SUN lights the flashlight).

Hear the BROOK, so sweetly *gurgling*
Babbling, prattling through the forest.
See the SQUIRRELS, gently *sporting,*
Gathering nuts to safely store them.
Comprehend the *situation,*
Calm, serene, and full of beauty.
But the restless WIND comes *sweeping,*
Sweeping onward o'er the fair SCENE.

Now the hero, CAPTAIN JOHN SMITH,
Is *a-stalking* through the forest.
Now our darling, POKEY HUNTUS,
Smirking, humming, trotting, trips in.

Watch our darling mincing onward,
Sweeping obstacles before her.
SMITH, he *sees* our blessed darling,
Fastens sad his EYES upon her. (SMITH pins eyes on Pokey.)
DANGER all about is *hovering,*

Lurking in obscurest places.
Then CHIEF POWDER CAN, the noble,
In his might, he comes *a-stalking*,
Calmly *steps* upon the FAIR SCENE,
While he *views* the SITUATION.

SMITH he *stands* in all his manhood,
Meets the red man's gaze of anger,
Watches while he *shows* his "WARRANT,"
Sees the block of execution
That the noble SMITH is led to.

Hold your tears! Stop all that weeping.
Fate! It isn't going to hurt him.
POKEY *wails* and *groans* and *shudders,*
Hands her dad her "MANIFESTO." ("If he goes, I go.")
Silence reigns. Then through the forest
Breaks the mighty rushing NORTH WIND,
Shakes each tree and makes it totter.

POWDER CAN deep thoughts is thinking,
"Shall I scalp him? Give him Pokey?"
Better thoughts at last prevailing,
He relents and *kicks* the bucket.
Now the SITUATION *changes.*
JOHN SMITH *gives his heart* to Pokey,
Begs her be his darling wifey.
Enter quick the HOLY FATHER,
Ties the knot. (FATHER fastens them together with rope.)
While from the forest
All the BIRDS sing happily carols (BIRDS whistle wedding march).

Now you've heard the noble story
Of the Princess Pokey Huntus,
How she saved the captive white man,
Saved the noble Captain John Smith.
Now 'tis time to end the drama.
Falls upon the SCENE the CURTAIN.

THE END

Variety Shows

A variety show is a group project unusually adaptable for severely handicapped individuals such as the cerebral palsied. It is popular with groups of all kinds because it offers an opportunity for a varied program of entertainment. It can include skits or stunts requiring only one or two people or a play or pageant with a large cast. In short, it is an excellent means for encouraging creative work in a group, since the poetry, songs, skits, dance acts, tableaux, and pantomimes can be entirely original. This type of activity offers opportunities to the members of the group to do something which they have already mastered, such as singing a particular song or reciting a favorite poem, or to display a talent.

One such group, when the possibility of a variety show was discussed showed immediate enthusiasm, and over half of the fifteen members volunteered some type of talent. One boy wanted to be master of ceremonies; another in a wheel chair wanted to play his harmonica, and eventually a dancing act was worked out to accompany his music. One girl volunteered to sing a song; two others asked to learn a magic act which they could perform. Usually the most severely handicapped, particularly those with severe speech difficulties and lack of coordination, have few if any ideas of how they can participate. If they do have ideas, they experience difficulty in explaining them to the leader, who must allow time to encourage expression and suggestions. Skits and stunts modeled on radio programs using simple sound effects are well suited to the severely handicapped group. If a child or young adult is able only to grunt, groan, or scream, he can play a sound effect in a skit of this type.

A Typical Skit

As a way of including them in a variety show, a skit entitled "A Ghost Story" was first introduced to a group of six severely handicapped youngsters with cerebral palsy. The author had been warned by well-meaning individuals that some of these young people were mentally incapable of responding properly and that very little should be expected of them. However, when the tryouts began, each person grunted, groaned, and screamed to his fullest capacity and was most eager to be cast in the play. One girl in a wheel chair, who was supposedly quite "dull," played the part of the "Timid Young Girl." She never missed a cue and each time managed a bloodcurdling scream. A boy of ten, whose only speech was a grunt, played the part of a ghost and evoked a very ghostly groan. Each participant in turn was able to produce the needed sound effect, and this particular skit became the most enjoyed in the show.

For a radio skit of this sort, a real microphone is most effective; however, if one is not available, a makeshift microphone can be constructed to add reality. Characters in the skit, no matter how small their parts, should be given full recognition. For example, players' names with their parts should be read at the beginning of the play or the players themselves should be presented for curtain calls at the end of the play. A printed or mimeographed program listing the cast of characters is actually the best means of providing the necessary recognition each participant so earnestly needs and desires. When skits are presented in the spirit of fun and simple enjoyment, they never fail to gain tremendous response and enthusiasm, even from the most severely handicapped.

"A Ghost Story" and other successful skits follow; sources of additional skits and stunts are included in the bibliography.

A GHOST STORY[3]

The following story should be read slowly and dramatically. Each time a character is mentioned, the designated person makes the noise indicated.

CHARACTERS

Timid Young Girl, *sobs or screams*
Old, Old Woman, *shrill cackle*
Large Black Cat, *mei-ow*
Long Black Snake, *hiss-ss-ss*
Tall Man, *groans*
Yellow Dog, *howl*
Big Black Crow, *caw-caw*
Four Black Bats, *whir-r-r*
Bogey Man, *boooooo-oo*
Ghost, *everyone screams together*

THE STORY

On a dark and stormy night in October, a stage coach rumbled along a country road. In it a Timid Young Girl . . . bounced up and down on the hard cushions and gazed with fright out into the darkness. Suddenly, the coach stopped, and in stepped an Old, Old Woman. . . . From under one arm peered a Large Black Cat . . . and around the other twisted a Long Black Snake. . . .

"Hoity toity! A Timid Young Girl . . . traveling alone tonight!" exclaimed the Old, Old Woman . . . with a hideous grin. "Let me tell your fortune, my pretty dear." The Old, Old Woman . . . stretched out a bony arm toward the Timid Young Girl . . . while the Large Black Cat . . . arched his back and growled and the Long Black Snake . . . watched with beady eyes. "No, no!" cried the Timid Young Girl . . . shrinking into a corner with her pretty hands behind her back.

[3] "A Ghost Story," *Handbook for Recreation*, Department of Health, Education, and Welfare, Children's Bureau, Washington, D.C., 1960, p. 103.

At that moment the door was thrown violently open, and in rushed a Tall Man . . . wearing a long raincoat. His face was hidden by a drooping hat, but his voice was low and pleasant. "Allow me," he said, and gently pushed between the Timid Young Girl . . . and the Old, Old Woman . . . who three times pointed her finger at the Tall Man. . . . A Yellow Dog . . . howled from under the seat, the Large Black Cat . . . growled again, and the Long Black Snake . . . hissed.

On the window sill a Big Black Crow . . . alighted and croaked most dismally. Into the coach flew Four Black Bats . . . and beat their wings in the face of the Timid Young Girl . . . while through each window peered the grotesque face of a Bogey Man. Nearer and nearer to the Old, Old Woman . . . bent the Tall Man . . ., fixed on the Old, Old Woman . . . two startling eyes, and pushed back his hat. With a terrified shriek, the Old, Old Woman . . . sprang to the door, followed by her Large Black Cat . . ., howling Yellow Dog . . ., Long Black Snake . . ., Four Black Bats . . ., and the Big Black Crow. . . . Inside the coach the Timid Young Girl . . . had fainted, for under the hat of the Tall Man . . . was the ghastly countenance of a ghost! . . .

THE END

THE KING WITH THE TERRIBLE TEMPER[4]

A Skit

Divide the group into five units as indicated. Each group makes the appropriate response when its key word is given in the reading of the story.

CHARACTERS	RESPONSE
The King	Gr-r-r-r-r-r!
Fat Daughter	Ka-plunk
Thin Daughter	Whistle
Beautiful Daughter	Ah-a-a-a-a-a-ah!
Handsome Prince	A-ha!
Galloping Horse	All make galloping noise with feet

THE STORY

There was once a king with a terrible temper (gr-r-r-r-r-r). He had three daughters. The eldest was very fat (ka-plunk); the second was exceedingly thin (whistle); but the youngest was exceedingly beautiful (ah-a-a-a-a-a-ah!).

Now in a nearby country there lived a handsome prince (a-ha!). One day he came to the palace of the king with a terrible temper (gr-r-r-r-r-r). "I have come," said he, "to seek a wife among your daughters" (ka-plunk, whistle, ah-a-a-a-a-a-ah!). First he was presented to the eldest and, well, the heaviest daughter (ka-plunk). "She would eat too much," said the handsome prince

[4] "Handy Stunts," Cooperative Recreation Service, Inc., Delaware, Ohio, 1932. Revised, 1961, p. 6.

(a-ha!). Then appeared the daughter who was very thin (whistle). She did not please him either, and he said, "But, I heard that you had a young and beautiful daughter!" (ah-a-a-a-a-a-a-ah!). This displeased the king with the terrible temper (gr-r-r-r-r-r). Said he, "You can't rob my nursery for a bride!" "Well," came the reply, "I cannot love your oldest daughter" (ka-plunk), "and I don't like your thin daughter" (whistle). Just then on the stairway appeared the youngest and most beautiful daughter (ah-a-a-a-a-a-a-ah!). Rapture filled the heart of the handsome prince (a-ha!) and he cried, "I will take your youngest daughter!" (ah-a-a-a-a-a-a-ah!). "Call out the guards," the King thundered, "and turn out this upstart of a prince!" (a-ha!). But the suitor immediately seized in his arms the willing princess (ah-a-a-a-a-a-a-ah!). With her he rushed out. When the royal court reached the door, all they could see was a cloud of dust raised by the hoofs of the galloping horse (galloping sounds which gradually die away).

So ends the romantic tale of the king with the terrible temper (gr-r-r-r-r-r), his fat daughter (ka-plunk), his thin daughter (whistle), his youngest and most beautiful daughter (ah-a-a-a-a-a-a-ah!) and the handsome prince (a-ha!) with the galloping horse (galloping sounds with feet).

THE END

LION HUNT IN DARKEST AFRICA[5]

A Skit

Divide the group into six units as indicated. Each group makes the appropriate response when its key word is given in the reading of the story.

CHARACTERS	RESPONSE
Lion	Roar
Rain	Hand clapping
Snake	Hiss-s-s-s-s
Army	Feet marching
Horse	Neigh
Gun	Bang

THE STORY

I served with the Third Army (feet marching) in Africa recently and promised myself that someday I would return. So, when I received my Army (feet marching) discharge, I jumped on my horse (neigh) and galloped off to hunt lions (roar) in the wilds of Africa.

We had many adventures. To begin with, it rained (hand clapping) for the first week, which, of course, reminded me of my life in the Army (feet marching). The rain (hand clapping) finally stopped, and we set out. At first the horse

[5] Novelty arrangement by Larry Eisenberg, Madison, Wisconsin.

(neigh) shied at the snakes (hiss-s-s-s-s) but soon forgot about them when he heard a lion (roar) in the distance. I might not be here now if it had not been for my gun (bang) practice in the Army, because suddenly a big lion (roar) crashed through the bushes near us, causing the horse (neigh) to buck. But I quickly shot the lion (roar) with my gun (bang). Then in my best Army style, I leaped from my horse (neigh), just missed landing on a snake (hiss-s-s-s-s), and prodded the dead lion (roar) with my gun (bang).

Now, as I sit by my fireside on a rainy (hand clapping) evening, gazing at the lion (roar) rug, I am reminded of Africa.

THE END

Puppetry

Puppetry is a very fine medium for initiating the handicapped into the realm of dramatics. It can be enjoyed by shy individuals who wish to appear only behind the scenes in their first experience with drama. It also presents an excellent opportunity for group effort as well as individual creative growth and expression. Puppetry can be coordinated with a great many other activities such as arts and crafts, music, and creative writing.

One group's interest in puppetry began in a pottery class in which the clay heads of "The Three Bears" were shaped and formed from potter's clay. These were used as models for the papier-mâché heads which were eventually made into hand puppets and which proved to be a great incentive in improving the manipulation of fingers and hands. Children who could talk but could not control their hands read the lines, while other children who could use their hands but could not talk manipulated the puppets. Puppetry proved an incentive to improve speech as well as coordination; many children would practice for hours in order to be able to speak a word or a few lines. Backdrops for the stage were made as a group project; each child or young person contributed one portion—a tree, the sky, and so on. One girl, who painted with her toes, took great delight in making many of the backdrop scenes. Eventually she wrote an original Thanksgiving play which was presented in puppet form by the entire group.

Types of Puppets

Rod or stick puppets are perhaps the easiest for the handicapped to use, since most individuals can hold the stick or rod which supports a puppet and perform the simple movements required. A Christmas puppet show, "The Three Wise Men," was produced with stick puppets by a group of children. The sticks were nailed together, and cloth tennis balls for heads, were stuck on the sticks; the faces were painted with tempera paints. Steel wool made excellent hair. Camels—in this instance, only flat figures were attempted—were made from painted cardboard and nailed on sticks.

Paper bag puppets, which are also very easy to make, can be attached to the sticks. These puppets are light, and the children find it easy to hold up their sticks while the rhyme is recited. One group of cerebral palsied children presented a dozen or more nursery rhymes with puppets made from paper bags. A stick can also be used with a simple string puppet, such as the spider who sits down beside Miss Muffet.

Hand puppets sometimes prove to be an incentive for better hand and finger coordination for individuals with cerebral palsy. Some are able, with practice, to make the puppet dance, sit down, and pick up objects.

Marionettes, which are puppets operated by strings, are quite difficult for persons with some physical handicaps to manipulate. However, with a little ingenuity and resourcefulness, marionettes can be adapted so that they can be manipulated by even the most severely handicapped. Very simple marionettes can be made from cardboard and joined with string at the arms, shoulders, and legs. They can then be fastened to guiding strings which are attached to the puppet stage itself. The end of the operating string can be fastened to a curtain ring which, in turn, is held by a cup hook when it is not in operation. Individuals work the marionettes by looping the curtain ring over one finger or toe, so even if an individual has only the use of one finger or toe, he can operate a marionette. In one instance, a girl of nineteen who could not use her hands at all was able to manipulate a dancing puppet by having the strings tied to her wrists. In this manner, she was able to make the marionette dance by moving her arms back and forth in rhythm to the song she sang. The marionette was the more effective because she made it dance in tempo with her own singing.

A marionette stage can be improvised or, if funds are available, simply constructed. In one instance an old restaurant counter was used for a marionette stage and lent itself remarkably well to the operation and use of marionettes in the recreation program (see illustration on p. 178). Sometimes the participants devise ways of constructing a stage.

Knight Rupert, a Play

Knight Rupert, an original Christmas play with music, was composed specifically for a group of thirty-eight cerebral palsied children whose ages ranged from three to twenty-one years. Before it was written, the group was studied in order to adapt the play to the limitations of the children and encourage the development of their hidden potentialities. A further consideration was to provide an activity in which every child, regardless of his or her handicap, might participate. Several members were confined to wheel chairs; others required crutches; still others lacked coordination in the use of their hands, legs, or arms; many had severe speech difficulties.

The section that follows describes the action, the sequence of scenes, the music, and the character adaptations in the original presentation. Suggestions are also offered as to costumes, lighting, scenery, and other aspects of producing the play.

THE PLAY[6]

The story of *Knight Rupert* was taken from an old German legend. According to the legend, each year at Christmas time Knight Rupert, a mythical being, visits the four corners of the earth to see if love and kindness still dwell in the hearts of all children. In the play, the four corners of the earth, North, South, East, and West, are portrayed by "islands."

Each island is represented by a child in his wheel chair. By decorations on the wheel chairs, the geographical and physical characteristics of the various islands are vividly illustrated. Surrounding each island is a group of children dressed to resemble the natives and animals of that island.

In the play, Knight Rupert and his four young messengers visit these islands, accompanied by their followers, who are small children carrying slender, tapered Christmas trees decorated with brightly colored ornaments. Upon his arrival at each island, Knight Rupert, assisted by a chorus of the younger children, sings to the inhabitants, asking if they have been good children all year. The islanders respond in song that they have, and Rupert presents them with a rare gift from one of the messenger's Christmas trees. After the presentations of the gift, the islanders' music, which is written for piano and rhythm band, begins. The islanders then interpret this music according to their physical ability and imagination.

After the last island has been visited, Knight Rupert leaves the stage briefly. He reenters bearing a large white Christmas tree heavily laden with ornaments, holly sprigs, and candy canes. The Knight then beckons to the islands, the natives, and the animals to join him in the center of the stage. The cast then groups itself around the tree and joyously sings "Deck the Hall," while Knight Rupert walks through the audience wishing all the members Christmas cheer as he presents them with sprigs of holly and candy canes.

[6] "Knight Rupert—A Christmas Pantomime." By permission of Carl Cherry Foundation.

MUSICAL NUMBERS

The musical numbers in order of presentation were:

1. Star-Hanging Music
2. Percussion Interlude
3. Knight Rupert's Music
4. Rupert's Song and Response
5. Northern Island Music
6. Knight Rupert's Music
7. Rupert's Song and Response
8. Southern Island Music
9. Knight Rupert's Music
10. Rupert's Song and Response
11. Eastern Island Music
12. Knight Rupert's Music
13. Rupert's Song and Response
14. Western Island Music
15. Star-Hanging Music
16. Christmas Tree Music
17. "Deck the Hall"

Sequence of Scenes

The action in each scene of the play is described here, together with a reference to the accompanying music. The piano score used in each scene is also reproduced.

Scene I—The Star-hanging Music. As this is played, the star raiser enters from the rear of the room or from a side door and walks to the center of the stage to hang the star nets on the racks. She then sits down with the choir.

1. Star-Hanging Music

2. Percussion Interlude

Scene II—Knight Rupert's Music. The Knight's music is played briefly, and Knight Rupert comes out and makes his introductory speech; then his music begins again, and his followers step out to follow him on his journey to the islands. The Knight's music ends as they arrive at the northern island.

3. Knight Rupert's Music

4. Rupert's Song and Response

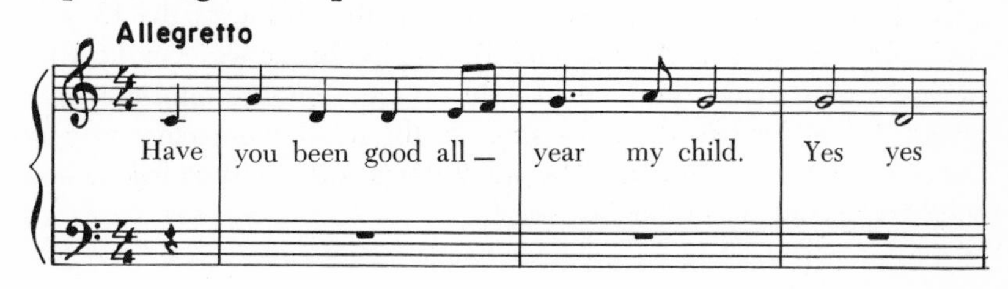

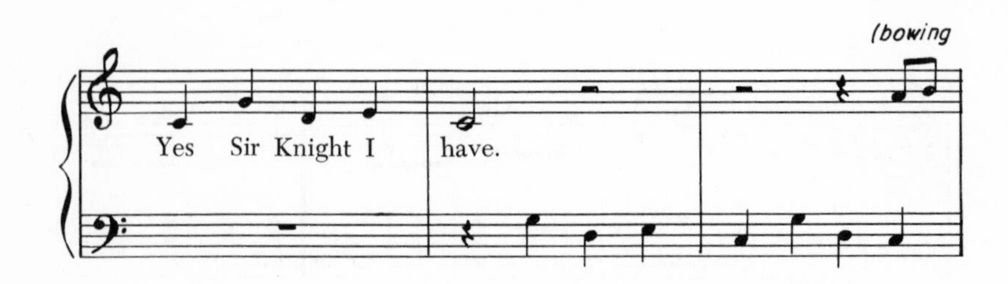

Scene III—Northern Island Music. Upon their arrival at the northern island, Knight Rupert and his messengers sing to the northern island. The inhabitants answer him as he presents them with gifts of candy canes from a messenger's tree, and the Eskimo music begins. The natives and animals of the northern island perform to this music as the Knight and his followers watch. At the end of the performance Knight Rupert's music begins again, and he and his retinue proceed to the southern island. On his arrival there, he sings to the inhabitants and, after receiving a response, he presents the inhabitants gifts of snowflakes, and the southern island music begins.

5. Northern Island Music

6. Knight Rupert's Music (repeat #3)

7. Rupert's Song and Response (repeat #4)

Scene IV—Southern Island Music. The southern island's inhabitants perform to this music as Knight Rupert and his followers stand by. At the end of this performance, the Knight's music begins again, and he leads his followers to the eastern island.

8. Southern Island Music

9. Knight Rupert's Music (repeat #3)

10. Rupert's Song and Response (repeat #4)

Scene V—Eastern Island Music. The Knight's music then begins again; the Knight sings to these islanders, and they in turn respond. He then presents the inhabitants with gifts of stars from the star tree. As they bow to him, the oriental or eastern island music begins. The natives and animals of the eastern island perform to their music.

11. Eastern Island Music

12. Knight Rupert's Music (repeat #3)

13. Rupert's Song and Response (repeat #4)

Scene VI—Western Island Music. Knight Rupert's music begins again, and he journeys to the last island—the western island. Upon his arrival, he sings to these inhabitants, and they respond in a manner similar to that mentioned for the previous islands. As he presents them with sprigs of holly from the "holly" tree, the western island music begins. The western islanders in turn also carry out their dance to the western music; the Knight's music follows immediately, and Rupert returns to the curtain entrance to bring in the Christmas tree. As he brings the Christmas tree to the center of the stage, he summons the rest of the cast to join him; as they do so, the strains of "Deck the Hall" are heard.

14. Western Island Music

15. Star-hanging Music (repeat #1)

16. Christmas Tree Music

Scene VII—"Deck the Hall." As the entire cast sings "Deck the Hall," Knight Rupert and his messengers pass out candy canes and holly sprigs to each member of the audience.

17. "Deck the Hall"

CHARACTER ADAPTATIONS

Knight Rupert proved the framework for a creative drama for severely handicapped children. A discussion of the character parts, a description of the handicaps of the original cast, and the interpretations of the cast are presented here merely as guides for the recreation leader or teacher. The original production was presented as a Christmas pageant in which thirty-eight children of a cerebral palsy school participated, but the play could be presented by only ten or twelve children merely by omitting or reducing the chorus or the orchestra or both, or by eliminating some of the natives or animals of the various islands. On the other hand, the island groups, and hence the cast, could be enlarged by adding more animals or inhabitants.

As the handicaps of another group of players would not necessarily correspond with those of the children who originally presented *Knight Rupert,* each group that considers producing the play should develop its own story dramatizations to suit its particular handicaps and abilities as well as its number. The recreation leader or teacher should assist the children in determining how each scene should be interpreted and how many characters it would need. Each child, however, should be encouraged to develop his own part and interpret it to the best of his individual ability.

The Star Raiser

In the original play, the star raiser at her first appearance transported the audience into the world of the play. With heavily braced legs, she walked toward the star racks with great effort and determination, swinging her crutches back and forth to the music. She managed to carry the star nets by draping them around her shoulders, and with resolution she braced herself with her crutches as she unfolded the nets over the star racks.

While the star-hanging music might be used by itself merely as an introduction, the star raiser could be portrayed in a manner similar to that of the original play by a child in his wheel chair, who could wheel himself to the star racks. Another possible variation of this part could be for a child to sing with the star-hanging music or to make a brief welcoming speech to the audience after the music ended.

Knight Rupert

The title role of *Knight Rupert* was effectively portrayed by a boy of nineteen, who was severely handicapped by cerebral palsy. His occasional facial distortions did not distract from his warm, spontaneous speech at the beginning of the play. His keen understanding of his role and of Knight Rupert's purpose in visiting the islands enabled him to enact his part with deep feeling and compassion. His concern for his four small followers, as he went from island to island in his lame, rhythmic walk, was indeed convincing and characteristic of a true medieval knight.

As in the original production, Knight Rupert should be played by a child who is a natural leader and who has a strong feeling for and under-

Knight Rupert and messengers.

standing of the role, as his part is the unifying one of the play and should inspire the other members of the cast with the desires and spontaneity necessary to make it a success.

Knight Rupert's Messengers

Knight Rupert's messengers were four young children handicapped from various types of cerebral palsy but able to walk. Although each child had some lack in motor coordination, all of them responded to the mood of the play and walked rhythmically side by side as they carried their small Christmas trees from island to island. Two of the children sang spontaneously with Knight Rupert as he addressed the islands and at the end of the play eagerly assisted the Knight in distributing holly and candy canes to the audience.

Although the messengers in the original production were about the same age and height and were able to walk, children with practically any handicap could play these parts. As an example, the children could be in wheel chairs and wheel themselves from island to island with Knight Rupert; their wheel chairs could be decorated with ornaments, and the children could hold the small gifts for the islands in their laps. It would be possible to have only two messengers if the cast was small.

The Islands

The islands were represented by children confined to their wheel chairs with various types of cerebral palsy and different degrees of handicap. Several actively interpreted their parts by joining the natives and animals in singing their response to Knight Rupert, while the children with speech impairments pantomimed the island response.

The islands may be built around a chair, bed or stool; however, a wheel chair lends itself as a frame for the necessary island decorations and makes it possible to include children in the play even if they are confined to wheel chairs. The islands, in addition to the interpretations described above, might participate by engaging in a conversation with the natives about their "homeland" or island; in another variation, they could be encouraged to sing a song in their "native" language.

Inhabitants of the Northern Island

The Eskimo and walrus, as inhabitants of the northern island, developed a simple pantomime together. The Eskimo, a boy of thirteen, had some speech difficulty and was lacking in motor coordination. The wal-

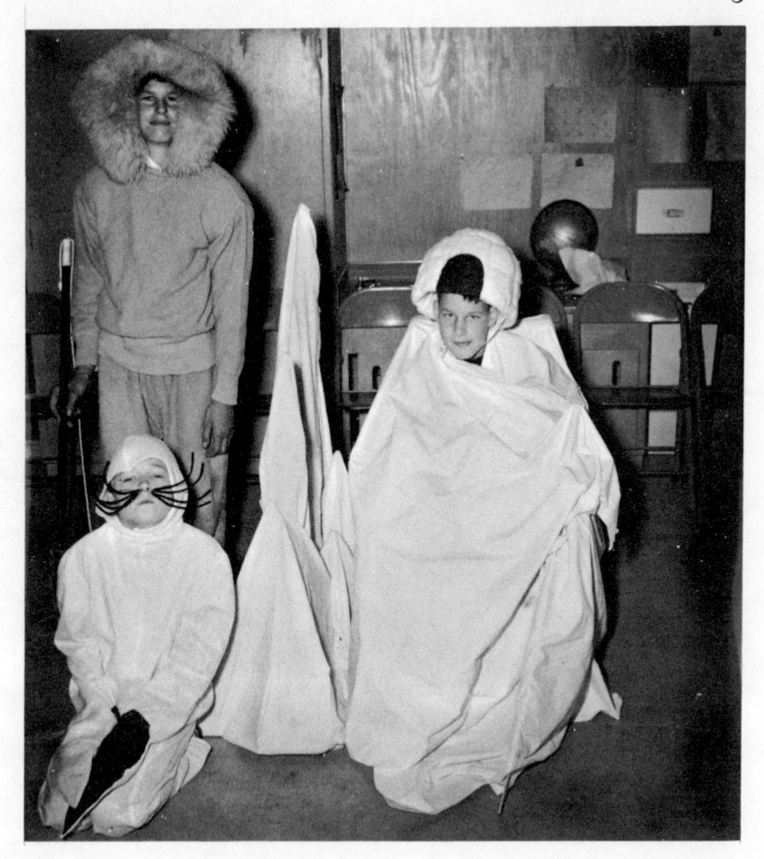

Inhabitants of northern island.

rus, another boy of thirteen, had a speech involvement and severe motor disorders. In rhythm to the music of the northern island, the Eskimo stabbed a fish with his long, black harpoon, while the walrus, who was unable to stand, crouched on his knees, flapped his fins, and tried to take the fish away from the Eskimo. The involuntary, jerky movements of the handicapped boy actually added to his interpretation of his part as walrus.

The action used by the inhabitants of the northern island in the original production was a pantomime developed by the children of that island. The island group could be changed by adding another animal or by portraying a different animal, in which case a different pantomime would be required. For example, if the children elected to have a polar

Inhabitants of southern island.

bear instead of a walrus, the bear and the Eskimo could dance together or perform some other routine to fit the Eskimo music.

Inhabitants of the Southern Island

The southern island inhabitants developed a scene in which two monkeys and a native Hawaiian girl participated. The native girl, who had a general lack of physical coordination and a speech handicap, was confined to a wheel chair. As a Hawaiian native, she sat in a wheel chair making flower leis as she watched the monkeys of her island.

Two boys selected the character parts of the monkeys; they especially enjoyed the pretense of the monkey actions—and operated completely independently. One monkey was compelled to sit on the floor because of occasional *grand mal* siezures; however, he played with coconuts and bananas, scratched his head, and tossed fruit to the other monkey. The second monkey, who had a severe speech impairment but who otherwise had good coordination, danced to the island music, played with the other monkey, and tried to steal the Hawaiian girl's lei.

As a variation on the scene in the original production, a Hawaiian native could perform a hula dance to the accompaniment of a rhythm band, while the monkeys or other animals might dance with each other or sing a song in the native Hawaiian tongue.

Inhabitants of the Eastern Island

The Oriental "native" was played by a girl of twenty-one who had a severe speech defect, a hearing loss, and tonic neck reflexes. Drawing upon her early childhood experiences in the Orient, she presented a charming dance which convincingly projected the mood of the Far East. Her balance was maintained by heavy arm braces which held her arms down, slightly extended them, and gave her, in Chinese costume, a true Oriental dancer's appearance.

Inhabitants of eastern island.

The Oriental pattern of the island was accentuated by the bird which was portrayed by a girl of nineteen. She imitated bird actions by flapping her "wings" in rhythm to the music while standing supported by crutches. She sang and bowed to Knight Rupert as he presented her with a golden star from a messenger's Christmas tree.

The Oriental, the bird, or any other inhabitants of the Orient could, of course, develop a "scene" together which would be representative of the Orient. If the Oriental were unable to walk, she could merely sit cross-legged with a Chinese fan and sing a native song.

Inhabitants of the Western Island

The Nordic and the reindeer, two young boys, developed their own scene in a dance together. Although both were lacking in motor coordination, the Nordic boy, holding a Swiss music box to his ear, danced to

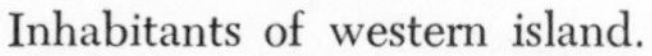
Inhabitants of western island.

Orchestra for "Knight Rupert."

the music of the Western island while the reindeer pretended to butt the dancing Nordic with his antlers.

Although this type of scene was developed in the original production, it would be just as effective for two Norsemen or two reindeer to stage a scene together. For example, two reindeer could fight with each other playfully, locking and unlocking horns, or several Norsemen might work out a native dance together.

Orchestra and Chorus

In the original production of *Knight Rupert*, a group of eight children comprised the orchestra. Their ages ranged from six to ten, and they had varying disabilities. All of them, however, could use their hands, or at least a hand, to play a drum, xylophone, the triangles, or a Chinese gong. For the most part, these children had no previous training in music or in the use of rhythm instruments, yet their response as members of the rhythm band or orchestra was exceptional. In only a few rehearsals they developed an exceptional sense of rhythm and learned how to play their instruments.

The orchestra as related to the play is extremely flexible in that any number of instruments can be used. Also it is possible to introduce instruments other than those called for in the score by writing additional arrangements.

The children who sang in the chorus were, for the most part, those who had severe handicaps and were unable to walk, although they were able to sing. They learned the island songs readily and proved to be invaluable to the production as a whole, since they responded for those "natives" who could not respond to Knight Rupert. As the number of children in the choir is not governed by any consideration in the play, the choir provided additional flexibility to the over-all production of *Knight Rupert.*

PRODUCTION NOTES

There are various ways in which *Knight Rupert* might be produced, depending upon the facilities and organization of the individual schools or recreation groups. It either could be presented as any other play, or it could be treated as an educational project. If it is presented in a recreation program, it is suggested that a director be appointed and that he begin preparations several months before the play is to be presented. He should organize committees to be responsible for casting, properties, and scenery. These committees should complete their work well in advance of the date of the performance. It is particularly important that the properties which are to be used in the pantomime actions of the children—that is, the messengers' Christmas trees, the Hawaiian leis, and the harpoon—be assembled for the first rehearsal.

The director should also select a pianist, preferably a teacher from the school, who would be available for the frequent rehearsals so necessary in producing this type of play. In his over-all approach to the production, the director should spend considerable time studying the history of each island country with the children and/or adults to stimulate creative thinking and to help them plan the settings, cast the characters, and decide what action each one can contribute.

As *Knight Rupert* provides an excellent framework for creative dramatics and lends itself to use as an educational project, it is believed that one of the most desirable production methods would be to use the play as a class or school project.

A suitable preparation for the production might include a study of the Christmas legends of various countries, as well as the geographic and cultural backgrounds of the specific "island" countries. The children should become thoroughly familiar with their size and location and their principal mountain ranges and rivers. Their study of the islands should emphasize the customs, folklore, and dress of the inhabitants and should provide the group with material for the play.

As their study progresses, the children should be encouraged to select the characteristics they deem important in representing the islands, in order to reinforce the mood and meaning of the play. In their arts and crafts classes, the cast should develop the settings they have chosen and make the properties and decorations for the wheel chair islands. For example, in the study of the Northern island, the children could improvise the necessary decorations from readily available materials to stimulate ice and snow, properties which also might suggest to them the suitability of the igloo headdress used in the original production. In their study of the Northern inhabitants, the children could be encouraged to collect authentic pictures of Eskimos as an aid in costume design.

In the creation of the animal costumes, the children's imaginations will suggest some simple distinguishing feature of the particular animals selected for the play, which will be sufficient to produce the desired illusion. For example, they would probably associate whiskers with the walrus, white fur with the polar bear, and antlers with the reindeer. In the course of the study of the island countries' folklore, a simplified arrangement of a dance, a short dialogue, or a song in the native tongue might be adapted for actual use in the play.

Regardless of what method is used in producing *Knight Rupert,* it will be found to hold endless possibilities as a creative musical drama, particularly for severely handicapped children. With sufficient stimulation and guidance from the teacher or recreation leader, the children themselves will respond with vivid, creative ideas, which will increase their desire for self-realization and will result in sound educational and emotional growth.

Casting and Rehearsals

The play might best be cast by having various members of the group interpret the parts and then with the aid of group discussion select the children to play them.

If a large group of children produces *Knight Rupert,* a wide range of ages will probably be encountered, which may actually simplify the matter of casting. The older children will be able to portray the "adult" roles with greater conviction, while the younger ones will feel at ease in the "children's" parts. The very small children, on the other hand, are well adapted when cast as a part of the chorus or orchestra or as "native children" on the islands.

The rehearsals can be greatly simplified by breaking the play into relatively small units and allowing only those members of the cast who are involved to be present at one time. For example, each island could be rehearsed separately with Knight Rupert and his messengers until actions, dialogues, and so on, were learned. The orchestra and chorus likewise could be rehearsed separately or together with only the piano. In order to weld the various scenes together and to assist the children in better understanding the over-all theme of the play and their relationships to each other, it is advisable to have several complete rehearsals with the costumes, lighting, and all properties.

Costumes

Much ingenuity was evidenced in the preparation of the inexpensive costumes. Descriptions of the costumes designed for various members of the cast follow.

MESSENGERS AND STAR RAISER. The messengers' costumes were old sheets dyed a turquoise blue. They were made according to a very simple two-piece pattern and were sewn only down the sides and sleeves. They were draped as robes and held in place by drawstrings at the neck and brightly colored cords at the waist. The messengers' foot covering consisted merely of brightly colored wool socks worn over their shoes.

The headdresses were made from wire covered with crepe paper and formed into a loop to fit the crown of the head. Stems were attached to this loop to support the stars, holly, candy canes, and snowflakes. The loop and the attached decorations were held in place with bobby pins. The candy canes were made by twisting together red and white pipe cleaners and bending them into a hook at one end. The snowflakes and stars were made of crepe paper and cardboard and then attached to the wire stems. The sprigs of holly can be made of crepe paper and wire, or as in the original production, real holly can be used.

The messengers' Christmas trees were made from heavy wire covered with black crepe paper. The decorations, that is the holly, candy canes, snowflakes, and stars, were made in the same way as for the messengers' headdresses and were attached to the trees with light wire.

The star raiser's costume was made in the same way as the messengers' costumes, except that it was left white and was tied with a metallic gold belt. The headdress was made in the same manner as that of the messengers, except that three very large gold stars were used. The stars were made out of cardboard and were painted with gold paint.

THE ISLANDS. The four islands were decorated by draping the four wheel chairs with white sheets. The mountains, icicles, and other characteristics shown in the photographs of the islands were simulated by draping other white sheets over three-quarter-inch dowels secured to one-by-ten-inch boards. The dowels were arranged and cut to length in such a way that the result approximated closely the peaks and shadows of the physical characteristics of the island sketches.

The evergreen tree and bamboo tree were portions of real plants sprayed with white paint and wired to the back of the island wheel chairs. The coral on the southern island was cut from a sheet of quarter-inch plywood and then sprayed with white paint.

The various headdresses were quite unusual and are described below.

NORTHERN ISLAND. The igloo headdress was made from the crown of an old felt hat which was covered with cotton batting. The cotton batting was stitched to the crown to resemble ice blocks of an igloo. The entrance, or door, of the igloo was a piece of appropriately cut black cloth sewn to the batting.

SOUTHERN ISLAND. The grass shack headdress was made from a square cardboard box. A hole was cut in the bottom of the box to fit the child's head; the sides and ends of the box were trimmed down to provide a base for a peaked roof. The roof, a piece of cardboard folded down the center, was fastened to the upper side of the box with Scotch tape. The roof was then "thatched" with strips of green crepe paper glued in place, while the sides were spotched with green poster paint to resemble grass shingles.

EASTERN ISLAND. The pagoda headdress was made from four round cardboard cartons of graduated size stapled together in a tierlike fashion and covered with green crepe paper. Chinese designs cut out of construction paper were pasted around the lowest tier. Wire covered with green crepe paper was attached to the top of each carton of the pagoda to resemble the "points" shown in the photograph.

WESTERN ISLAND. The western island headdress was made from a cardboard box in much the same way as the grass shack headdress, and the doors, windows, and other features were painted on the box with poster paints.

THE ESKIMO. An oversize sweat suit was heavily padded to simulate the costume of an Eskimo. The headdress was made from a skull cap with the fur collar from and old coat sewn over the crown. The Eskimo's boots were heavy ski socks pulled on over shoes.

THE HAWAIIAN. A native grass skirt was used as the basis for the Hawaiian's costume; however, a sarong of brightly colored cloth would have been very suitable. A brightly colored paper lei could be used, but in the original production a real lei was available.

THE ORIENTAL. The Oriental costume was simply made by using a Chinese pajama set or coolie outfit of embroidered cloth. The headdress was made by using a skullcap as a base, to which was attached a crown cut from light cardboard to resemble the outline of the headdress shown in the photograph. Poster paints were used to decorate the crown.

THE NORDIC. A Turkish towel bathrobe dyed a suitable color and modified by the addition of piping of a contrasting color to match the cap was used as the basic Nordic costume. A simple stocking cap and matching sash were made from cotton cloth of a contrasting color.

ANIMALS. The animal costumes were made of white sheeting, which is available at department and ten-cent stores, cut to a basic animal pattern. The tails, markings, and other features were painted on the costumes with poster paints or were formed from crepe paper and wire and attached to the costumes. The monkeys' tails were made in this fashion; however, the walrus's whiskers were made from black pipe cleaners. The reindeer horns were made from heavy wire covered with cotton batting and were sewn to the costume. The bird's wing and neck feathers were cut from gold and silver crepe paper and sewn to the costume. The bird's beak was made from papier-mâché and painted with poster paints.

KNIGHT RUPERT. Knight Rupert's costume was rather simply made from cotton Shantung. The cape was made with two straight pieces of material long enough to reach from the shoulders to the floor; the cape was gathered across the shoulders and held in place on the robe by several hook and eye fasteners. The robe itself was cut from a simple two-piece pattern and was seamed at the sides and across the shoulders. The cross was made from metallic cloth and sewn to the robe. Similarly, black braid, which is available at any ten-cent store, was sewn in place as seen in the photograph. The sleeves and drape under the chin were made from blue cotton material. The sleeves were cut from a standard pattern to fit the actor, but were cut to provide considerable fullness at the shoulders. The drape was made from an uncut piece of material which was attached to the headpiece in order to provide fullness at the throat. The designs on the sleeves, on the bottom of the cape, and on the oversize black socks were painted with poster paints.

Knight Rupert's headdress had a skullcap as a base, to which a crown of light cardboard was attached with staples. Poster paints were used with spangles to obtain the jeweled effect shown in the photograph.

Properties

The various properties used by the children in the original production of *Knight Rupert* were relatively simple and were made from readily available materials. These properties and a description of how they were made follows:

1. *Star Net.* The star nets were made from approximately four yards of mosquito netting to which were sewn irregularly placed gold paper stars.

2. *Star Racks.* The star racks, over which the star raiser placed the nets in the opening scene, were made to resemble short hat racks. The center post was a three-quarter-inch dowel, which was drilled in three places to accommodate quarter-inch dowel "branches" at the upper end. The base of the rack was a piece of two-by-twelve-inch board which had been drilled to accommodate the center post.

3. *Instrument Racks.* The instrument "racks" for the gong and xylophone were made in the same fashion as the star racks but had only one branch near the top.

4. *Harpoon.* The harpoon was made from a length of three-quarter-inch dowel stock. One end was slotted to receive a triangularly shaped point made from quarter-inch plywood; the line was made of a six-foot length of window sash cord which was tied to the other end of the harpoon. The shank and the point were painted with black lacquer.

5. *Music Box.* The Swiss music box used in the original production was a real music box. However, it need not be real, as it does not have

to play. Any small wooden box could be painted to resemble a music box.

6. *Fish.* The fish used by the walrus can easily be made of papier-mâché. However, a plastic, toy fish was used in the original production. The fish was approximately eighteen inches long.

7. *Fruit.* The fruit used by the natives of the southern island could also be made of papier-mâché; however, real fruit was used in the original production.

8. *Christmas Tree.* The large Christmas tree used in the final scene of *Knight Rupert* was a real tree about six feet in height. It was sprayed with white Kemtone to make the decorations—the holly, candy canes, and so on—stand out. The base for the tree should be of the ready-made metal variety, as this type is more stable than most wooden bases.

Lighting

In the original production of *Knight Rupert*, the only lighting used was from two six-inch spotlights which were made available to the school. One was equipped with a blue gelatin filter, the other with pink. They were placed in the rear corners of the room, and during the performance the beams were used to follow Knight Rupert from island to island.

If spotlights were not readily available, it is suggested that two spotlight bulbs, which are very nominal in price, be purchased for use. The Westinghouse R–40 bulb in the three-hundred-watt size, with a louver, would be very adequate. Standard color media could, of course, be fastened to the front of the louver. If further directions on inexpensive lighting are needed or desired, it is suggested that Herbert V. Hake's book *Here's How!* be consulted.

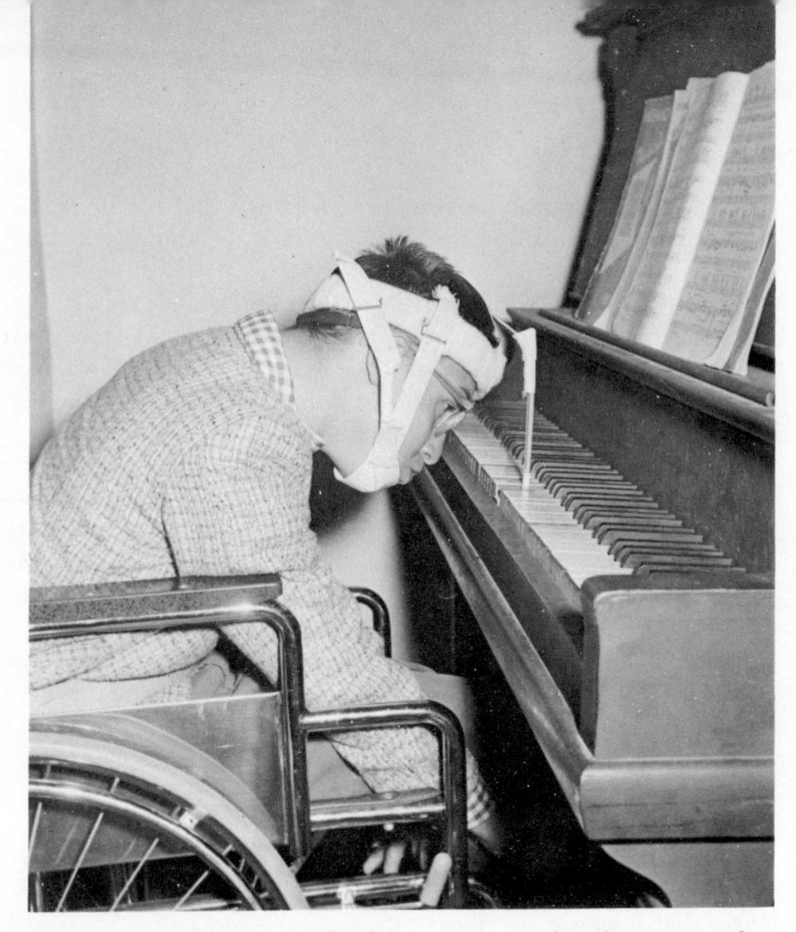

A severely handicapped cerebral palsied boy learns to play the piano with a head attachment. He has also learned to type, which is his only method of communication.

CHAPTER 16

Music

I am MUSIC, most ancient of the Arts. I am more than ancient: I am eternal. Even before life commenced upon this earth, I was here—in the winds and the waves. When the first trees and flowers and grasses appeared, I was among them. . . . For I speak to all men, in a language that all understand. Even the deaf hear me, if they but listen to the voices of their own souls. I am the food of love. I have taught men gentleness and peace; and I have led them onward to heroic deeds. I comfort the lonely, and I harmonize the discord of crowds. I am a necessary luxury to all men. I am MUSIC.[1]

[1] Allan C. Inman, "I Am Music" from a Supplement, *The Performing Arts as Recreation,* to the publication *Recreation* of the National Recreation Association, New York, 1961, p. 260. (Quoted in part.)

Music is truly the universal language and has been called the most delicate, most subtle, and most powerful medium for the expression of man's emotions.

It would be impossible to omit music completely from any recreation program, for music is so closely related to almost all other recreation activities. In many forms of social activity, dramatics, and dance, it is essential. It plays an important part in games, sports, camping, club activities, pageants, and celebrations. Music has many inherent values. "It engenders devotion to an interest for its own sake, releases energies, provokes excitement, brings about good will among neighbors, makes one feel alive, gives one a mental and physical toning up, provides relaxation, and in general enlivens the present and brightens the future. Moreover, music deepens one's sensibilities, broadens one's understanding, and enriches the personality."[2]

Music should be considered an essential part in recreation programs for the physically handicapped. It offers limitless opportunities for enjoyment and for active participation of even the most severely handicapped person, regardless of age or sex. Music for the handicapped can replace "lonely and endured time" with happy and interesting activity.

Obviously the physically handicapped cannot take part in all music activities, but many forms have been included successfully in recreation programs for this group. Several of these activities are described in the pages that follow.

Singing

Informal and community singing, choruses, quartets, and other ensembles, glee clubs, *a cappella* choirs, madrigal groups, and solos are all possible forms of singing activity for the handicapped. Singing is one activity that does not require the participation of the total body. For example, persons who may be otherwise literally helpless may still be able to express themselves through song while sitting down or even lying in bed. Singing does not exclude persons with speech impairments. If a song is sung very, very slowly, these individuals are often able to participate. A cerebral palsied woman of twenty-seven, who had a severe speech impairment, was so determined to sing a solo for a Christmas music festival that she practiced diligently for months. She finally real-

[2] National Recreation Association, "Music Is Recreation," *The Performing Arts as Recreation*, New York, 1961, p. 243.

ized her ambition when she was able to sing "Ave Maria" before an audience. She sang very slowly but her performance was most effective and enjoyable.

Persons with speech impairments have also enjoyed pantomiming to recorded songs. Imitating a singer in this manner requires a great deal of practice, however. Nevertheless, this type of performance can be realistic and pleasurable.

Action songs have proved to be most popular with severely physically handicapped persons. Even those who have speech impairments enjoy performing the actions, even if they have difficulty in singing the words.

Hints for the Song Leader

There are some general points to remember which apply to all song leaders. Persons who work with the severely physically handicapped, however, need to realize the fact that usually songs should be sung more slowly, particularly where there are speech impairments. Each group should indicate its own tempo.

There is no set rule for leading a song. Leaders acquire different methods. Some leaders develop elaborate expressions with the hands, arms, and body; others use simple hand gestures to obtain response from the group. "The song leader sets the mood of the singers by his manner of conducting. If he shouts and waves his arms violently, he can soon wear the people out with loud singing and artificial enthusiasm. If he is merely sharing with them the songs he obviously enjoys, they, too, will enjoy them in very much the same spirit."[3] It is of primary importance that the leader develop his own style based on his unique personality, rather than attempt to emulate other song leaders. Imaginative interpretation inspires lively group response to a song.

A leader should:

1. *Be natural,* original, and alert for new methods of presenting songs.
2. *Be enthusiastic,* full of fun, and have a sense of humor.
3. *Love to sing* and be able to put the singers at ease.
4. *Be thoroughly familiar with the song,* sure of himself and of his material.

[3] *Handbook for Recreation,* U.S. Dept. of Health, Education, and Welfare, Social Security Administration, Children's Bureau, Washington, D.C., 1960, p. 108.

5. *Practice his speaking voice* to make it pleasant but strong enough to be heard and understood.

6. *Acquire a large repertoire* of songs and continually add new ones.[4]

When introducing a new song, a leader should:

1. Select one that is simple and short with a catchy tune, then lead up to a longer one.

2. Repeat the words slowly, calling attention to the story or sequence of events.

3. Sing the song through to give tempo and spirit.

4. Know that good singing can be achieved without accompaniment. However, when accompaniment is used, it should support, not dominate the singing. Some of the acceptable instruments for recreational singing are the auto harp, guitar, harmonica, accordion, ukelele, and piano.

The type of songs to be sung depends upon the nature of the occasion, but in general a leader should use a variety of songs, i.e., happy, sad, plaintive, rollicking, thoughtful, sentimental, and nonsensical. He should stress harmony, diction, rhythm, and pitch. The singing period should be brought to a close with enthusiasm, while enthusiasm is still high. There should be no boisterous singing. Among the many wonderful songs are the old-time favorites such as "I've Been Working on the Railroad," "Daisy," and "The Bicycle Built for Two," which are familiar and enjoyable with any group, including the handicapped.

Action Songs

Numerous action songs are fun to do and are popular with all age groups. Following are some of the action songs that have been very popular with the severely physically handicapped at the Recreation Center.

ONE FINGER, ONE THUMB[5]

Words accompanied by gesticulation with fingers, thumbs, stamping of feet, standing up, turning around and sitting down actions. Each verse progressively adds one new action.

[4] MIA Music Manual, Published by Church of Jesus Christ Latter Day Saints, Deseret News Press, 1956.

[5] From Action Songs by permission of National Recreation Association, New York.

1. One finger, one thumb together
   One finger, one thumb together
   One finger, one thumb together
   Together all the time.
2. Two fingers, two thumbs together (Repeat three times)
   Together all the time.
3. Two fingers, two thumbs, one leg together (Repeat three times)
   Together all the time.
4. Two fingers, two thumbs, two legs together (Repeat three times)
   Together all the time.
5. Two fingers, two thumbs, two legs, stand up, sit down together
   (Repeat three times)
   Together all the time.
6. Two fingers, two thumbs, two legs, stand up, turn around, sit down together
   (Repeat three times)
   Together all the time.

ONE FINGER, ONE THUMB

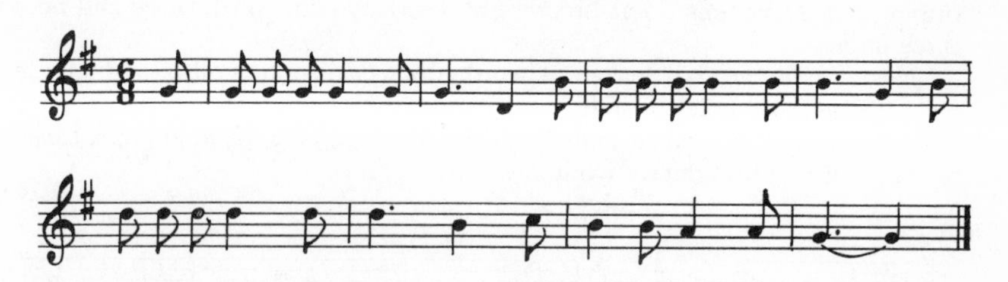

OH, CHESTER[6]

Tune: "Yankee Doodle"

Sing slowly until everyone gets the actions, then sing two or three times, each one faster than the last.

Oh, *Chest*-er have you *'ear*'d about *Har*-ry?

(On *Chester,* put your right hand to your chest; on *'ear'd* to your ear; and on *Harry,* touch your hair.)

He's *chest* got *back* from the *arm*-y.

(With your right hand touch your chest on *chest;* your back on *back;* and on

[6] *Ibid.*

army cross your arms, touching first your left arm between the elbow and shoulder with your right hand and then your right arm with your left hand.)

I 'ear'e knows how to *wear a rose.*

(On *I* point to your eye with your right hand; to your right ear on *ear,* to your nose on *knows;* and on *wear a rose* put both hands over your heart.)

Hip, Hip, Hooray for the *army.*

(Touch your right hip with your right hand on the first *hip;* your left hip with your left hand on the second *hip;* wave your right hand in the air on *hooray,* and on *army* repeat the same action as described previously for this word.)

MY HAT IT HAS THREE CORNERS[7]

My hat it has three corners
Three corners has my hat
And had it not three corners
It would not be my hat.

Sing through once; on repeating leave out the word *hat* but touch head as if tipping hat. Next time do as before, but also leave out word *Three* and hold up three fingers.

Next—as before but leave out word *corners* and touch elbow. Finally leave out word *my* and point to self.

Anyone singing a word that should be silent may be made to pay a forfeit or to sing it through perfectly while facing the group.

LITTLE PETER RABBIT[8]

(Sung to the tune "Battle Hymn of the Republic")

Little (*indicate size*) Peter (*hands on chest like a rabbit's forepaws when sitting on his haunches*) Rabbit (*hands on either side of head, forefingers pointing up*) had a flea (*snap finger in front of you as you "hop" your hand*) upon his ear (*point to ear*).

[7] *Ibid.*
[8] *Ibid.*

Little Peter Rabbit had a flea upon his ear
Little Peter Rabbit had a flea upon his ear
And he flipped it (*flip open hand as though flipping ear*)
till it flew (*both hands fly away to right*) away.

Sing entire song without action first time. Then each successive time add one action in place of a word until all action suggestions have been substituted.

JOHN BROWN'S BABY[9]

(Also sung to the tune, "Battle Hymn of the Republic")

John Brown's Baby had a cold upon his chest,
John Brown's Baby had a cold upon his chest,
John Brown's Baby had a cold upon his chest,
So they rubbed it with camphorated oil.

The verse is first sung without action. When singing it the second time, the word "Baby" is omitted. Whenever this word is reached, all the players make the motion of rocking a baby. For the third verse, the word "cold" is also omitted. The baby is rocked when the word "Baby" is reached, and a little cough is given instead of the word "cold." The fourth verse is similar to the third verse and singers also omit the word "chest." Instead of singing it, the players tap their chest with their open hand. During the fifth verse, the word "rubbed" is dropped and a gentle rubbing movement of the chest is substituted. For the sixth verse, "camphorated oil" is omitted and a little sniff is given.

THE CROCODILE[10]

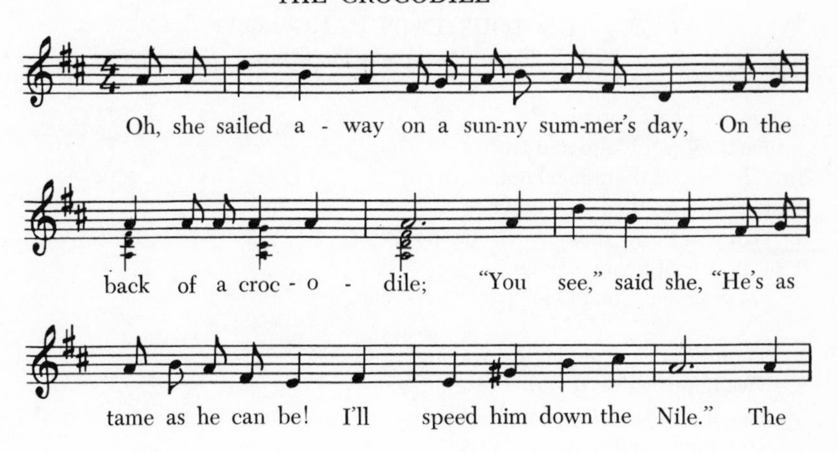
Oh, she sailed a - way on a sun-ny sum-mer's day, On the
back of a croc - o - dile; "You see," said she, "He's as
tame as he can be! I'll speed him down the Nile." The

[9] *Ibid.*
[10] *Handbook for Recreation*, U.S. Dept. of Health, Education, and Welfare, Social Security Administration, Children's Bureau, Washington, D.C., p. 115.

croc winked his eye as she bade them all good-by,

Wear-ing a hap - py smile. At the end of the ride The

la-dy was in-side. And the smile was on the croc - o - dile.

Oh, she sailed away on a sunny summer's day (*flutter hands*)
On the back of a crocodile (*make crocodile mouth by flapping hands*);
"You see," said she, "he's as tame as he can be (*pat back of hand*)!
I'll speed him down the Nile" (*flutter fingers*).
The croc winked his eye as she bade them all goodbye (*point to wink, wave goodbye*)
Wearing a happy smile (*outline smile*)
At the end of the ride (*whirl hands*)
The lady was inside (*hands on stomach*),
And the smile was on the crocodile (*outline smile and make crocodile mouth*).

DO YOUR EARS HANG LOW?

Tune: *Turkey in the Straw*

1. Do your ears hang low?
2. Do they wobble to and fro?
3. Can you tie them in a knot?
4. Can you tie them in a bow?
5. Can you throw them over your shoulder?
6. Like a continental soldier?
7. Do your ears hang low?

1. Thumbs at ears and fingers waving
2. Two hands palms together to and fro
3. Two hands roll around each other
4. Two hands pull out
5. Two hands throw over shoulder
6. Salute
7. Repeat 1.

SKUNK SONG

Tune: Dixie

Oh, I stuck my head in a little skunk's hole,
And the little skunk said, "Doggone your sole."
Take it out! Take it out! Take it out! Remove it!

Now, I didn't take it out and the little skunk said,
"If you don't take it out you'll wish you were dead."
Take it out! Take it out! Wheeeeeeeewwwwwwwww!!!! I removed it! (hold nose)

SHE'LL BE COMIN' ROUND THE MOUNTAIN

She'll be comin' round the mountain when she comes (pull train cord, say "Toot, toot"),
She'll be comin' round the mountain when she comes (same),
She'll be comin' round the mountain,
She'll be comin' round the mountain,
She'll be comin' round the mountain when she comes (same).

She'll be drivin' six white horses when she comes (pull back reins, "Whoa, back"),
She'll be drivin' six white horses when she comes (same),
She'll be drivin' six white horses,
She'll be drivin' six white horses,
She'll be drivin' six white horses when she comes ("Whoa, back; Toot, toot").

Oh, we'll all go out to meet her when she comes (vertical wave, "Hi, Babe"),
Oh, we'll all go out to meet her when she comes (same),
Oh, we'll all go out to meet her,
Oh, we'll all go out to meet her,
Oh, we'll all go out to meet her when she comes ("Hi, Babe; Whoa, back; Toot, toot").

Oh, we'll kill the old red rooster when she comes (chop left wrist, "Hack, hack"),
Oh, we'll kill the old red rooster when she comes (same),
Oh, we'll kill the old red rooster,
Oh, we'll kill the old red rooster,
Oh, we'll kill the old red rooster when she comes ("Hack, hack; Hi, Babe; Whoa, back; Toot, toot").

Oh, we'll all have chicken and dumplings when she comes (rub stomach, "Yum, yum"),

Oh, we'll all have chicken and dumplings when she comes (same),
Oh, we'll all have chicken and dumplings,
Oh, we'll all have chicken and dumplings,
Oh, we'll all have chicken and dumplings when she comes ("Yum, yum;
Hack, hack; Hi, Babe; Whoa, back; Toot, toot").

We'll be wearing red pajamas when she comes (make scratching motion with arms, "Scratch, scratch"),
We'll be wearing red pajamas when she comes (same),
We'll be wearing red pajamas,
We'll be wearing red pajamas,
We'll be wearing red pajamas when she comes ("Scratch, scratch; Yum, yum;
Hack, hack; Hi, Babe; Whoa, back; Toot, toot").

Oh, we'll have to sleep with Grandma when she comes (snoring sound and whistle, "Snore, snore"),
Oh, we'll have to sleep with Grandma when she comes (same),
Oh, we'll have to sleep with Grandma,
Oh, we'll have to sleep with Grandma,
Oh, we'll have to sleep with Grandma when she comes ("Snore, snore;
Scratch, scratch; Yum, yum; Hack, hack; Hi, Babe; Whoa, back; Toot, toot").

WE ARE THE RED MEN[11]

(Arranged by Carol M. Brown)

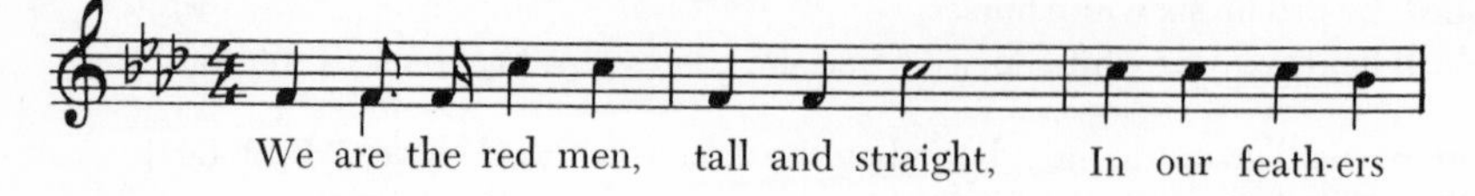
We are the red men, tall and straight, In our feath-ers

and war paint, pow wow, pow wow. We're the

men of the old Cow - Tow. We are the red men,

feath-ers in our head men, down a-mong the dead men pow wow.

[11] By permission of Carol M. Brown.

We can fight with sticks and stones
Bows and arrows
Bricks and bones

Chorus

Pow wow, Pow wow,
We're the men of the old Cow Tow
We are the red men
Feathers in our head men
Down among the dead men
Pow wow.

We return from hunting afar
Greeted by our long-nosed squaw.

Chorus (as above)

ACTION

Verse One

1. We are the red men, tall and straight,
   In our feathers and war paint
   (Stand tall and straight with arms crossed on chest, right hand on left shoulder and left hand on right shoulder.)

Chorus

2. Pow wow, Pow wow
   (Nod head as words are sung.)
3. We're the men of the old Cow Tow
   (Stretch arms straight out in front of body.)
4. We are the red men,
   Feathers in our head men
   (Hold hands up at head to indicate feathers.)
5. Down among the dead men,
   (Indicate down motion with hands and arms.)
6. Pow wow
   (At the words *Pow wow*, cross arms again as described in Action One.)

Verse Two

(Stand same as Action One.)

7. We can fight with sticks and stones,
   Bows and arrows,
   Bricks and bones
   (Indicate motion of shooting with bow and arrow.)

Chorus (Same as above)

Verse Three

(Stand same as Action One.)

8. We return from hunting afar
Greeted by our long-nosed squaw
(Indicate long nose by extending nose with hand.)

Chorus (Same as Motion 6)

Rounds

The simplest way to obtain harmony is through the use of rounds. Rounds are easy to learn; for once a group knows the melody line, the harmony comes automatically with each entering part.

When teaching a round it is best to teach the song as a straight song to the entire group first before dividing the singers into smaller sections or parts. Rounds may be sung with two to nine parts depending upon the size and ability of the group. The leader must be specific as to where each part enters the round and how many times the round is to be sung. When first learning the round, the group should sing it through twice and later expand to four times.

In order that each section can sing as a unit, the singers should be standing or sitting close to one another. They should also be encouraged to listen to other parts of the round so that they may hear and appreciate the harmony they are creating through the medium of the round.

Rounds are popular with both young and old. Following are several rounds that have been enjoyed by the handicapped of all ages at the Recreation Center.

UPWARD TRAIL (ROUND)

1.
2.
We're on the up - ward trail! We're on the up - ward trail!

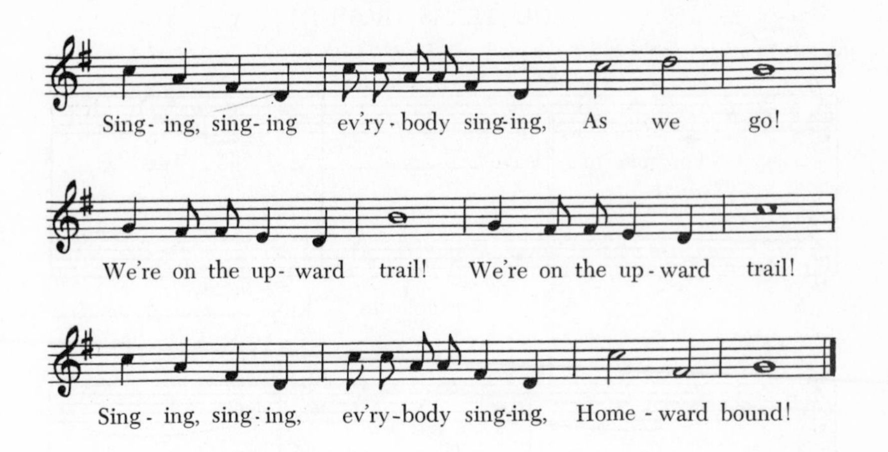
Sing- ing, sing- ing ev'ry - body sing-ing, As we go!
We're on the up- ward trail! We're on the up - ward trail!
Sing - ing, sing - ing, ev'ry-body sing-ing, Home - ward bound!

COME, FOLLOW, FOLLOW (ROUND)

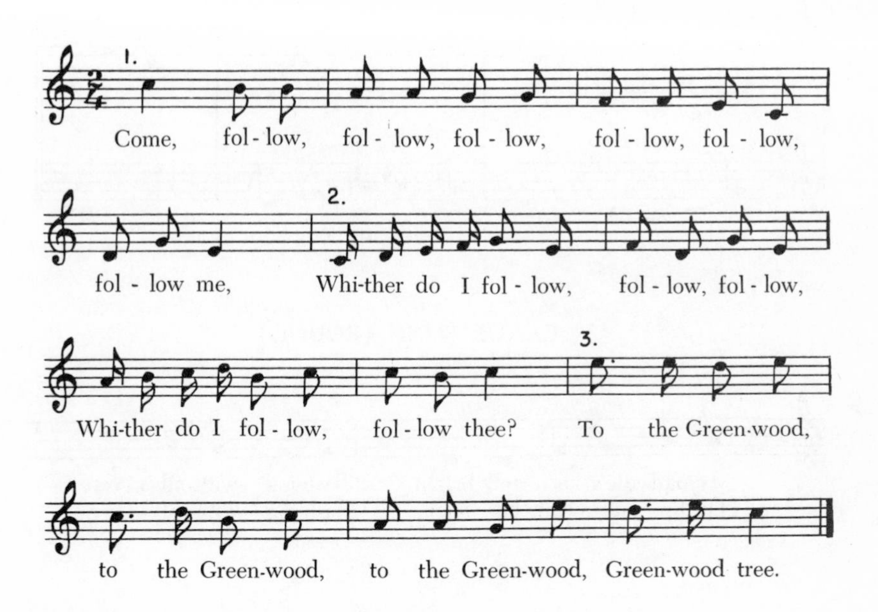
1.
Come, fol - low, fol - low, fol - low, fol - low, fol - low,
fol - low me,
2.
Whi-ther do I fol - low, fol - low, fol - low,
Whi-ther do I fol - low, fol - low thee?
3.
To the Green-wood,
to the Green-wood, to the Green-wood, Green-wood tree.

OL' TEXAS (ROUND)

I'm goin' to leave old Tex - as
I'm goin' to leave
now They've got no use
old Tex - as now They've got no
for the long-horn cow.
use for the long horn cow.
D.S.

CANOE SONG (ROUND)

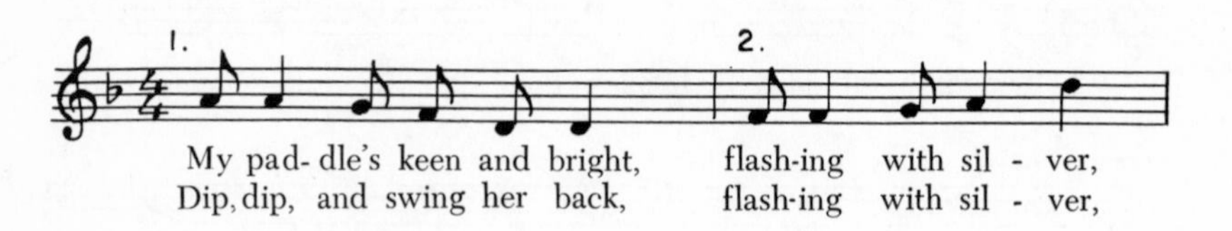
1.
2.
My pad- dle's keen and bright, flash-ing with sil - ver,
Dip, dip, and swing her back, flash-ing with sil - ver,

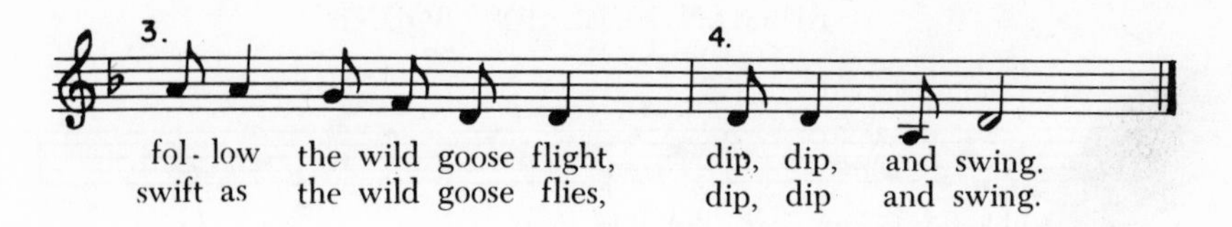
3.
4.
fol- low the wild goose flight, dip, dip, and swing.
swift as the wild goose flies, dip, dip and swing.

KOOKABURRA (ROUND)

1.
Kook-a - bur - ra sits on the old gum tree, —

2.
mer-ry mer-ry king of the bush is he,— Laugh, Kook-a-bur-ra,

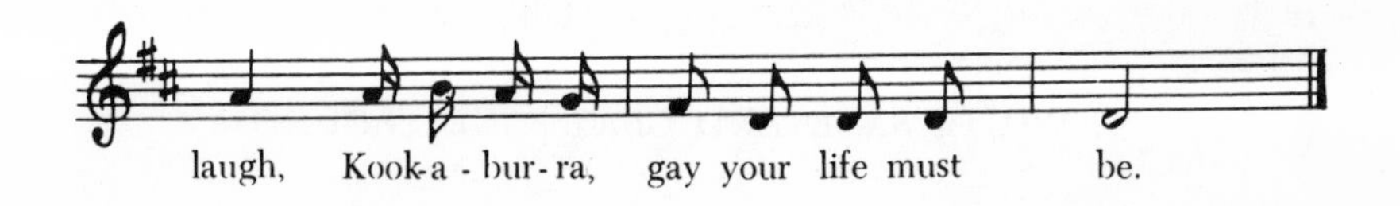
laugh, Kook-a - bur - ra, gay your life must be.

HEY, HO! NOBODY HOME (ROUND)

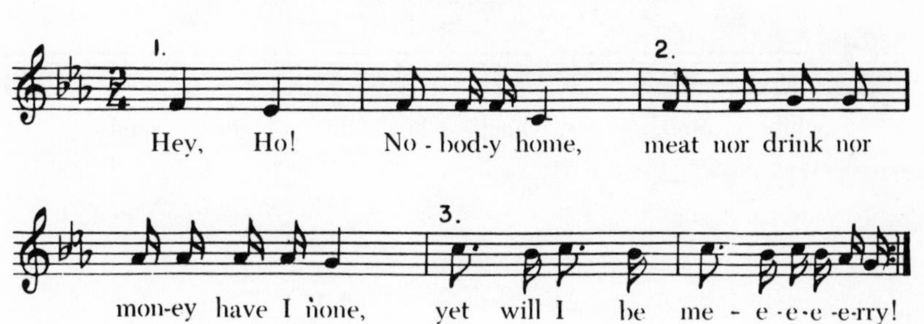
1.
2.
Hey, Ho! No - bod-y home, meat nor drink nor
3.
mon-ey have I none, yet will I be me - e -e-e -e-rry!

RUSSIAN LULLABY (ROUND)

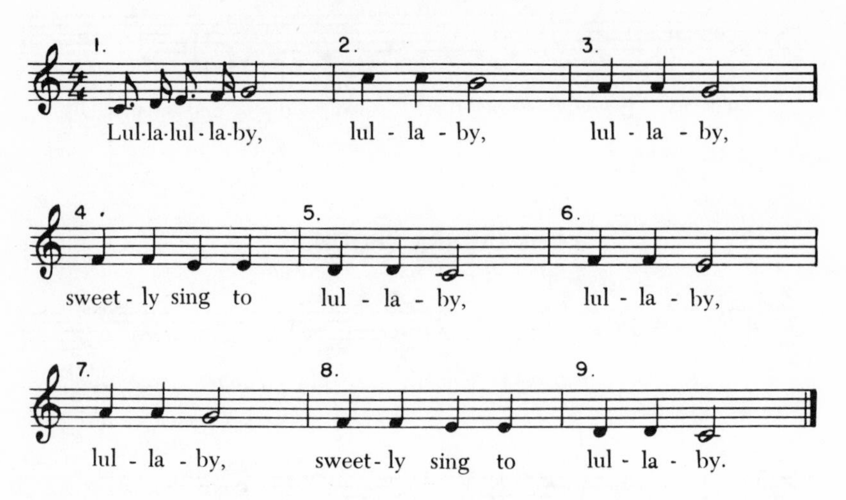
1.
2.
3.
Lul-la-lul-la-by, lul - la - by, lul - la - by,
4.
5.
6.
sweet - ly sing to lul - la - by, lul - la - by,
7.
8.
9.
lul - la - by, sweet - ly sing to lul - la - by.

WHITE SAND AND GRAY SAND (ROUND)

1.
2.
White sand and gray sand, who'll buy my
3.
white sand, who'll buy my gray sand?

Folk Songs

INGOMBE—AFRICAN FOLK SONG[12]

(Arranged by Carol M. Brown)

O - li-khwe-bwa in- gom-be om - wan - a -ma ma-ma
omul- aan - do ma ma-ma
ngo - nam - ga nim-bar - a

in - gom - be om - wan- a ma ma - ma in - gom - be
omul- aan- do ma ma - ma
ngo- nam- ga nim-bar- a

om-wan - a ma ma- ma in - gom - be
omul- aan - do ma ma- ma
ngo-nam- go nim - bar - a.

This is a folk song of Africa, in the Luhanga language. It is generally sung with a leader and the group responding. The following translations and pronunciations may be helpful in singing the song.

Olikhwebwa (Ole–h'way–bwa)—a dowry will be paid for you
Ingombe (Ei–ome–bay)—neutral word for cattle (this is what will be paid)
Omwana ma mama—child of my mother
Omulaando (mul–an–do)—my beautiful (lovely) sister
Ngomanga (go–nam–ga)—I sleep
Nimbara (Nim–bah–rah)—while thinking (I sleep thinking of you)

[12] *Ibid.*

TENNESHAY[13]
(Arranged by Carol M. Brown)

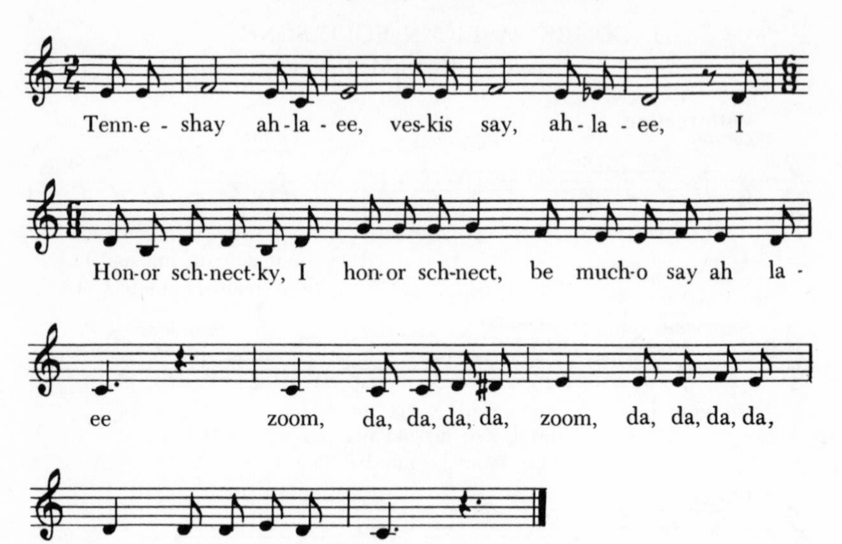
Tenn-e - shay ah-la - ee, ves-kis say, ah-la - ee, I
Hon-or sch-nect-ky, I hon-or sch-nect, be much-o say ah la -
ee zoom, da, da, da, da, zoom, da, da, da, da,
zoom, da, da, da, da, zoom.

Singing Games

All children love singing games. They provide opportunities for physical movement, for play acting, and for mixing up a group. They also help develop a social sense and teach good sportsmanship. They have unpretentious tunes, simple rhythms, and when sung unaccompanied, they tend to develop accurate pitch. Several singing games that can be adapted to use by the handicapped follow.

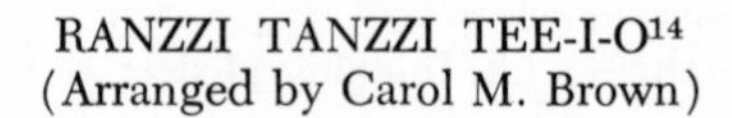

RANZZI TANZZI TEE-I-O[14]
(Arranged by Carol M. Brown)

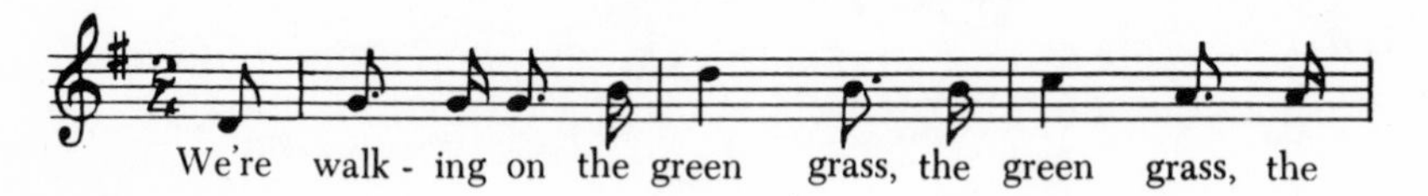
We're walk - ing on the green grass, the green grass, the

[13] *Ibid.*
[14] *Ibid.*

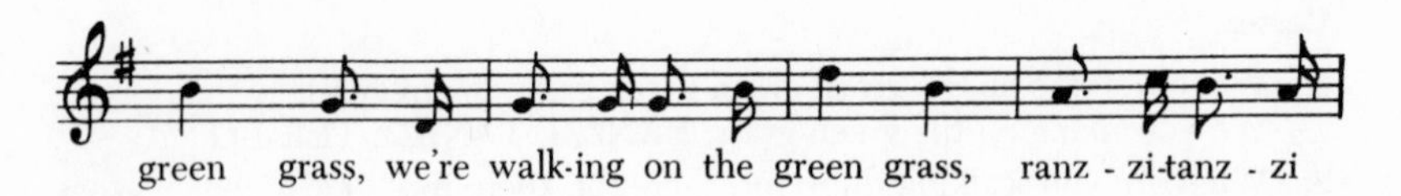
green grass, we're walk-ing on the green grass, ranz - zi-tanz - zi

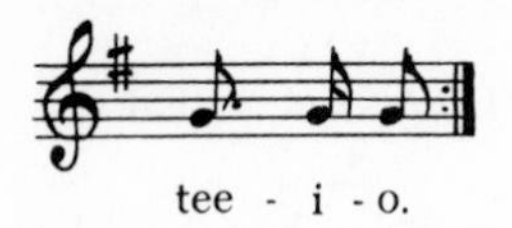
tee - i - o.

The above singing game is played for fun rather than for competition. It can be played with large or small groups as the number of persons is not important. It has been extremely popular and enjoyable for children of all ages and both sexes.

FORMATION

Two equal lines facing each other. Each group joins hands. Adaptations: Persons who are unable to walk may be sitting down on benches, wheel chairs, etc. Persons bed-bound may also be included.

ACTION

X→ O 1. First group starts out by singing first verse while walking or wheeling, forward four steps and back four steps, for a total of sixteen steps. Persons in wheel chairs or beds who are unable to propel themselves may be pushed by others.

X O 2. The second group sings verse two and repeats the action.

X O 3. The same actions are repeated throughout the game with each group alternating verses.

X O 4. Before the fifth verse, the group selects a member from the other group and inserts his name.

X O 5. Before verse seven, the group selects a gift of some type.

X ←O 6. The second group consults with the selected player before singing the last verse. If the selected player does not wish to "accept" the gift, then the first group must think of another gift. When the gift is finally accepted, the selected player crosses over to the other side and becomes a member of the other group.

7. Repeat with the second group starting the game.

Verses:

1. We're walking on the green grass, green grass, green grass,
   We're walking on the green grass, RANZZI, TANZZI, TEE-I-O.
2. What are you walking there for, there for, there for?
   What are you walking there for, RANZZI, TANZZI, TEE-I-O.
3. We're walking there to get married, etc.
   (Each verse repeats the line, ending with RANZZI, TANZZI, TEE-I-O.
4. Who are you going to marry?
5. We're going to marry________________(Name girl or boy they choose.)
6. What are you going to give her?
7. We're going to give her a________________(Name any gift—one at a time; i.e., mink coat, sports car, etc.)
8. Yes, you may (or No, you may not) have her.

AH, WOONEY COONEY[15]

(Arranged by Carol M. Brown)

Ah, woon-ie coon-ie cha, ah woon-ie, ah,

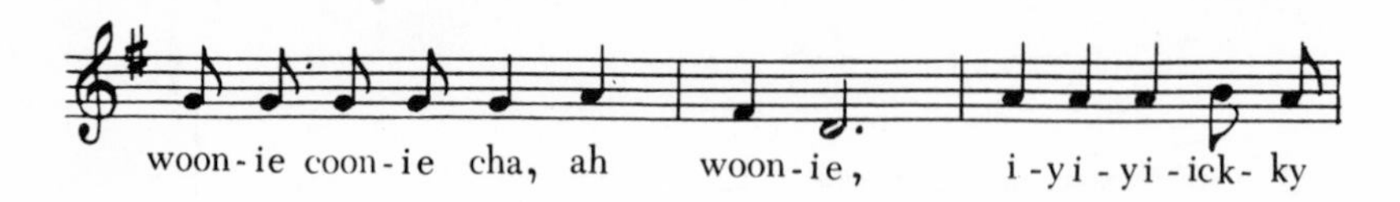
woon-ie coon-ie cha, ah woon-ie, i-yi-yi-ick-ky

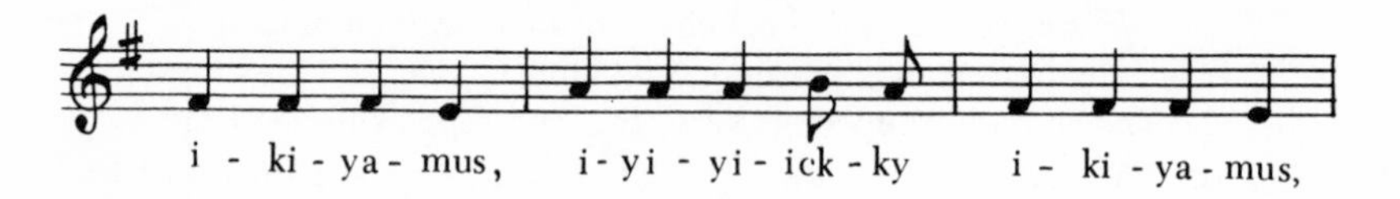
i-ki-ya-mus, i-yi-yi-ick-ky i-ki-ya-mus,

ah, woo, ah, woon-ie keetch-ie.

ACTION

1st Round

1. Slap both hands on your own thighs

[15] *Ibid.*

2. Slap both hands on thighs of person on left
3. Slap both hands on own thighs
4. Slap both hands on thighs of person on right
5. Repeat as above.

2nd Round

1. Slap hands on own thighs
2. Cross hands and slap own thighs
3. Slap hands on own thighs
4. With left hand, slap thigh of person to the left of you
   With right hand, slap thigh of person to the right of you
5. Repeat as above.

3rd Round—Put right hand straight out on first "Ah"

1. Tap right wrist with left hand
2. Tap right shoulder with left hand and leave left hand on right shoulder (some find it easier to tap wrist, elbow, and shoulder on the third beat)
3. Bring right hand over to left shoulder
4. Put left hand straight out
5. Tap left wrist with right hand
6. Tap left shoulder with right hand and leave right hand on left shoulder
7. Bring left hand over to right shoulder
8. Repeat until end of song and end with hands up, palms out.

HERE IS A BEEHIVE[16]
(Arranged by Carol M. Brown)

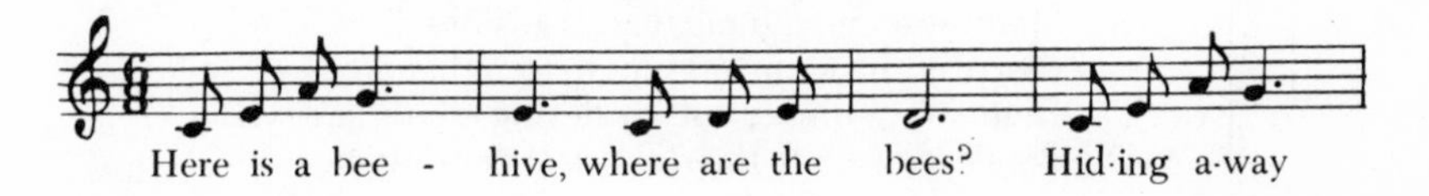
Here is a bee - hive, where are the bees? Hid-ing a-way

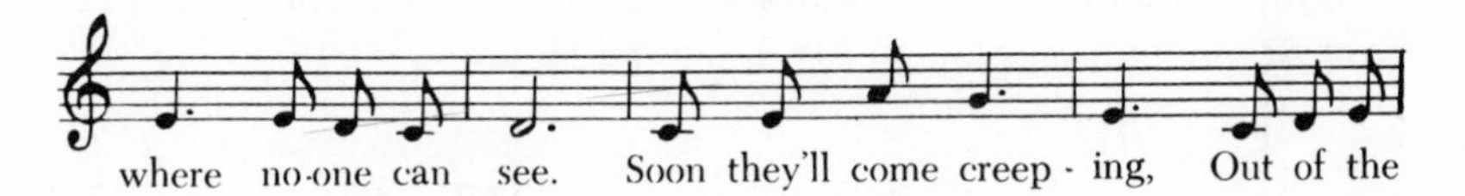
where no-one can see. Soon they'll come creep - ing, Out of the

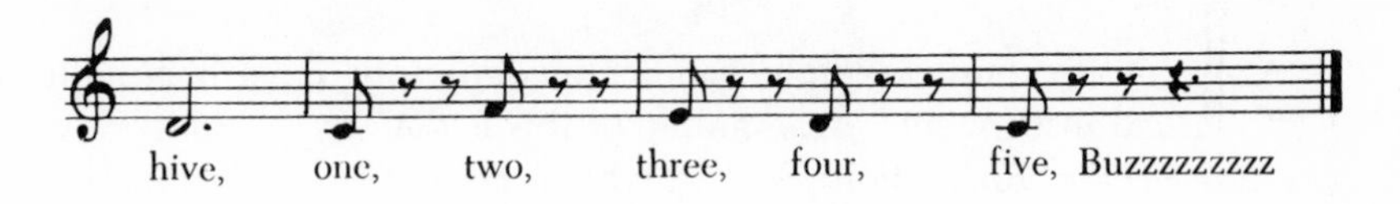
hive, one, two, three, four, five, Buzzzzzzzzz

[16] *Ibid.*

ACTION

Place back of hands together, fingers interlocked. Close hand to form the "beehive." When the counting starts, release each pair of fingers one at a time, starting with the thumbs, forefingers, etc. On the count of five, all fingers become bees, and they swarm over the closest person while making the appropriate buzzing sound.

I'M A LITTLE TEAPOT[17]

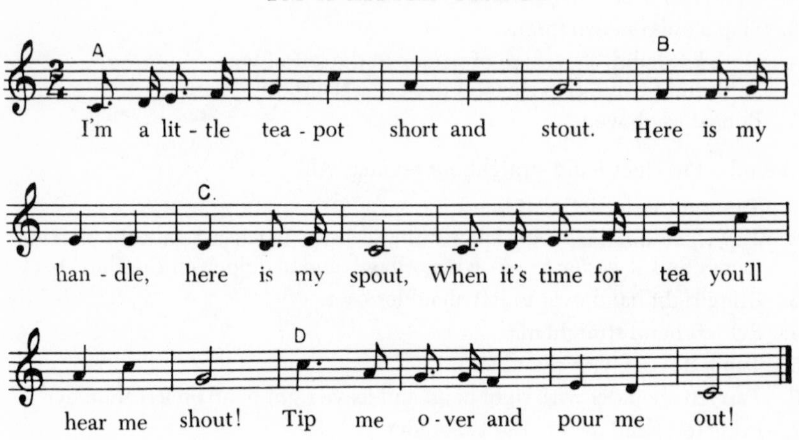
A
B.
I'm a lit - tle tea - pot short and stout. Here is my
C.
han - dle, here is my spout, When it's time for tea you'll
D
hear me shout! Tip me o - ver and pour me out!

ACTION

A—Stand straight and tall, hands at sides
B—Place left hand on left hip, to form handle
C—Right arm forms spout, by flexing elbow and wrist
D—Bend sideways to the right, as if pouring the tea

Other suitable singing games are the Farmer In The Dell, Did You Ever See A Lassee, Skip to My Lou, and so on.

Playing Instruments

Many of the most severely handicapped persons have been able to play musical instruments. An example of this is the case of a fifteen-year-old boy at the Recreation Center, who is multiple handicapped as a result of cerebral palsy. Because of the extreme involuntary motion of

[17] *Ibid.*

his arms and legs, it is necessary to strap him in his wheel chair so that he can sit upright. Although he is unable to speak, or to use his hands or arms, he has learned to play the piano with an attachment worn on his head (see illustration on p. 225). He has enjoyed playing solos at various performances given by participants of the Recreation Center.

A man of twenty-four, also cerebral palsied, with a great deal of involuntary motion, particularly in his arms and hands, learned to steady his hands sufficiently to play the xylophone. His determination to play "Silent Night" at the annual Christmas party was the incentive for his accomplishment.

Persons who are bedfast can learn to play wind, string, and percussion instruments; for example, one bedfast girl of twenty-three learned to play the tambourine with her toes.

All physically handicapped children can participate at some level in rhythm activities by shaking or kicking a rhythm instrument or by keeping time with the head, arms, hands, or feet. According to Zanzig, simple

A bed-fast girl learned to play the tambourine with her feet.

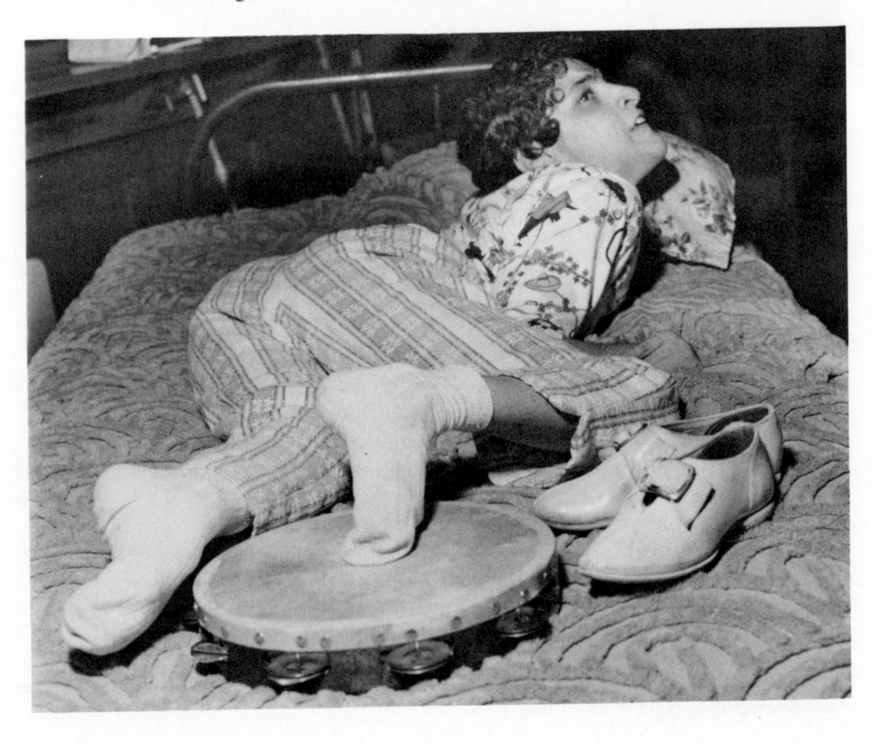

percussion instruments used to mark rhythm, particularly when associated with the melody and harmony of the piano, phonograph, or singing, can contribute much to the musical interest and development of the players, especially of children.[18] Interest in music and in crafts can be combined through the making of simple instruments for use by rhythm bands. Directions for making several types of simple rhythm instruments follow.

How to Make Rhythm Instruments

Roller Rattle

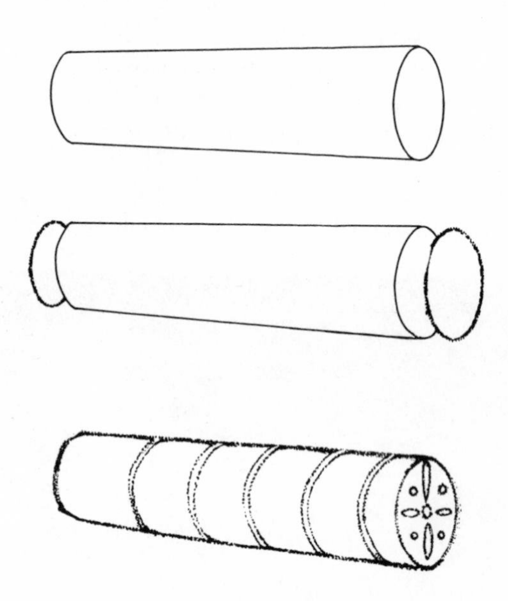

Materials:
- Paper towel roll
- Beans or small pebbles
- Paper (colored or plain)
- String or ribbon

How to make:
- Put beans in roll
- Cover roll with paper, leaving 1½″ of paper overlapping each end
- Tie ends with string
- Decorate with crayon, poster or other paint

Rattles may also be made with toilet paper or aluminum foil rolls, milk cartons, etc.

[18] Augustus D. Zanzig, *Starting and Developing a Rhythm Band,* National Recreation Association, New York, 1954, p. 5.

Aluminum Plate Rattle

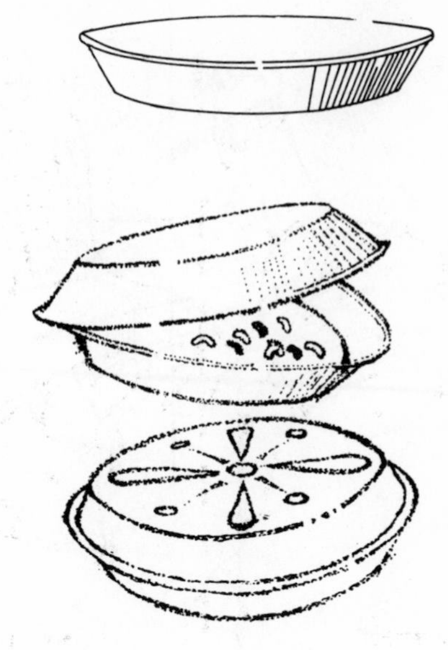

Materials:

Two aluminum plates
Stapler and staples
Beans or pebbles

How to make:

Put beans in one aluminum plate
Put other plate face down on top of first one
Staple or sew plates together. (If sewn, use colored yarns)
Decorate with brightly colored lacquers. Paper plates may also be used, but they are not as durable

Sand Blocks

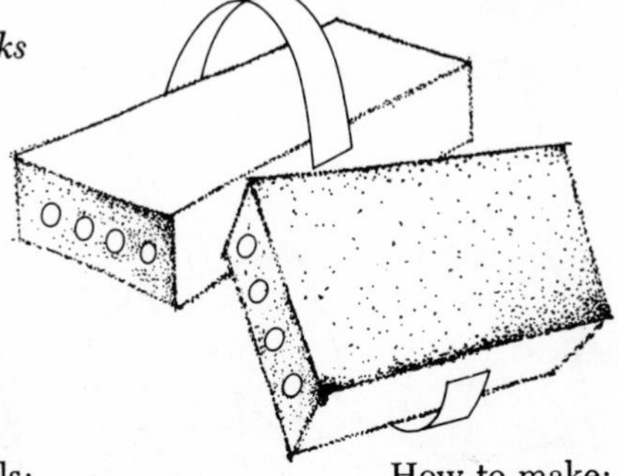

Materials:

Two blocks of wood (2″x4″x1″)
Sand paper
Colored thumb tacks
Elastic bands

How to make:

Tack sandpaper to ends of blocks
Tack elastic bands to center of side of blocks

Gourd Morocca

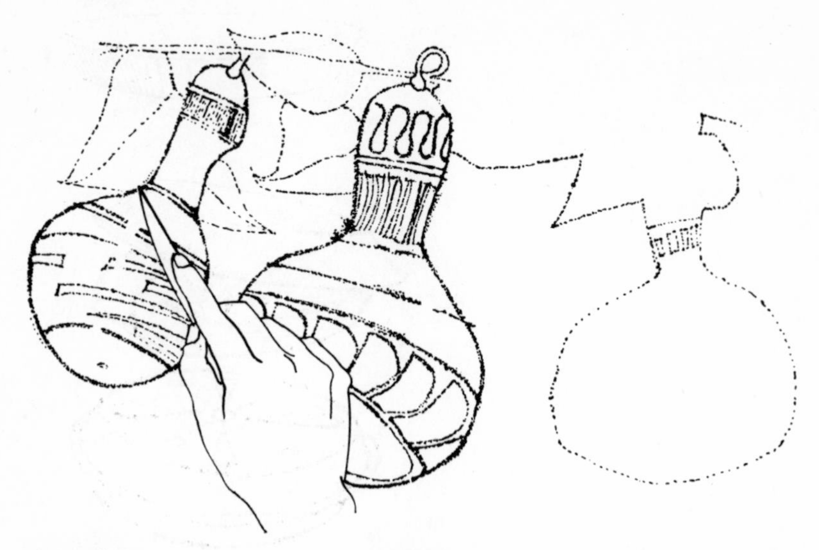

Materials:

- Hard-shell gourds, must be dry enough for the seeds to break loose and rattle
- Lacquer, stains, or oil paint
- Shellac or varnish (optional)

How to make:

- Designs may be carved, burned, or painted, or a combination of these
- If home grown, design may be carved on when gourd is mature

Sound or Bell Cups

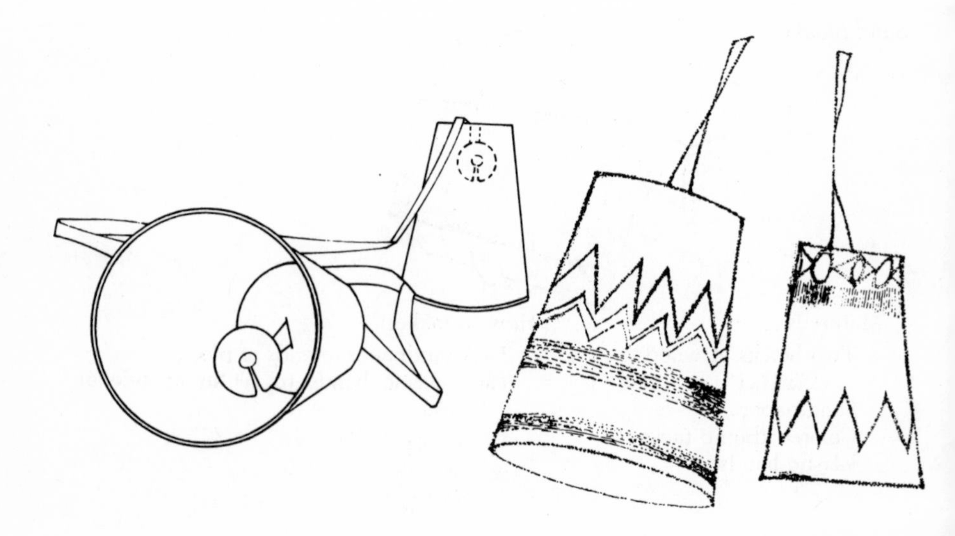

Materials:

Two paper cups
Ribbon (1 yard)
Paint (optional)

How to make:

Punch hole in bottom of cup
Measure ribbon to length of arms
Put ribbons through holes in cups and tie knots in ends
Paint

Pop Bottle Xylophone

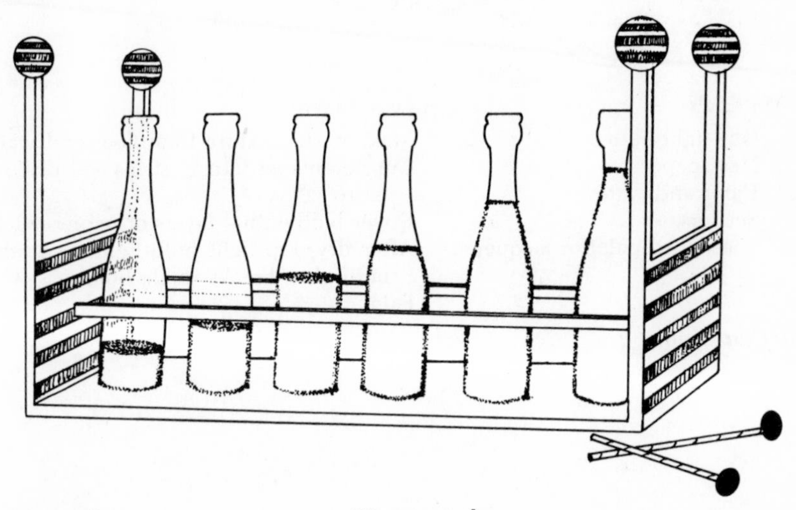

Materials:

Seven pop bottles
Wood
Large beads
Two dowels 8″ long

How to make:

Starting with middle "C" on the piano, put water in each bottle until you have scale
Make rack for the bottles
Push dowel through hole in bead

Light Bulb Morocca

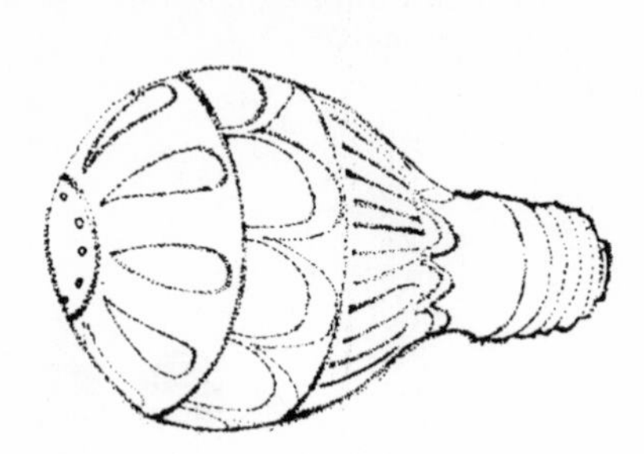

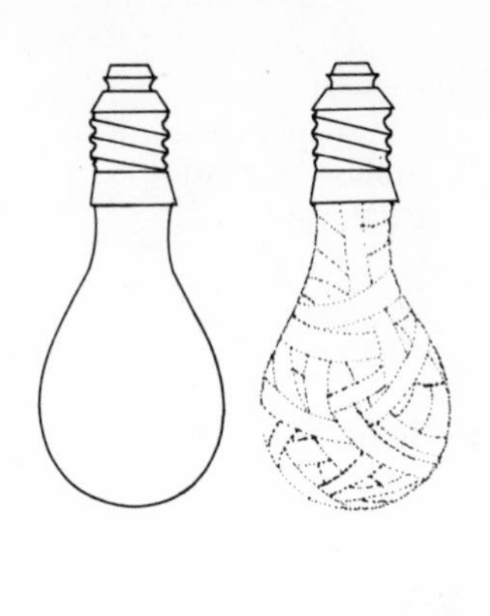

Materials:

One light bulb
Newspaper
Flour and water
Scissors
Show card paint or lacquer

How to make:

Make paste mixture from flour and water
Cut newspaper into 1″ strips and place in paste
Cover bulb with 4 layers of papier-mâché
After dry, tap light bulb lightly on table until glass breaks inside bulb.
Paint

Tin Can Drum

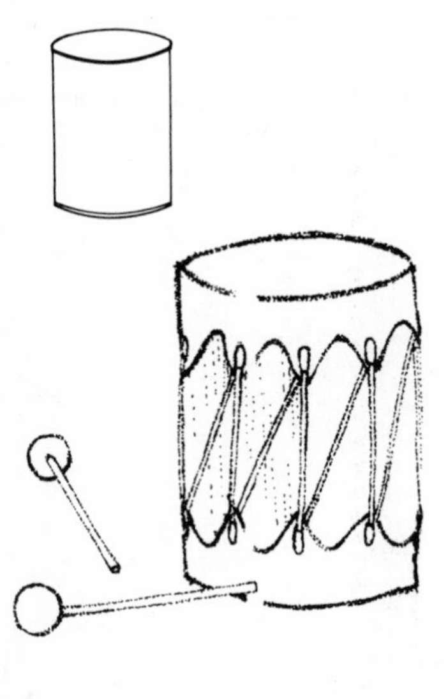

Materials:

Tin can
Two round pieces of inner tube 1½″ larger than lid
String
Two dowels, 8″ long
Two small rubber balls

How to make:

Cut the top and bottom out of tin can
Place one rubber inner tube over the other and punch holes 1″ apart all the way around the outside of both pieces of rubber
With one piece of rubber on top of can and one on the bottom lace the two together tightly with string
Secure dowels in rubber balls for drumsticks

Ping-pong Paddle Tambourine

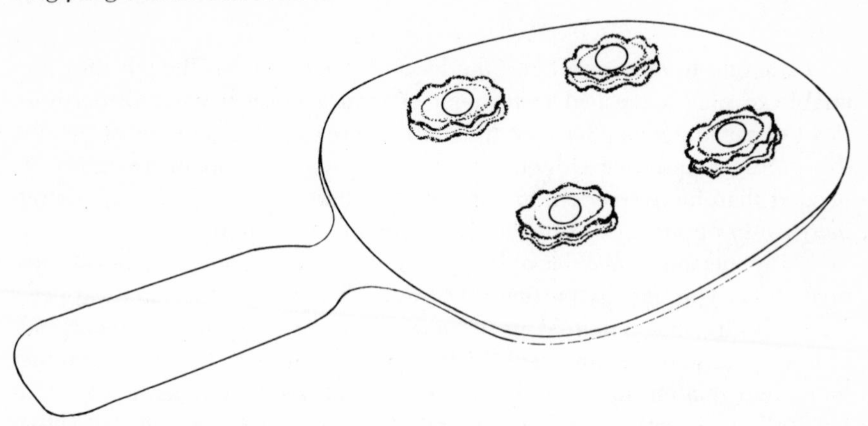

Materials:

One old ping-pong paddle
Four nails
Sixteen bottle tops
Paint

How to make:

Flatten bottle tops with hammer
Hammer the nail through 4 tops and into paddle
Paint

Egg Carton Tambourine

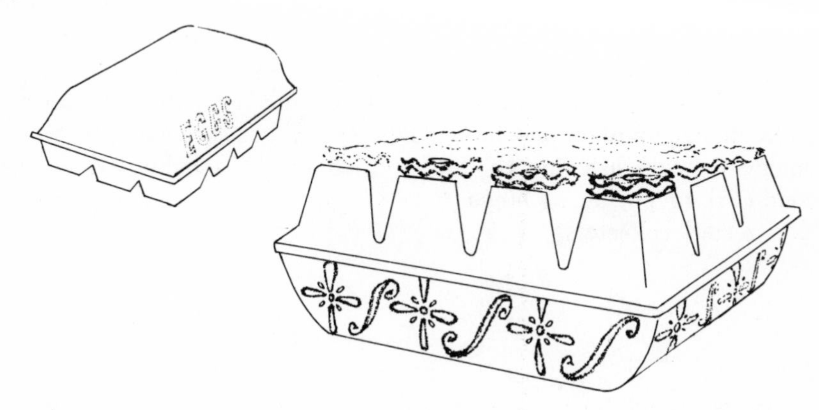

Materials:

Egg Carton
24 bottle caps
Paint or lacquer
String, wire, or ribbon

How to make:

Punch two holes through end of egg rest and bottle caps
Secure bottle caps to egg rest with string or wire
Tie loosely inside of carton
Staple or lace carton together
Paint

Listening

Listening to music enriches the lives of persons, even though they are unable to play a musical instrument or read a musical note. Opportunities to hear fine music have continued to increase. "For millions of people the gates of full musical enjoyment are now wide open. Yet more is needed than mere freedom to enter them. There must be a corresponding increase in opportunities for guidance for this full enjoyment."[7]

Many persons have lacked opportunities for guidance in music appreciation. This fact is particularly tragic as it affects the handicapped, for music has the potential to become a major source of enjoyment and of leisure enrichment for them. Listening is one activity that has a unique individual relationship. Zanzig points out that what happens to a person musically is directly between him and the sounds he hears and that there can be no substitute for this direct experience of the music itself.

Two illustrations are cited to show that listening to music, both recorded and live, can become an interesting hobby for handicapped persons, who have so much leisure. Several handicapped young adults who were encouraged to form a music appreciation club studied a variety of composers and their works. Some club members learned musical composition while others studied symphonic arrangements and opera. Ultimately they became interested in attending live concerts, special musical programs, and grand opera.

Members of a teen-age club were given a jukebox with many records. Even though most of the individuals were in wheel chairs, they thoroughly enjoyed listening to the recorded music, a hobby which they continued to pursue at home. Several members of the group became avid record collectors.

Combined Activities

The ways in which music can be combined with other activities are numerous. For example, it can be combined with drama in variety and talent shows, pageants, festivals, ceremonies, ballads, puppet shows, and monologues, to name only a few. In dance, it can be related to rhythms, interpretive dance, social, folk, and many other forms of dance. It is effec-

[7] Augustus D. Zanzig, *Roads to Music Appreciation,* National Recreation Association, New York, 1958, p. 4.

Painting a wheel chair dragon for an original musical play titled "Prince Yo Yo."

tively used with many games with such sports as synchronized swimming and with camping and other outing activities. The description of the Christmas pantomime in Chapter 15 indicated activities in which music and drama are combined and are particularly well suited for groups of handicapped.

One group of handicapped teen-agers with the assistance of the leader wrote and produced a parody based on *The Mikado* for a spring music festival. Thirty-eight children, some of whom were totally blind and multiple handicapped, participated actively in the musical production.

Christmas caroling has also proved to be a popular service project for a group of severely handicapped children and young adults. Each Christmas the children visit the local children's hospital to sing Christmas carols, while the young adults have found real pleasure in caroling for elderly folk in a resident home for the aged.

Interpretive dance—dancing can be enjoyed sitting or lying down.

CHAPTER 17

Dance

It has been said that if a person can think, feel, and move, he can dance. This broad concept of one's ability to dance is particularly applicable to the severely handicapped person, who can "dance" on his crutches, in his wheel chair, or even in his bed. "The fact that there has always been dance, compels us to accept it as an old and deeply rooted human activity whose foundations reside in the nature of man. It will continue as long as the rhythmic flow of energy operates, and until man ceases to respond to the forces of life and the universe. As long as there is life, there will be dance."[1]

Values of Dance

Children express themselves through spontaneous bodily activity, and this is as natural to them as breathing. This free form of expression should be encouraged for all persons and especially for the severely handicapped individuals who all too often are expected to sit on the side lines and watch, rather than to participate actively. The body is capable of a wide variety and range of movement, and this is true of many of the most severely disabled persons. Movement in this sense is used as a medium of expression, not as an activity designed for exhibition.

Dance, however, contrived for expression, has numerous values for all persons. In addition to the fact that it is one of the finest of all social activities for pure fun and enjoyment, it is both relaxing and exhilarating. It can break down needless inhibitions and free the personality for a wider and more enriching emotional life. Dance can satisfy and deepen the aesthetic sense, and through music and dance one can express feelings without words.

Dance is said to be the most generally available of all art forms, since the instrument needed is one's own body. Anyone who understands this can create his own dance or can find meaning in forms created by others. Dance is an activity that can provide numerous opportunities for group feeling, belonging, and for social integration. Among the types that can be introduced in programs for the handicapped are social and modern dancing, folk and square dancing, creative rhythms, ritual dancing, and tap, clog, and character dancing. Modifications in these activities are necessary for many handicapped persons.

[1] Margaret N. H'Doubler, *Dance, A Creative Art Experience* (Madison, Wisc.: U. of Wisconsin, 1957), p. 168.

Experiences of Handicapped Groups

One group of severely handicapped young adults, some in wheel chairs and some in beds, were introduced to dance through the study of its early history. They became particularly interested in primitive dance and rituals and proceeded to work out their own rhythms and movements. They made their own drums and costumes and learned that they could "dance" while sitting or lying down and that they could use their hands, heads, shoulders, or feet to interpret the rhythm, time, and melody of music in dancing. (See photograph.)

Other handicapped persons have learned to hop, to rock and roll, and to twist, some even from their wheel chairs. Teen-age clubs from the Recreation Center have held twist contests among their members, one of which was won by a boy who twisted from his wheel chair. The involuntary motion which is common to some of the cerebral palsied individuals seems to be an asset in dancing the twist. Dance forms which do not require exact patterns stimulate and encourage individual expression; not only are they popular with handicapped persons but they are dances in which everyone can participate.

The love for music and the desire to dance provided the incentive for one severely handicapped young man to learn to stand and to walk with heavy braces and crutches. Ultimately he was able to "dance," even though he could only move his whole body from side to side in slow rhythm to the music. The fact that he was on his feet dancing with others was a thrilling and satisfying experience for him.

Simple folk dancing is most popular with handicapped groups, as it does not require highly developed skills, and can be easily adapted to all ages and to all types of handicaps. Folk and square dancing in wheel chairs can range from simple slow dances to highly skilled and more complicated dances for persons capable of fast manipulation of their chairs. Persons on crutches often enjoy pushing a wheel-chaired individual, particularly if the person is unable to propel his own chair. In this case they put aside their crutches and use the chair for balance.

Music for folk dancing and square dancing with the handicapped need not be slowed down, but the calling is of primary importance. Such calling requires an experienced person who can watch the dancers, calling to tempo but ad-libbing according to their ability to move about. A singing call cannot be adapted in this manner. Calls should be of the hoe-down type patter. For example: "Forward six, and fall back six, forward two and fall back two." Some adaptable folk dances are the Virginian Reel, Turkey In the Straw, Waltz of the Bells, Oklahoma Mixer, Wooden Shoes, Dashing White Sargent, and many others of the hoe-down type.

Suggestions for Dance Adaptations

1. Substitute swaying, swinging, walking, sliding, balancing, or wheeling for regular dance steps.

2. Decrease tempo of music for slow dance steps for waltz, fox trot, two-step, and so on.

3. Encourage each person to create his own dance pattern, adapted to his individual capacity. For example: Swinging trunk from side to side, using a variety of arm and leg movements, i.e., forward, backward, tapping out rhythm with feet (sitting down); clapping hands in time with music, using fingers to dance a variety of steps (fingers may be dressed as puppets for dancing); using head to dance from side to side and around and around.

4. Use another dancer as a partner for a person in a wheel chair or for one who is bedfast. In this manner, the partner can push the chair or bed in marches, folk dances, ritual dances, or in creative modern dances such as the twist or rock and roll.

Folk Dancing for Children

Many simple folk dances can be adapted for handicapped preschool and older children. Among them are the Shoemaker, Klappdans, and Seven Jumps. In the Shoemaker dance, for example, almost everyone can do the first part, which is winding the thread and tapping the shoes, from a sitting or standing position. In the second part, which consists of a circle or polka steps, wheel-chaired persons who are unable to propel themselves may be pushed in time to the music. If it is difficult to move at all, they may sit in a circle and join hands. The clasped hands or arm movements are then used instead of the foot work.

In Seven Jumps, the Danish dance, after dancing in a circle the group is supposed to get down on their knees. Children who can only sit in their chairs can achieve the same effect by using the elbows on the lap to swing the arms back and forth to depict dancing in a circle. In this manner the group follows the regular dance instructions but adapts to what the children can do. Persons who are bedfast may also participate in many phases of the dances, especially those like the Klappdans, by clapping with someone, even from his bed.

Many other single and double circle dances are simple to do with handicapped children. Examples of these are Here We Go Round the Mountain, Way Down In The Paw-Paw Patch, and The Hoki Poki.

Making a papier-mâché relief map was educational as well as fun.

CHAPTER 18

Arts and Crafts

Arts and crafts is a phase of the recreation program that "is as broad as there are individuals or groups of people and as varied as there are different types and combinations of material to treat and manipulate."[1] Arts and crafts represents one of the many outlets for human expression; it can fulfill the natural urge to create with one's hands, to express ideas in materials. It can, by stimulating the imagination and releasing the creative urge, become an emotional outlet and thereby contribute to the maintenance of even the restoration of physical and mental health.

Arts and crafts may be readily correlated with many other activities such as music, drama, dance, and special events; however, it is unique in its own contribution and deserves the important place it occupies in most recreation programs.

Arts and crafts offers limitless possibilities to the most severely handicapped persons; and one of its greatest values lies in the potential for developing hobbies that can be pursued by individuals in their homes. In addition, a sense of achievement and satisfaction may be gained by those who may not be able to participate in more strenuous and active forms of recreation. The usefulness and lasting values of various articles made in arts and crafts can be a particular source of satisfaction and appreciation for all persons participating in this activity. Although it is one of the finest leisure time activities for individual participation—a factor which must be considered in any activity for the handicapped—numerous arts and crafts activities can be adapted for groups. The following activities have been selected to illustrate the methods by which arts and crafts may be used successfully in a recreation program for the physically handicapped.

Pottery

Almost everyone, if given the opportunity, likes to model in clay. Perhaps, as has been suggested by a psychiatrist, every child has a need to play in mud and dirt. Every child has a need to create, from the simplest of materials, objects which appeal to his imagination or help him in his attempts to understand the uses to which materials can be put. Clay offers an opportunity to fulfill these desires, particularly in the case of handicapped children who have so little opportunity to play creatively.

[1] The Athletic Institute, *The Recreation Program,* The Athletic Institute, Chicago, 1954, p. 16.

Pottery is an activity which lends itself to adaptation and thus is a suitable medium for even the most severely handicapped. Its scope extends from the simplest clay bead or ashtray to objects of art. By the very nature of its many manifestations and the opportunities it offers for creative expression, pottery can be one of the finest media for growth and development among individuals with severe physical handicaps.

The making of pottery is an excellent opportunity for group activity because it can include everyone. If a child has only the use of one finger, he can press small balls of clay into a mold in order to create an ashtray, a vase, or a tile. The chunks of clay pressed in the mold create an unusual pattern, and the finished object has more interest than would one made in a more conventional manner.

Experiences of Pottery Groups

Through pottery a new world was opened up for a girl of nineteen, with cerebral palsy, who had spent most of her life in bed and who had the additional handicap of a double curvature of the spine which prevented her from sitting up for more than an hour or so at a time. When she first came to the Recreation Center she was so shy that she would not allow her mother out of her sight. Gradually, as she learned the ways of the Recreation Center, came to know the leaders, and watched the others engaged in various activities, she became less afraid of the group

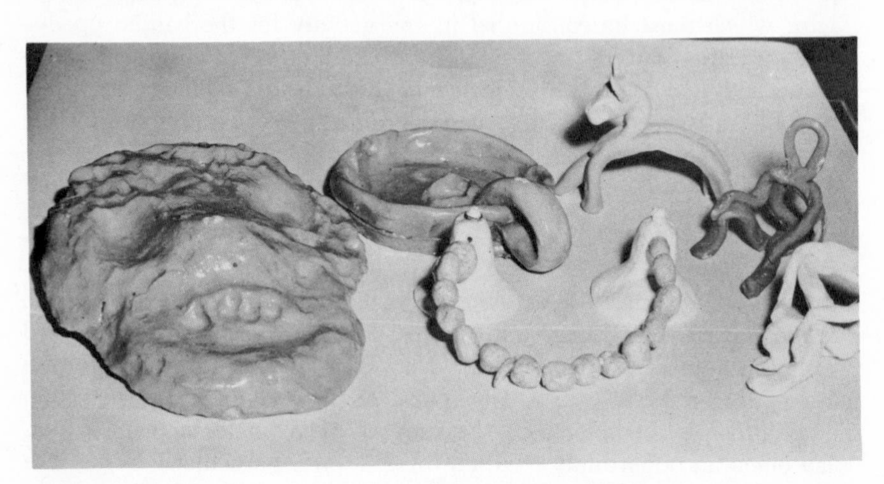

Original clay objects made by severely handicapped individuals. On extreme left is a mask which was made by an individual who used her feet. The mouth and hair were formed by toe prints, and the eyes were impressions made with her heels.

and was able to participate in activities from her portable cot. It was found that she could open and close one hand, and so she was given small chunks of clay to squeeze. She learned to squeeze the clay into the shape she desired; a hole was then punched in the chunk of clay to make a bead for a necklace. When the beads were ready for glazing, she pushed them around with her toes in a shallow pan. Eventually she learned to hold a glaze brush between her toes. The fact that each bead was of a slightly different shape made the completed necklace interesting. She has since learned to work in clay with her toes and has made several masks. Pottery proved to be a further reward for her when she was able, for the first time in her life, to give Christmas gifts she had made herself. She subsequently was able to spend more and more time at the Recreation Center and took part in a number of activities previously too difficult for her.

A group of twelve children with cerebral palsy, whose ages ranged from ten to twenty-one, formed a pottery club. It was the first chance many of them had had to belong to a club. With the guidance of the recreation leader, they elected officers, chose a club project, and selected the club name of "The Jolly Mudslingers." They decided to make ashtrays, bowls, and tiles which were to be offered for sale at a Halloween bazaar. Those who had only slight hand coordination were taught to work with a potter's wheel, an activity which, incidentally, was effective therapy as well as fun. One girl who could not use her hands at all was taught to use a potter's wheel with her toes. She made several ashtrays and eventually designed and made the club's pins, using only her toes. The group often utilized the assembly line process. Those who were seriously handicapped and had only slight use of a hand, for example, contributed to the group effort by sanding the objects in order to make them ready for firing. Others were able to roll coils of clay to be used in making coil vases, bowls, and ashtrays. Still others learned to make decorative slab pieces by flattening clay with a rolling pin and cutting out objects with blunt-edged instruments or cooky cutters. Several members of the group learned to coordinate their hands well enough to use glazing brushes; others, whose hands were unsteady, were encouraged to drip glaze on the objects to be fired. Dripped glaze, on certain pieces, frequently created an original and most pleasing effect. Molded pieces—in one instance, Christmas bells—were finished in an interesting manner by a girl who could only dab the glaze on unevenly. By using a number of different colors, the girl achieved many individual and striking effects. "The Jolly Mudslingers," who had learned to work together for the benefit of the club project, became a closely knit group.

One example of gradual adjustment involves a twelve-year-old girl whose handicap was slight, except for her speech. She appeared physically normal, but when she spoke she had little control of her salivary glands. Children in her neighborhood, so she told the recreation leader, called her "slobberpuss," and it was perhaps as a result of this nickname that she had come to resist the efforts of those who wished to help her. From the beginning of the class in pottery instruction, she demanded attention, annoyed the other children, interrupted the leaders when they were giving instruction or attending to others, and in various ways sought special consideration. She insisted that she was "no good" at making pottery and could not participate because her hands would not allow the coordination necessary for the making of small objects. One day the leader suggested that she turn the foot pedal on the potter's wheel for another girl whose legs were crippled but who had the full use of her hands. She accepted this suggestion and together the two girls made a beautiful bowl. They agreed to put both names on the bowl, since it was a mutual accomplishment. After this experience, the unruly girl helped many of the other children, and finally, with grim determination, learned to make her own pieces. They were not as small and as delicately designed as she would have liked them to be, but the leader could honestly compliment her on the boldness and originality of the large bowls and ashtrays she designed. She was of much help in assisting others who were less capable, and eventually she was elected vice-president of the pottery club. For the most part, her aggressiveness had disappeared. Several years later, she became one of the best leaders at the Recreation Center; she served as a program aide and taught wheel work in the pottery classes.

Leadership Methods in Adapting Pottery

Certain principles already discussed apply specifically to the leader of any creative activity in any recreation program, but they have special significance for leaders working with the severely handicapped. In pottery, as in other art forms, emphasis must be placed on the creative process itself rather than on the final product.

Pottery would seem to be an activity which stimulates the creative urge in almost everyone, and a leader must be unusually careful not to interfere with the handicapped child's creative expression by helping him too much. It has been noted, time and time again, that a leader who is himself a beginner, whether in pottery or in any other activity, in attempting to teach, has a tendency to lose himself in the creation of

Blindness does not prevent one from enjoying pottery.

an object and shortly to take over the participant's role. Many objects supposedly created by a handicapped individual show clearly that the achievement really belongs to the leader. The handicapped person, having been thus robbed of his own sense of achievement, may well have acquired not only an aversion to the creation of pottery, but a belief that he could not have done as well on his own. The object, as far as possible, should be the creation of the participant, not the leader; only when no means can be devised for the participant to complete an object he has begun should a leader offer to help.

In one instance, a group of eight camp counselors with no previous experience in pottery were given several workshop experiences so they could assist cerebral palsied individuals. However, the fifteen or twenty hours of instruction in the basic essentials of pottery making were not enough to fulfill their own creative urges so that they would guide effectively and refrain from helping too much. Each leader tended to inject his own ideas into the object to be created, choosing, color, form, and finished product. Many leaders, wishing to be kind, cannot resist the desire to take a crude or primitive object made by a handicapped individual and add the finishing touches which will improve its appearance. The handicapped individual is rarely pleased by such help, and prefers that the object be his own, however crude. Such interference tends to dampen his enthusiasm and lessen or destroy his creative desires and abilities.

Methods and Adaptations

The pages that follow describe several pottery techniques with adaptations that can be used in programs for handicapped groups.

SCULPTURING. The pinch method in pottery is particularly suitable for individuals who do not have perfect use and control of their hands and fingers. It is especially appropriate for making such figures as animals, since the idea is to squeeze a cylinder of clay in such a way as to suggest a form or figure. Details such as ears, nose, and so on, are pinched into shape. The fingers are the only modeling tools used, and the charm of the finished object is in its originality and simplicity. Small bowls and pots can also be made by the pinch method.

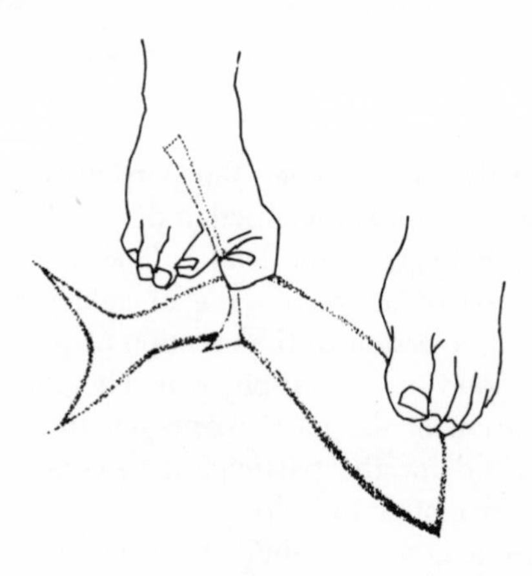

SCULPTURE

COILS. The use of coils is one of the easiest and most creative methods of pottery making for the handicapped. Coils of clay can be rolled and formed by individuals who have the use of only one hand, one finger,

A blind girl creates an animal in clay.

or the toes. Coil pieces can be made in many sizes and shapes, allowing the individual a wide variety of choices, such as bowls, pitchers, vases, ashtrays, and figures of animals and of people. Coils may be placed inside ice cream cartons, shoe boxes, cereal boxes, and other containers to create forms for such items as lamp bases. Depending upon the form chosen, any animal can be made by using three coils; two are used to form the body and legs, and one is used for the head and neck.

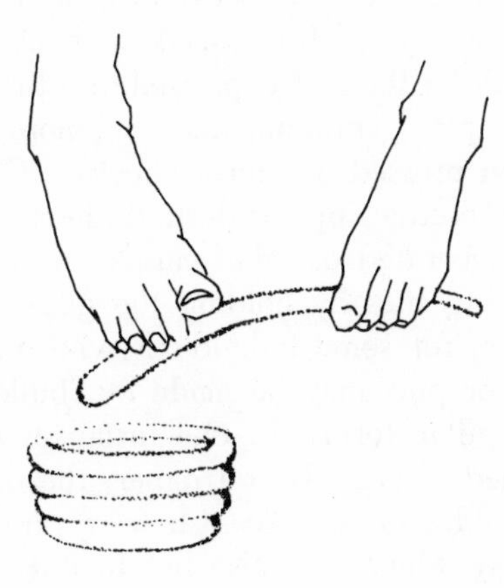

COIL

SLABS. The use of slabs in pottery is as simple as rolling dough and cutting biscuits or cookies. In this technique, one uses flat sheets of clay for cutting various shapes and forms to create the desired object. Guide sticks help to obtain uniform thickness, and the clay is rolled with a rolling pin in the same manner as pie crust. This is an easy method for individuals who use their toes or have the use of only one hand.

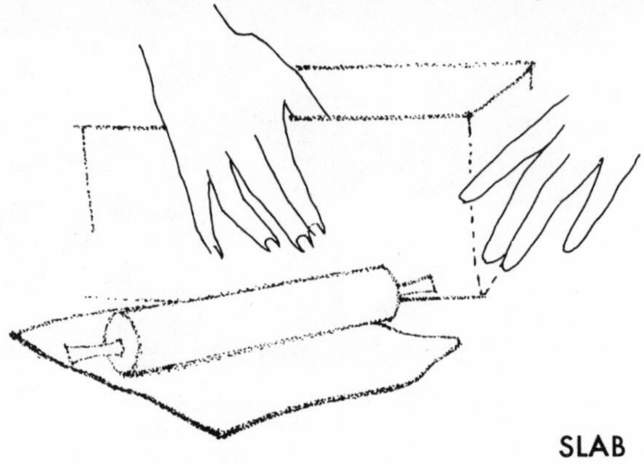

SLAB

For very small children, or for individuals who have limited use of their hands or feet, this method is excellent for making original hand or foot plaques, which are simply made by pressing the hand or foot into a wet piece of clay. The clay should be at least an inch thick in order to allow for a sufficiently deep print. Painting around the print, rather than over the print, allows lines and form to stand out on the finished piece.

Use of plant leaves makes possible another method of creating design in slabs. Leaves pressed into clay provide forms and designs that can be used for decorations or for useful objects such as ashtrays or center pieces. The bottom side of the leaf is pressed into the clay. Large leaves, such as magnolia, maple, geranium, and sycamore, which accentuate form and design when pressed, are most effective. One may cut around the design and turn the edges up for desired effect.

Flat tiles simply decorated or relief carved make attractive tea tiles and plaques. Decorating tiles by holding the glaze brush between the toes is an easy process for some individuals who work with their toes. Slab boxes, planters, or pots may be made by "building" with slabs, in either regular or irregular forms. In one instance, a girl who worked with her toes, sketched a large fish on paper; the design was then cut out in clay, and the sides of the clay fish were raised slightly in order to resemble an ashtray. Slabs may also be cut out and joined together with "slip" (liquid clay) in order to make objects such as a box. In order to make sure that the parts will fit, however, patterns of the box should first be made from cardboard or paper. The patterns of the various components are then placed upon the sheet of clay and cut out. Care should be taken to assure that inside and outside joints are thoroughly sealed. This can be achieved best by pressing additional clay along the inside angles. Outside joints can be sealed by forming the excess clay with a modeling tool or with the fingers. These techniques may be used by a handicapped person having the use of only one hand.

Slab sculpture is created by a similar method. Patterns of animals and other figures may be cut out and formed over a temporary support until they are "leather dry" and permanently formed; such pieces can then be put together to make three-dimensional decorative figures. The term *leather dry* is used for clay that has reached a point when it will no longer sag, yet is not completely dry.

MOLDS. If an individual can control only one thumb or finger or press the back of his hand, he can press clay into an open-mouthed mold to obtain a desired shape and thereby create a sturdy ashtray, bowl, or pot. The small balls, odd shapes, or chunks of clay are pressed with one finger, for example, into every detail of the mold to obtain its shape. The thickness of the form should depend upon the type of object to be

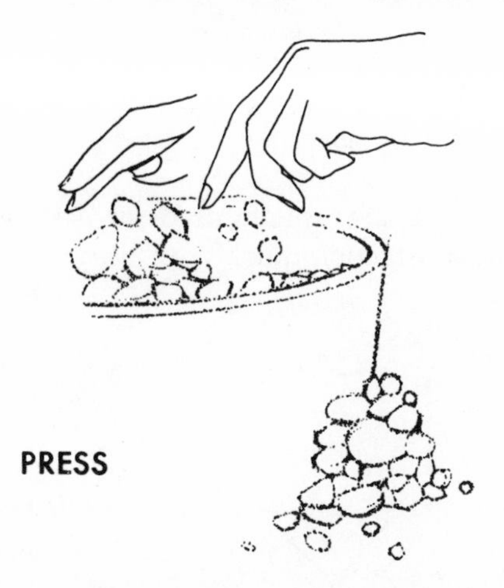

made and should be uniform throughout. If the balls of clay are uniform in size, one can, when pressing, create a free-form pattern. This will give an interesting texture to the outside of the finished object. After the mold has been pressed throughout, excess clay can be removed with a modeling tool or a tongue depressor. In order to obtain a smooth, even finish inside the piece, wet fingers or a wet sponge can be used to smooth over the uneven clay. When the pressed form is dry enough to pull away from

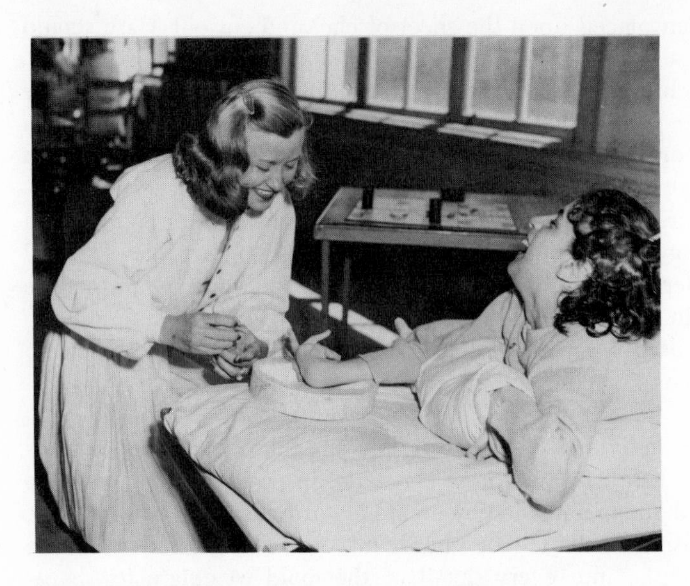

The author teaches a bedfast girl how to press clay into a mold.

the mold and appears to be loose, it is ready to be removed and set aside for thorough drying. A well-designed bowl may be used in the same manner as a mold by covering the inside of the bowl with a thin piece of cloth.

Plaster of Paris molds are usually used for casting with liquid clay. For those who want satisfaction quickly, casting with slip is good. Cast-

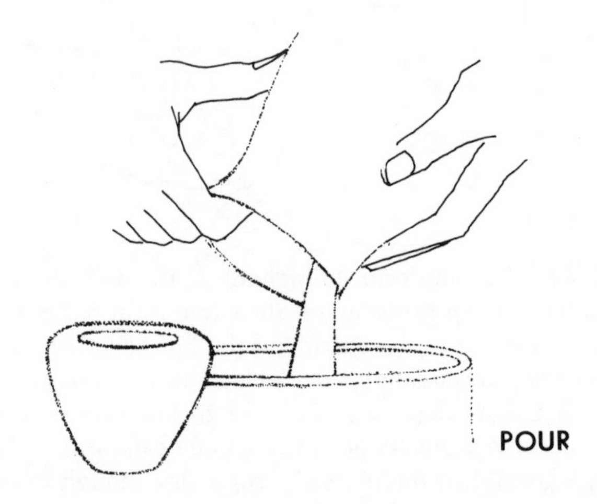

ing, however, does not wholly satisfy the urge to create, and except for the decoration of the object, the piece produced is not original. On the other hand, casting is an excellent group activity for making several identical gifts. For example, a group of handicapped participants made a dozen monogrammed coffee mugs for a person who had made a considerable financial grant to their program. The pottery group was extremely pleased to be able to make a personalized gift to their benefactor, and he was delighted to have a gift made by the handicapped.

THE POTTER'S WHEEL. Throwing is an exacting technique and demands many hours of patient effort for one to master, but learning to throw a bowl, a pot, or an ashtray on the potter's wheel is a tremendous satisfac-

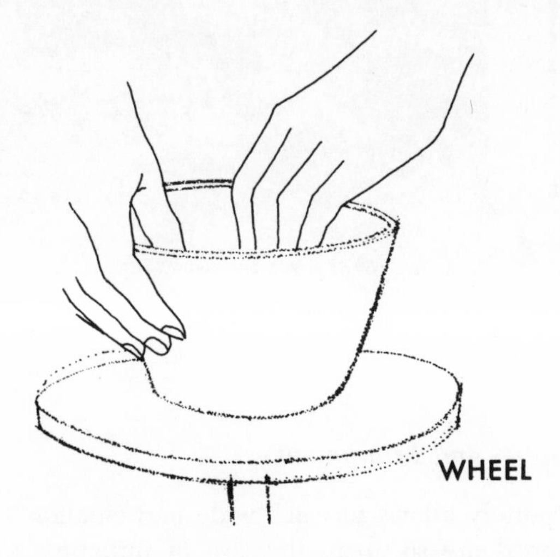

tion. It offers an additional challenge to those handicapped individuals who have involuntary motion of their hands or arms or who have arthritis or other hand-crippling diseases. Individuals who could not use their hands at all have actually had some success with the potter's wheel by using their feet and toes. A good instructor is necessary; one who has patience and understanding can develop proficiency in the participant and create an interesting and worthwhile hobby for many handicapped individuals.

Some individuals who are less severely handicapped prefer the kick wheel, because the speed can be easily regulated by the foot. Persons in wheel chairs, who have hand use but are unable to use their feet or legs, naturally require an electric wheel, the speed of which can be regulated according to individual needs.

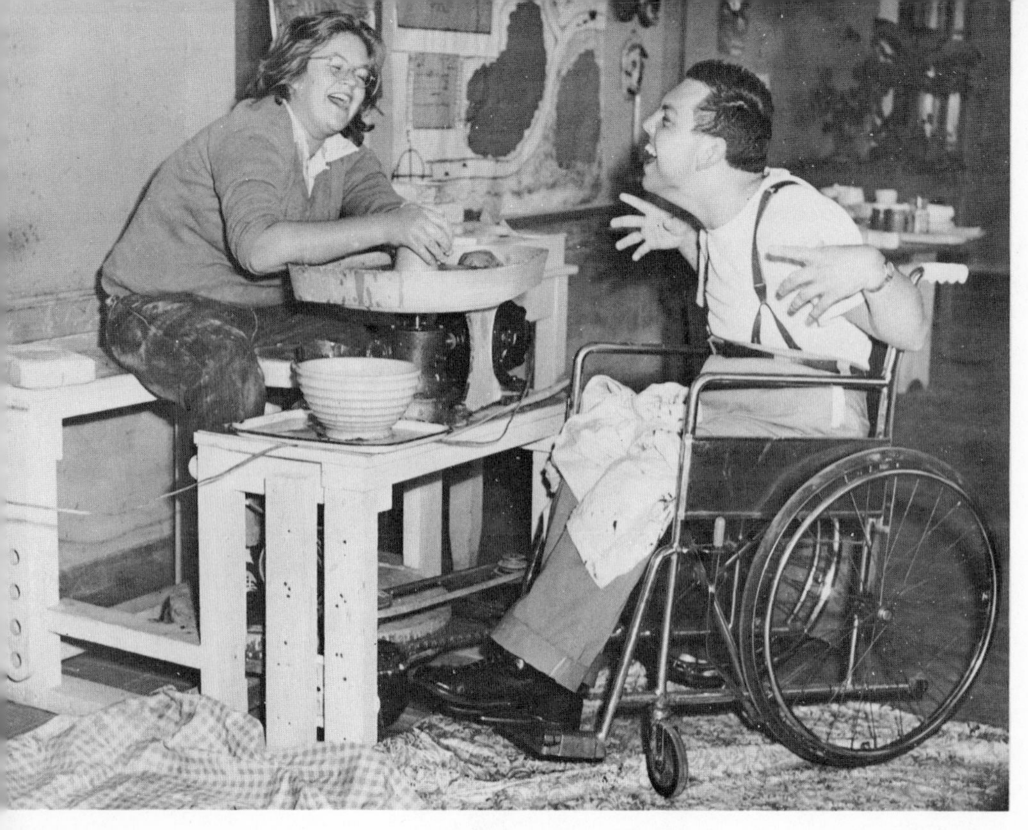

Working on the potter's wheel.

Pottery Supplies and Equipment

Because pottery allows for such wide participation and its benefits to the handicapped are so great, the cost of initiating a program is well worth the money spent. A program can actually begin with a few pounds of clay, glazes, and engobes, and simple tools. Clay can be purchased commercially in small amounts and is relatively inexpensive. Any clay which can be fired is suitable. Some clays are ready for use; others need to be wedged to remove air bubbles. Wedging the clay is good activity for handicapped persons who need to use their hands and/or feet. The pinch, coil, and slab methods can be used with little or no additional equipment. Objects made in clay can be left the natural color of the clay, which is usually white, red, or buff. They need only to have a coat of clear glaze in order to be given a finished look and to make them waterproof.

Many types of glazes are obtainable commercially and can be purchased in varied colors and in small amounts. Engobes, or colored slips, are reasonably priced, easy to apply, and can be used on unfired clay.

Many types of modeling tools can be purchased commercially, but kitchen utensils make an excellent substitute for pottery tools. The following items are useful and adequate for a limited budget:

Rolling pins	Cookie cutters
Knives	Cheese cutters
Spoons	Oilcloth
Sponges	Tongue depressors

Dull knives are needed in cutting out slab work or in trimming or carving objects. Spoons can be used to dig out excess clay in modeled pieces; cookie cutters, for actual design and form in slab work; cheese cutters for cutting the clay into chunks in order to look for air bubbles. Sponges have many uses, such as smoothing out objects, cleaning up after the pottery activity, and, when used wet, covering unfinished pieces in order to keep them moist and pliable until they can be completed. Oilcloth provides an excellent cover for the working surface of benches or tables where wet clay is being used. The wrong side of the oilcloth is more flexible and is better to use next to the clay than the right side. Since no sharp objects should be used on a mold, tongue depressors are excellent to scrape away excess clay from the mold which has been poured or pressed.

The minimum supplies and equipment suggested above can be purchased reasonably from ceramic supply houses. Some commercial agencies will also fire objects for individuals and groups. Used molds can be purchased at a minimum cost, or original ones can easily be made from plaster of Paris. All molds must be made of plaster of Paris because it serves as a blotter to absorb the water from the clay.

Since many schools and public and private recreation programs include pottery activity, supplies and equipment may be purchased through the agencies conducting them. These agencies may also give assistance in firing, although small electric kilns are reasonably priced, inexpensive to operate, and are useful in the pottery program.

Papier-mâché

Papier-mâché crafts, which have been most popular with handicapped persons, form an activity that is interesting and enjoyable for all age groups. Articles made range from toy animals for children to relief maps for adults. Papier-mâché craft is very inexpensive and is an excellent individual or group project for even the most severely handicapped. The fact that it is not an exacting craft activity makes it especially desirable and satisfying for persons who have difficulty with hand and arm coordination. Strips of newspaper can be torn easily with one hand or even with toes; and applying the material to an object or modeling with pulp is a simple procedure.

Large objects are especially easy to make and can serve as a most interesting and enjoyable group activity. An example of this is shown in the following illustration:

A group of severely handicapped teen-age children decided to make a large reindeer for the Christmas play and for use in other Christmas festivities. And old sawhorse made an excellent frame for the legs and body. Chicken wire was used to expand the body and legs and to form the neck and horns. Papier-mâché was then applied in layers to the entire surface. The object was large enough so that several persons could work

Making a papier-mâché reindeer.

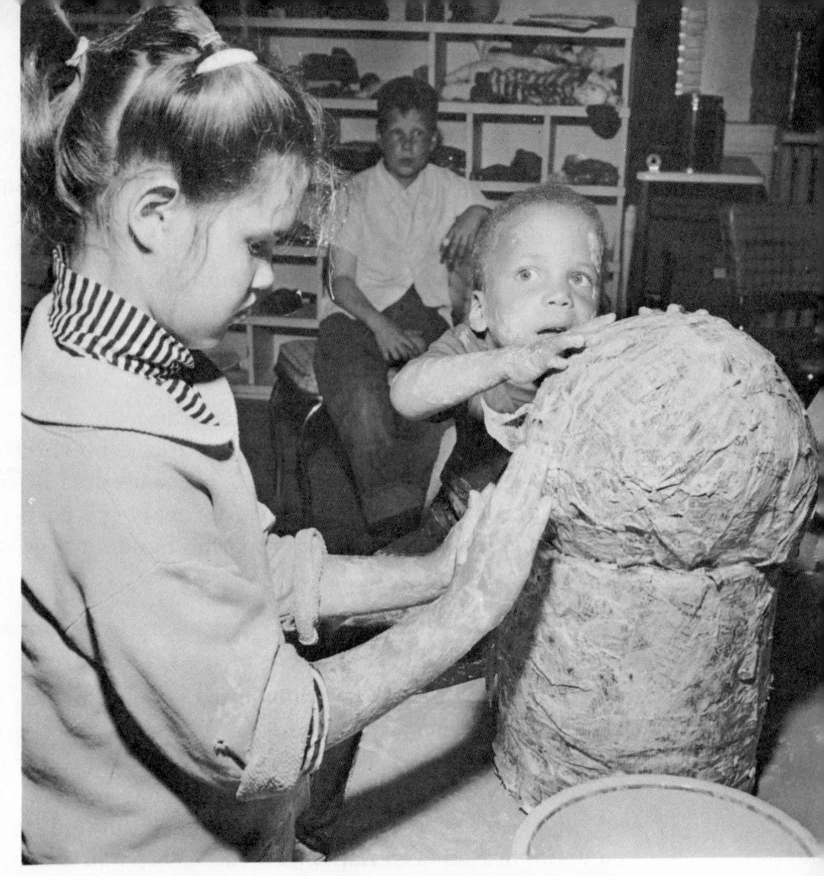

A blind girl and a cerebral palsied boy make a papier-mâché clown's head.

on it at one time. Every person in the group had an opportunity to participate in the making of the reindeer by tearing newspaper strips and soaking them in water, by taking part in the pasting process, or by painting the object when it was completed. Several individuals who had a great deal of involuntary motion in their hands and arms and who experienced difficulty in grasping or holding small brushes were delighted to discover that they could paint the reindeer by using large paint brushes, which were easier to hold and manipulate. In this manner, several persons who had never painted before enjoyed tempera painting and felt real satisfaction with the completed project. (See illustration.)

Making a papier-mâché relief map can be educational as well as enjoyable. For example, a group of handicapped young adults chose to make a relief map of California to further their study and understanding of the state's history and government. The map, which was made to scale, was modeled on a piece of plywood. The project, which required a great deal of study and research, took several months to complete. During this time the group visited various places of interest and studied native wildlife. This stimulated them to make for the map papier-mâché objects such as fruits and vegetables and animals.

Method of Making Papier-mâché

Papier-mâché can be used to reproduce an object such as a puppet head modeled in clay, a piece of fruit, or a bowl; or it can serve as a medium for modeling objects. It is often used as a substitute for clay; for example, when clay is too heavy for making a particular object. There are two different methods for preparing papier-mâché, the uncooked and the cooked method.

1. The *uncooked method* is used primarily to obtain an exact duplicate of an object such as a piece of fruit, a bowl, or a puppet head.

Procedure: Tear newspapers into strips or small pieces, depending on the size needed for a particular object. Wet and squeeze out excess water. In a large flat tin such as a pie tin mix flour and water to the consistency of thick cream; or thinned library paste may be used. Dip the pieces of wet paper in the paste until thoroughly saturated and apply to object being duplicated. Overlap pieces of newspaper smoothly, so that they follow the contour of the object. Continue building layers until the desired thickness is obtained. The object should be allowed to dry thoroughly after the fourth layer has been applied. The last layer should consist of torn pieces of paper towel, since this make a better surface for painting. Do not dip these pieces into the paste but put paste over the papier-mâché surface and apply pieces of paper towel to the object. When object is thoroughly dry, cut completely through cover to form two halves; tape halves together and paint.

2. With the *cooked method* a pulp is used as a medium for modeling objects. Papier-mâché pulp may also be prepared uncooked; but it is coarser grained and does not model as well as when cooked.

Procedure: Tear newspaper into strips and soak overnight in water. Soaking overnight shortens the cooking time, as it helps to disintegrate the paper. Use twice as much newspaper as the amount of pulp desired. When paper has been well soaked, boil until it is mushy. Drain off excess water, but do not squeeze water from the pulp. Add generous amount of paste, the consistency of thick cream, and stir into the pulp. A few drops of preservative, such as alum or oil of clove, may be added to keep the pulp from souring. The pulp is now ready for modeling.

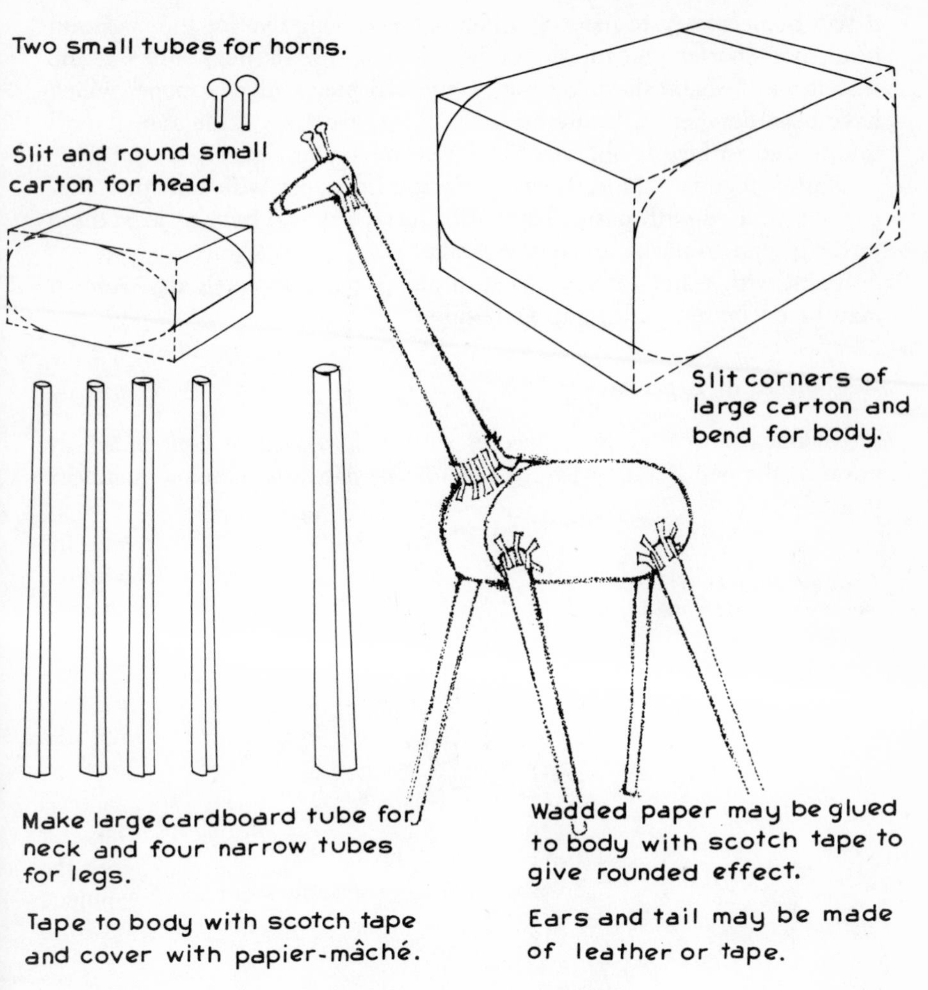
Two small tubes for horns.
Slit and round small carton for head.
Slit corners of large carton and bend for body.
Make large cardboard tube for neck and four narrow tubes for legs.
Tape to body with scotch tape and cover with papier-mâché.
Wadded paper may be glued to body with scotch tape to give rounded effect.
Ears and tail may be made of leather or tape.

Making a papier-mâché giraffe.

Animals

MATERIALS: Newspaper, paper towels; flour or wheat paste or thinned library paste; string or gummed tape; pie pan or flat dish; tempera paint; miscellaneous scrap materials.

General Procedure: Make form first by wrapping, rolling, or crushing the paper and securing it firmly with gummed tape or string. Newspapers rolled into tight, hard rolls of varying lengths serve as a skeleton upon which to build a papier-mâché animal. If the animal is to be a giraffe, it will be necessary to have six rolls: one very long one for the neck and head, one shorter one for the body, and four for the legs. Fill out the skeleton and shape the body with crumpled pieces of newspaper which have been dampened. Continue to build the structure of the animal until the desired surface is obtained. (See accompanying figure.)

Fasten together these pieces of dampened paper with torn pieces of paper saturated with paste. The entire surface should have at least three layers of papier-mâché, uncooked method.

Paint with water tempera when the object is completely dry. Animal may be decorated with scrap material.

Vegetables or Fruit

MATERIALS: A very firm piece of fruit or a vegetable; flour or wheat paste or thinned library paste; paper towels; flat dish; Vaseline; tempera paint.

Papier-mâché fruit.

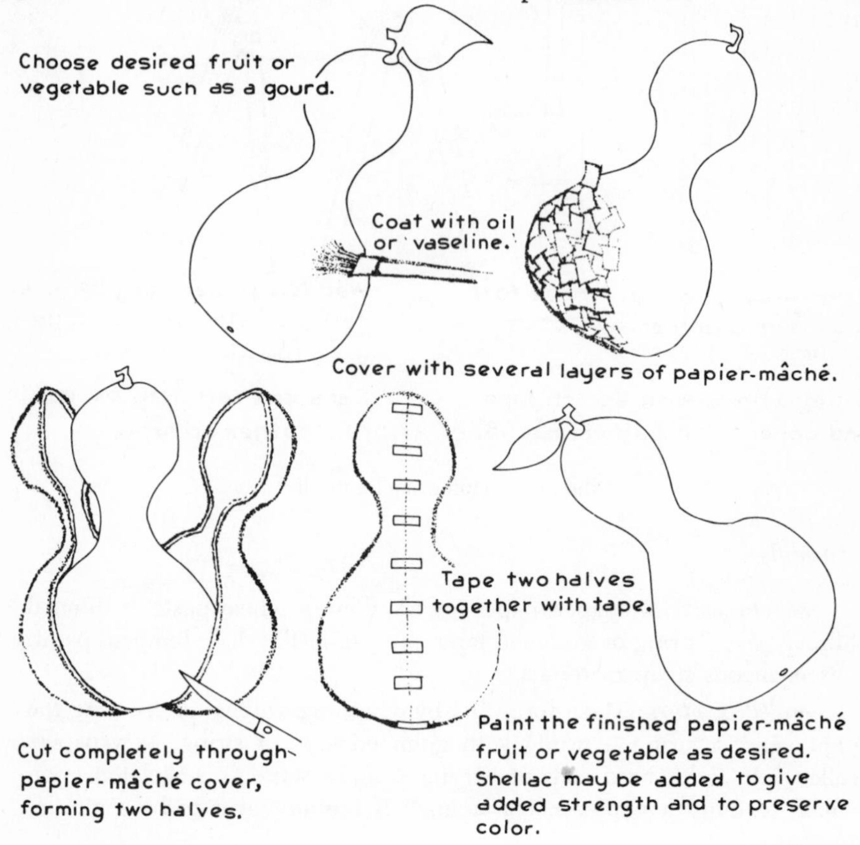

Choose desired fruit or vegetable such as a gourd.
Coat with oil or vaseline.
Cover with several layers of papier-mâché.
Tape two halves together with tape.
Cut completely through papier-mâché cover, forming two halves.
Paint the finished papier-mâché fruit or vegetable as desired. Shellac may be added to give added strength and to preserve color.

General Procedure: Grease the fruit or vegetable with Vaseline, and cover with several layers of uncooked papier-mâché. After the papier-mâché is completely dry, cut through shell and around object. (See figures.) Fasten the two halves of papier-mâché together with torn pieces of towels, to form a strong seam. Paint and, if desired, cover with white shellac, which gives additional strength and preserves the painted surface. NOTE: Vegetables and fruit may also be modeled with papier-mâché pulp.

Relief Map

MATERIALS: Newspaper; flour or wheat paste or thinned library paste; oil of cloves or wintergreen; flat dish; tempera paint; piece of ply board or chip board; spackle.

General Procedure: Draw an outline of the map to scale on the board. Then model the map with papier-mâché pulp onto the board using fingers or a simple tool. After the map has been allowed to dry thoroughly, spread over the entire map a thin layer of spackle mixed with water to the consistency of thick cream. The spackle gives a smooth finish to the map and makes possible additional modeling. Spackle must be allowed to dry thoroughly, which takes several hours. Paint with tempera paint and with shellac, if desired. (See illustration photograph.)

Among the other objects which are simple to make from papier-mâché and which are useful in a recreation program are model scenery and props, marionettes, and puppets. Participants enjoy making personal items or gifts such as jewelry, figurines, trays, pictures, bowls, and numerous other useful and decorative articles.

Graphic Arts

Creative painting in oils, water tempera, charcoal and pencil sketching, finger painting, and sand painting are all within the realm of possibility for even the most severely handicapped person. Several persons have learned to paint with their toes or by holding a paint brush between their teeth. One cerebral palsied young woman learned, after many months and with much patience and persistence, to steady her unruly, shaky hand with the other. (See photograph.) In this manner, she then experimented with various types of brushes and numerous angles from which to paint. After gaining confidence in the technique established, she painted many interesting seascapes and landscapes, thereby developing

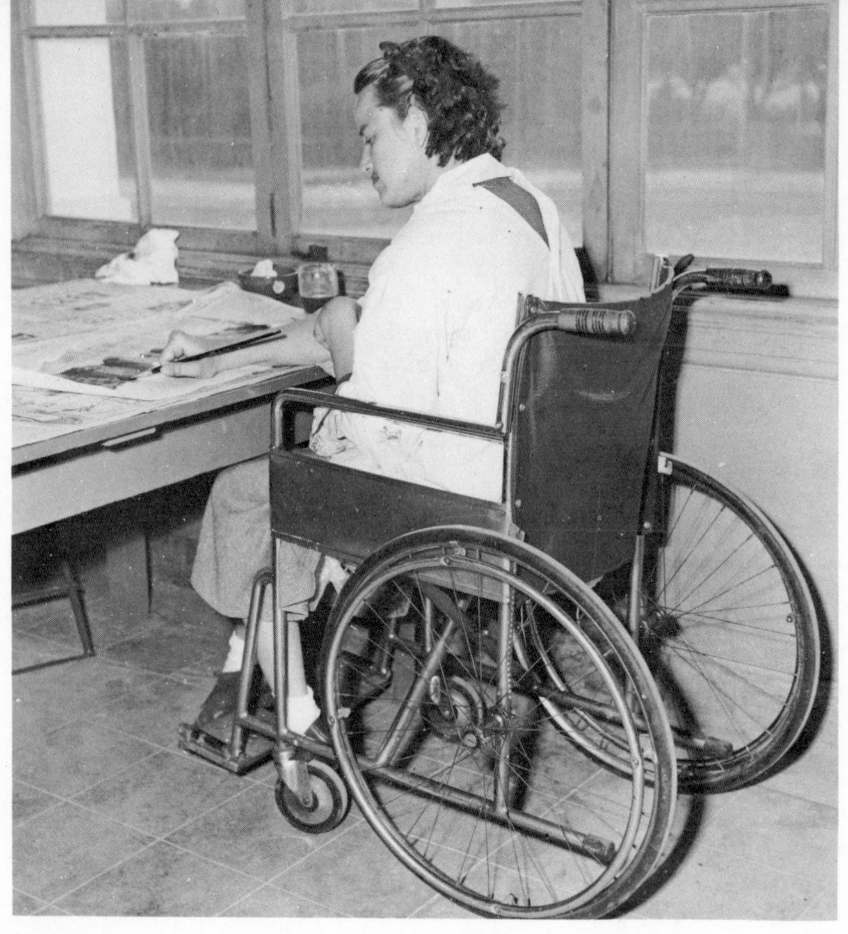

Learning to steady one hand with the other was an achievement which finally enabled this person to paint.

a hobby which she never before thought possible. Another similarly handicapped person was able to paint in oil with a sponge which had been secured to her elbow. The texture of the sponge aided in the design of her paintings. A third person with no use of her hands whatsoever has learned to paint in oils and to sketch while holding the brush or pencil between her toes.

Sand Painting

Sand painting, a process whereby sand is used to create the color and design of a picture or drawing, has proved to be a popular activity in recreation programs for the handicapped. The only materials needed are white beach sand, powdered tempera, glue, and construction paper. A list of the procedures used in sand painting follows.

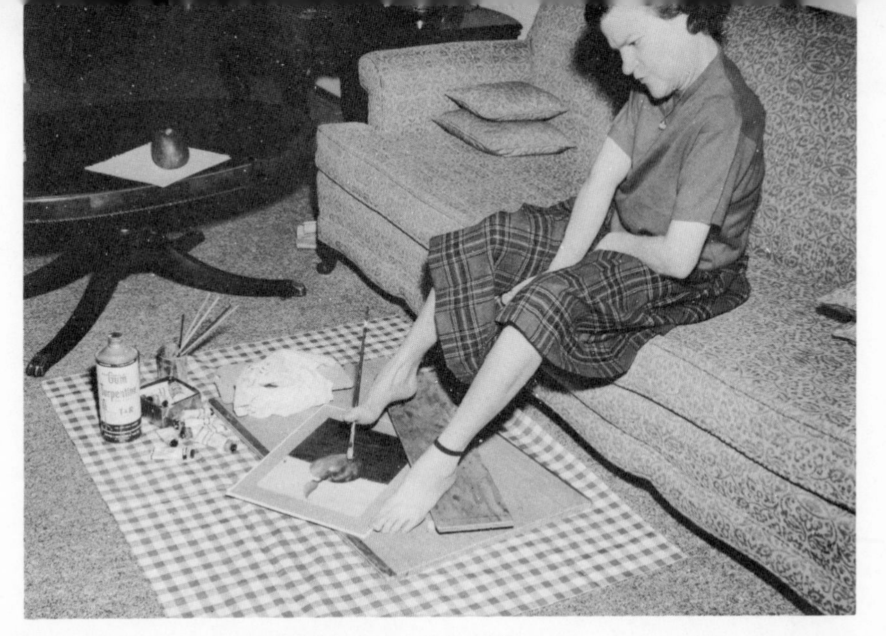

Painting in oils with toes.

Paintings made with toes.

1. Draw the outline of the painting on paper.
2. Prepare sand by sifting through a sieve to remove extraneous objects.
3. Put small quantities of sand into separate containers or in a muffin type tin.
4. Select desired colors from powdered tempera and mix with sand for desired shade, using a teaspoon of tempera to ¼ cup of sand.

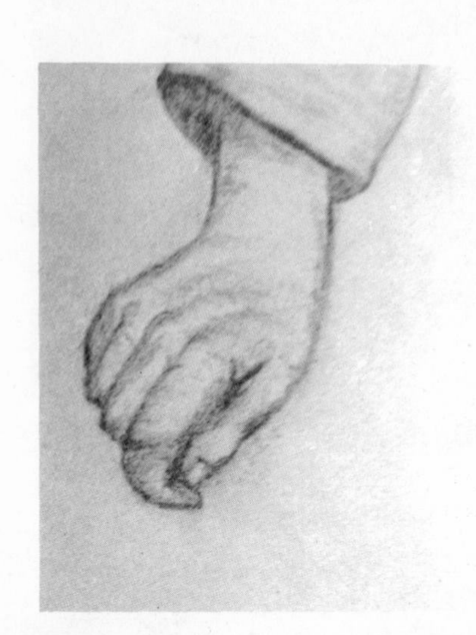

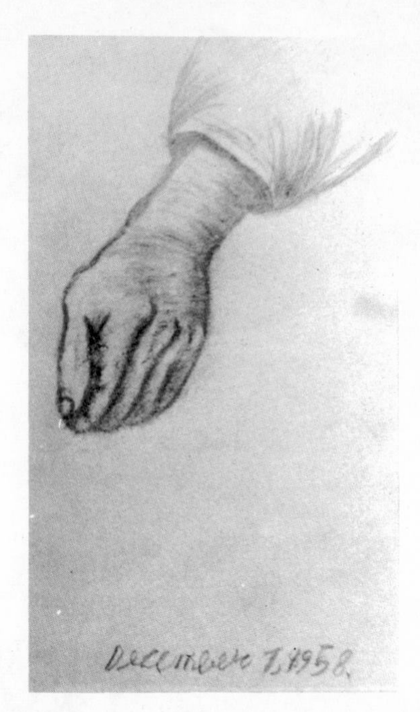

Sketches drawn with toes.

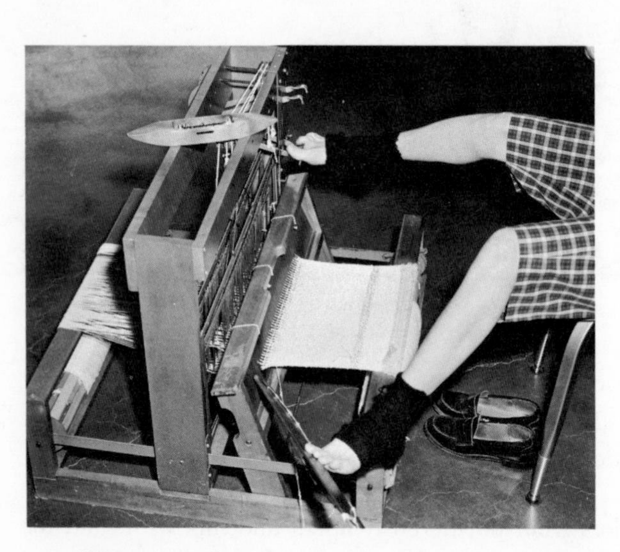

Weaving with toes.

5. Cover with glue the individual sections of the sketch where each color is to go, one section at a time.
6. With a knife or spoon, drop colored sand slowly over the glue and let this set until it is completely dry.
7. Shake off excess sand, and repeat the process on each succeeding section until the painting is completed. The glue will hold the colored sand to the various portions of the sketch.

SAND PAINTING

A turtle made with colored sand.

Mosaics

A mosaic can be described as the orderly arrangement of enduring materials, such as stone, tile, or glass, into a unified whole which has been set into cement or adhesive. The surface of a mosaic can be smooth or rough with an uneven texture, depending on the materials used and the purpose of the mosaic.

The art of mosaic is centuries old. There has been a revival of this interesting and decorative process, and due to the availability of new types of cement and adhesives, it has been greatly simplified and is well within the abilities of all age groups. Handicapped children as well as adults have found real pleasure in making mosaics. Part of the fun is in the collecting of the various materials such as pebbles, shells, and pieces of driftwood gathered at the beach, pieces of broken glass and bits of colored ceramic tile that can be used in making a mosaic. Designs can be free form or conventional. Useful and interesting articles can be made such as plaques, patio table tops, pictures, and trays. Walls, doors, and floors are some of the more elaborate projects.

Experiences of the Handicapped

Children and adults at the Recreation Center particularly enjoyed making free form mosaics. Some of the adults made patio tables, while

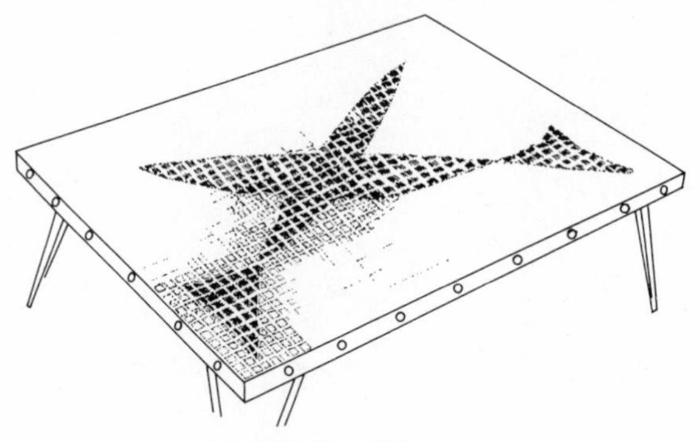

Mosaic table.

the children made plaques, trays, and pictures. One teen-age boy, unable to speak or to use his hands or feet, indicated a desire to make a mosaic. After a great deal of exploration, the recreation leader worked out an arrangement whereby the handicapped youth could nod his head to indicate the design and color of the mosaic. In this manner, the leader was able to help him create the design he had visualized but could not physically achieve.

Suggested Materials

Making mosaics can be a very inexpensive craft because scrap materials can be used successfully. As mentioned previously, objects such as pebbles and shells can be found at the beach. Broken colored tile may be obtained free of charge from ceramic tile supply companies. Frames for the mosaics can be made from scrap wood. Coffee can lids or aluminum pie plates may be used for molds.

Many of the glues, adhesives, and cements such as grout, magnesite, and mortar are inexpensive and easy to obtain.

Mosaic plaques and pottery items made by handicapped young adults.

Suggested Methods

There are several methods of mosaic making. They fall mainly into two categories, the "direct" and the "indirect" methods. In the "direct" method, the materials are placed directly into the cement or glued directly onto the backing and grouted. The "indirect" method is one in which the objects are arranged upside down in a pattern first and then either placed into the cement or the cement is poured over it. In each method it is best to make a drawing of the desired pattern and to arrange the mosaic pieces on the paper before final placement on backing.

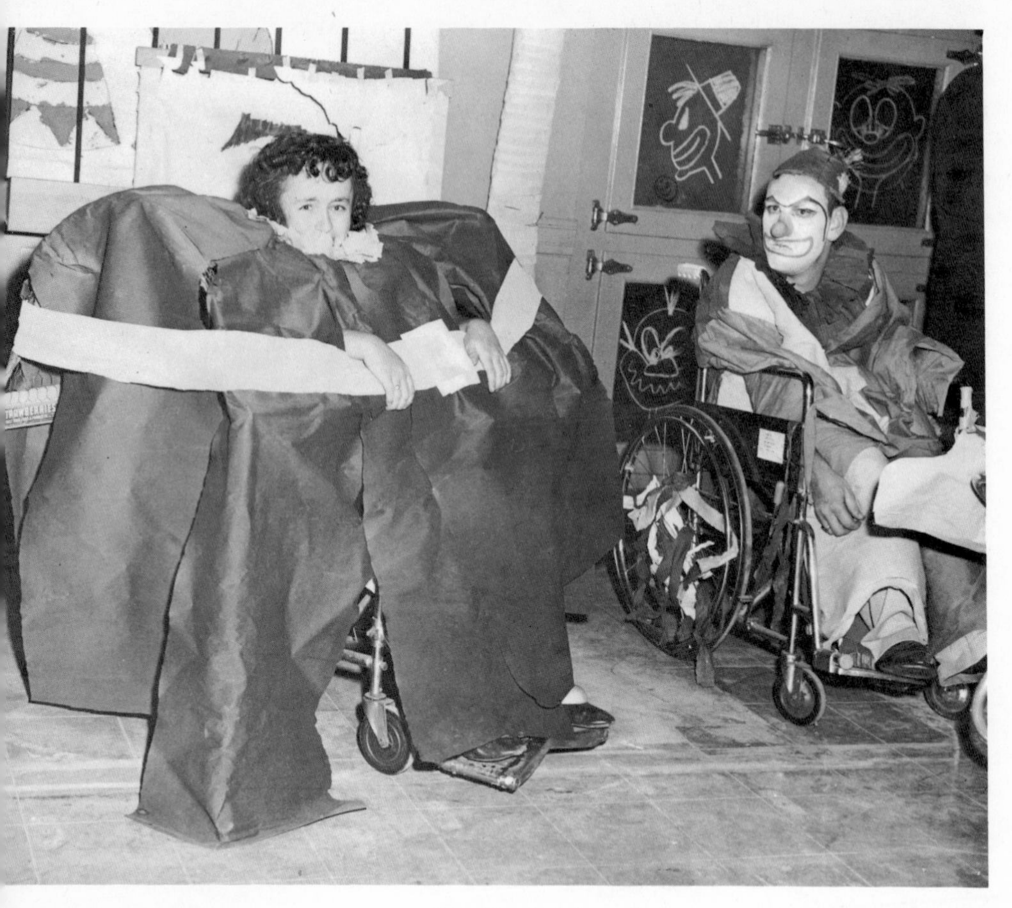

The "fat lady" in the circus.

CHAPTER 19

Special Events

Special events offer the handicapped tremendous opportunities for enjoyment and for creative participation. Circuses, carnivals, festivals, and funfests are just a few of the many events which provide an excellent framework for group endeavor. These activities are various enough to include all handicapped, of whatever age or disability. They can be large enough for all the students in a special school for the handicapped, or they can be small enough for a group in a recreation program. They can be either simply done at little cost or expensive and elaborately done, and they can be presented indoors or outdoors.

Special events provide an excellent opportunity for interpreting to the general public the value of recreation for the handicapped. At the same time they are a useful means of educating the community in the general acceptance of these persons and of promoting interest in the continued need to provide opportunities for them to engage in recreation. In addition, they give the handicapped a means of learning cooperation by working on committees and by assuming the responsibilities of conducting an activity. They offer opportunities to meet and enjoy other groups,

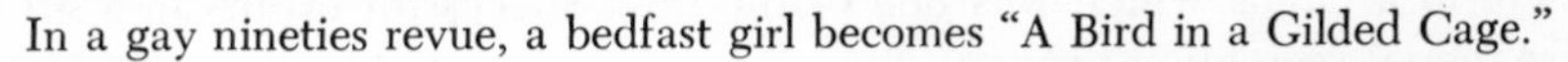
In a gay nineties revue, a bedfast girl becomes "A Bird in a Gilded Cage."

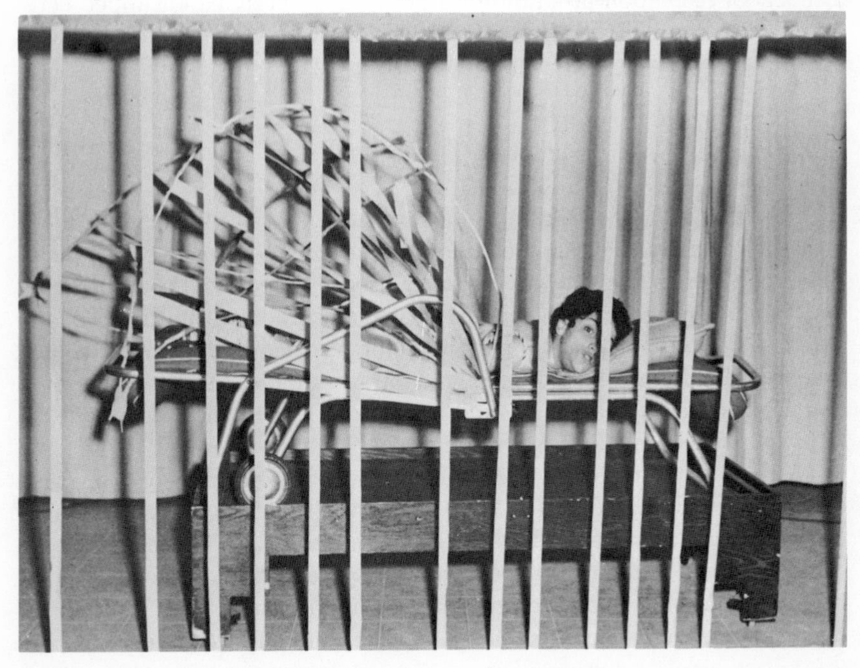

handicapped or nonhandicapped. They also serve as a stimulus for individual and group accomplishment.

It should be remembered that the type of performance or the action of the individual is of secondary importance. The primary objective is that each person has a chance to be included in a creative group effort for the sheer fun of taking part in a special event. All of the other benefits—the learning of group cooperation, the feeling of achievement and of belonging, and the opportunity to gain new confidence and a sense of personal worth—will come about naturally with good leadership. The benefits resulting from participation in special events are clearly demonstrated by the experiences recorded in this chapter.

The Circus

The production of a circus offers an exceptional opportunity for the use of ingenuity and makes possible the participation of even the most seriously handicapped. Fewer activities have a stronger appeal, especially to children. Some of the experiences reported in the following pages relate to a circus which was one of the most successful events in a summer school recreation program for a group of severely handicapped cerebral palsied individuals. The entire group of twenty-five students, whose ages ranged from five to twenty-one, had a part in the circus.

Adaptation of Space, Facilities, Equipment

The setting for the "big top," in this instance, was a secluded outdoor area sheltered by the wings of the building, which formed two walls of the circus arena. The site was normally used by the school as a play area and as a place for physical therapy practice. Equipment in the area consisted of two sets of parallel bars used for physical therapy and walking practice, a chinning bar, a seesaw, a large sandbox, playpen, tricycles, and a barrel horse. The space and equipment lent themselves exceptionally well to the creation of a small circus.

With a little ingenuity and imagination the parallel bars became cages for "wild animals." The cage effect was achieved by tying streamers of crepe paper into the bars in crisscross fashion. "Wild animals," who could not walk without holding onto bars, paced up and down the cages in bear, tiger, and leopard costumes, growling in true animal fashion and making an effective and realistic act. The chinning and climbing bars

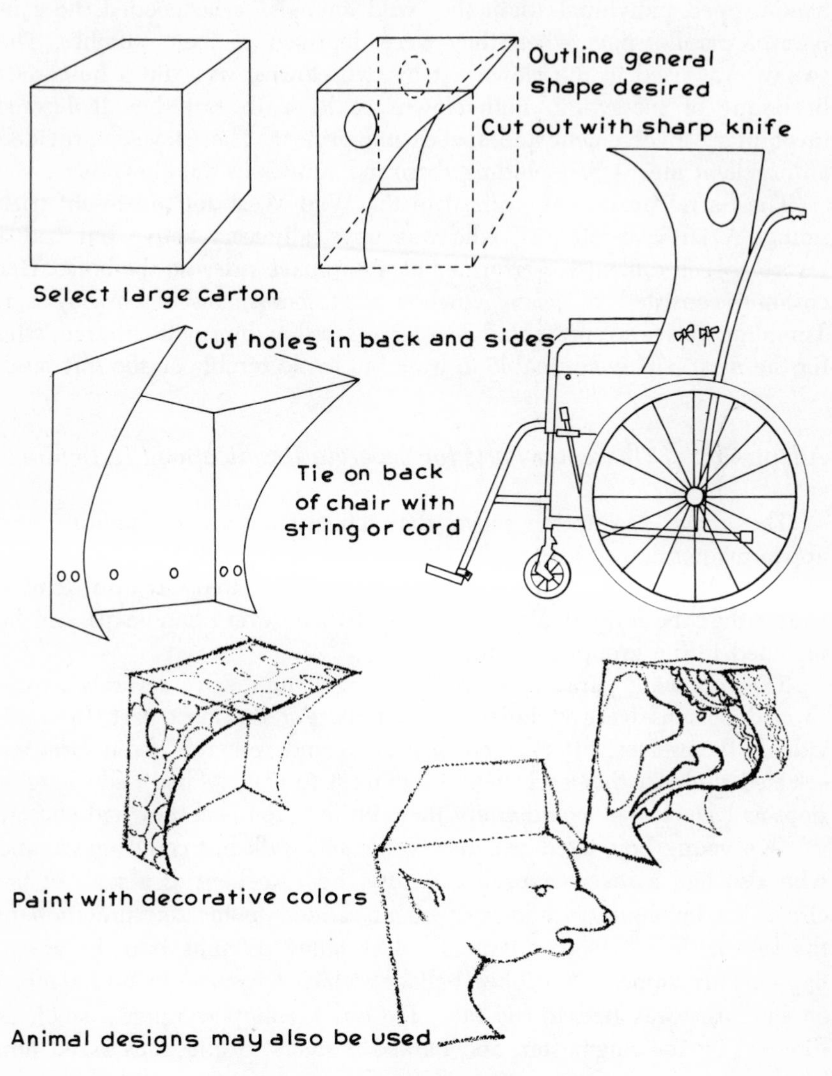
CIRCUS
Outline general shape desired
Cut out with sharp knife
Select large carton
Cut holes in back and sides
Tie on back of chair with string or cord
Paint with decorative colors
Animal designs may also be used

Decorating a wheel chair for a circus.

were used for the trapeze artists who performed simple tricks on them. The "tricks" were simple climbing, swinging, or chinning, but in trapeze costumes the performers were very effective. These performers were less handicapped individuals than the "wild animals," who needed the support of parallel bars when they were deprived of their crutches. The seesaw was used in the clown act by two clowns, who did a humorous burlesque of seesawing. Both clowns could walk, but they had some involuntary involvement and speech impairment. The tricycles provided an excellent means of including these individuals in the clown act.

The barrel horse was utilized in the Wild West act to present trick riding. A ten-year-old girl, who was physically very active but had a severe speech difficulty, performed as a bareback rider on the horse. Her costume consisted of jeans, cowboy shirt, boots, and a cowboy hat. Tumbling acts were presented in a large sandbox by small children, who for the most part were unable to walk but could tumble on the soft sand.

Adaptation of Character Parts for Severely Handicapped Individuals

The above description shows that the existing space, facilities, and apparatus normally used for the treatment of the physically handicapped can actually become assets in the creation of a circus. It also demonstrates that the individuals, regardless of their severe handicaps, can be included in the group as performers.

The following paragraphs explain how a number of severely handicapped persons were included in a circus. For the most part, the individuals themselves, after much discussion and research about circuses, selected the part that each would like most to play. Many made suggestions as to how they could adapt themselves to the part they had chosen.

One young boy, aged ten, who could not walk but could crawl, and who also had a severe speech difficulty, was excellent as a seal. In the circus his involuntary jerky movements added to his interpretation of the seal as he crawled out in his black shiny costume into the arena, flapping his flippers. A rubber balloon, which appeared to be balanced on his nose, was tied to his face. He put his flippers upon a stool, as directed by the ringmaster, and barked answers to questions asked him by the ringmaster.

A girl of nineteen, who could walk but could not talk or use her arms or hands, was the tightrope walker. Because of the extreme involuntary motion in her arms, she habitually wore a laced band which fitted around her diaphragm and arms and held her arms down to her sides. Since her

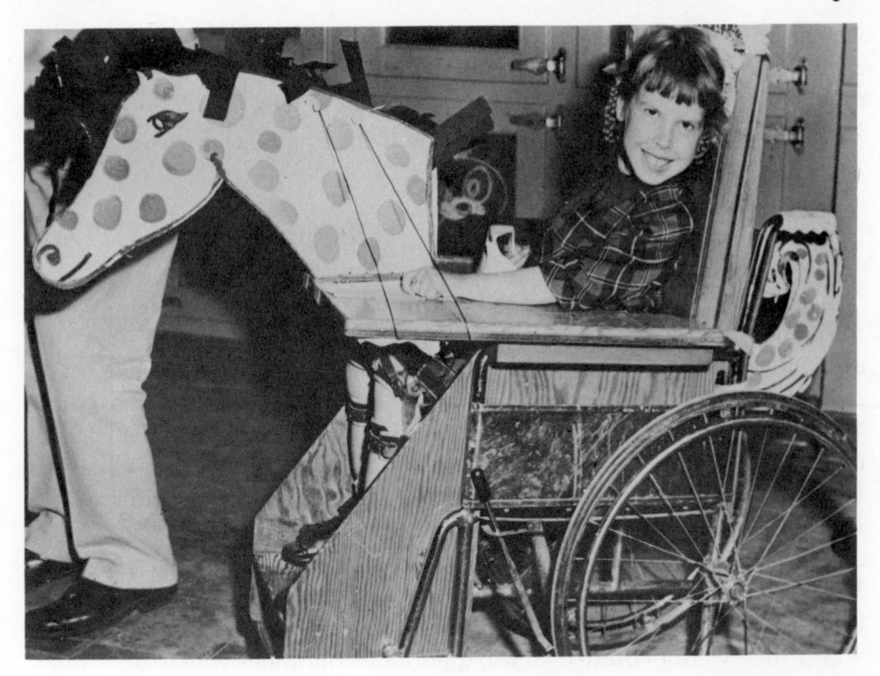

A severely handicapped child in a wheel chair becomes a dancing pony in a circus.

arms were held close to her body, she was forced to walk with a swaying movement, from side to side, and was most natural and effective as the tightrope walker, with the rope laid on the ground. Small umbrellas were tied to each of her hand braces to make her appear in a realistic balancing role.

A girl in her wheel chair made a wonderful "fat lady." Pillows and cardboard were used in her lap and fastened around her chair to create the necessary effect. The entire frame was then draped to cover the chair. Jewelry and bright make-up added to the girl's appearance. When she was pushed into the arena she was an amazingly realistic "fat lady." (See illustration on p. 286.)

The "strong man" was an eight-year-old boy on crutches. He lifted a "weight" which was made by attaching two large paper bags to a long stick. The bags were painted black with white numbers which read "2,000 lbs." Tattoos were painted on his arms and chest with washable tempera paint.

Two small children were Siamese twins. This effect was achieved by having the girls appear in one dress with heads together and inside arms around each other's waist. The girls were approximately the same size and height, and although they wore braces on their legs, they were able to walk without the use of crutches. They sang a song as part of their act and marched in the parade around the arena.

Decorated Wheel Day

Decorated Wheel Day is another special event which can be successfully used in a recreation program for the severely handicapped. It is fun, especially for those in wheel chairs, to decorate their chairs, while other individuals decorate wagons, tricycles, or their own crutches. Decorated Wheel Day provides an excellent opportunity for the handicapped and the nonhandicapped to be together, as demonstrated by an occasion when this event was cooperatively planned by a group of cerebral palsied individuals and the children attending a city playground.

The possibility of coordinating the activity was first discussed with both groups, and they were enthusiastic about it. The playground director then held a discussion with the children on the playground during which they were permitted to ask questions—questions which are always in the minds of nonhandicapped children when they see a handicapped child. Among them were "Is it catching?" "Do they hurt?" "Why can't they talk?" After reassuring them that cerebral palsy was only a condition, the director explained that the handicapped children were really more like them than unlike them and that they could all have fun together. After a further exchange of questions and opinions, one sage youngster of eight summed up the whole discussion when he said, "I understand; God made them that way." The group accepted this and began to prepare for the event. The experience confirmed the observation that with proper orientation nonhandicapped children will accept handicapped persons more readily than do some adults.

The morning of Decorated Wheel Day was spent by both groups in decorating their "wheels." Each handicapped child was responsible, insofar as he was able, for decorating his own wheel chair, crutches, wagon, tricycle, or doll buggy. Some individuals were able to wind crepe paper through the spokes of their wheel chairs or around their crutches, while others were only able to help as a part of the group. However, all could make suggestions, select their own colors and types of decorations, and assist in some phase of the decorating process.

The handicapped children were brought by bus from the school to the park, where they joined the playground group. The program for the

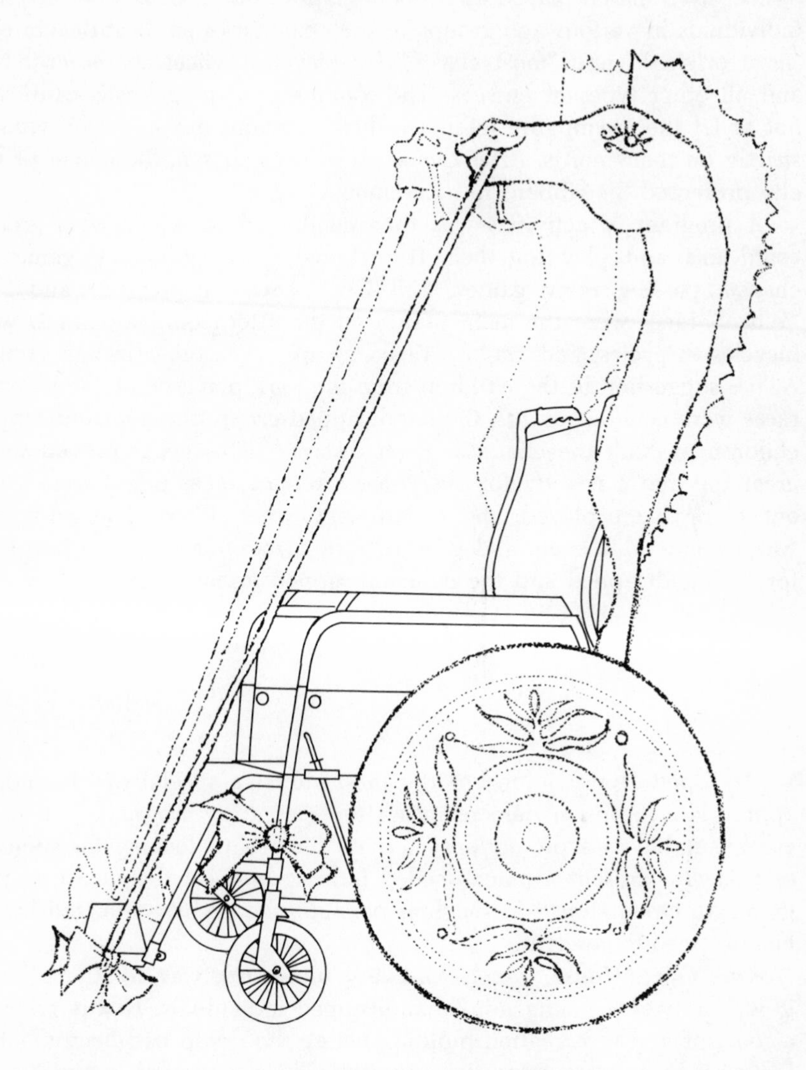

DECORATED WHEEL DAY

afternoon began with a grand parade in which each person paraded his "wheel" to a march played on a phonograph. Blue ribbons were given to individuals in various age groups in such categories as "best decorated," "most original," and "most clever," for bicycles, wheel chairs, crutches, and all other types of entrees. The committee of judges was cautioned not to let their sympathy influence their decisions but to select winners strictly on their merits. After the winners were chosen, the mayor of the city presented the ribbons in a ceremony.

A program of activities was then conducted, in which both groups could mix and play together. It included guessing games, games of chance, passing relay games, and Give. (See Chapters 21 and 22.) "Wheel" races were the main feature of the afternoon. Individuals with bicycles, tricycles, and wagons raced against each other in age groups. At the suggestion of the children from the park playground, wheel chair races were conducted with the handicapped group, the nonhandicapped children pushing the chairs a given distance. This event proved to be great fun and a novelty for everyone. After the races prizes were given out, games were played, and refreshments were served. The entire day was a memorable event and proved to be a most successful opportunity for the handicapped and the nonhandicapped to have fun together.

Open House

An Open House is one of the most effective special events and an appropriate means of demonstrating the recreation program. It is especially suitable as a promotional activity for groups looking for sponsors or trying to present a much-needed interpretation of their existing program. An Open House, as much as possible, should be conducted by the handicapped themselves.

One Open House, which was very successful, was conducted by a group of twenty young adult handicapped individuals. It was given in a room of a city recreation building where the group had been meeting for several weeks for recreation activities. The group made the invitations and mailed them to friends, current sponsors, community clubs, and various groups. The activities at the Open House included the presentation of a play written and produced by the group and exhibits of their work in arts and crafts and painting. As a result of actually seeing what this group had achieved, many visitors had a better understanding of the recreation program and became aware of the need for its continuance.

Planning council—children and young adults plan their own activities.

CHAPTER 20

Clubs and Interest Groups

Club activities, general and special interest groups, and hobbies play an important part in a well-rounded recreation program. Many activities of the handicapped as well as the nonhandicapped are organized on a club basis, and clubs are popular with children, young people, and adults. In some cities handicapped individuals and groups utilize for their group meetings facilities, leadership, and equipment furnished by the public recreation department.

Values

Club activities offer the handicapped a rare opportunity to learn self-government and to acquire the techniques and skills essential for effective leadership. As previously mentioned, many handicapped persons, lacking formal education, have had no opportunity to participate in student government and are only vaguely aware of the workings of the democratic process. They have not had the experience of undertaking the responsibilities or of performing the duties of committee members or of sharing in a creative group process. Club activities provide a natural means whereby handicapped teen-agers can set standards for their own conduct and solve their own problems. Teen-age clubs with handicapped or nonhandicapped members need considerable guidance, but the leader should encourage them to develop their capacity for self-leadership.

Club groups usually elect officers, charge a membership fee, and adopt a constitution and by-laws which define their purpose and the responsibility of the members. Formation of a club not only tends to stimulate greater interest in the activities and to encourage unity among the members, but the club meetings provide opportunities for self-expression and cooperative planning and action.

Types of Clubs

Some clubs are organized around a particular interest; others are formed by groups primarily for the purpose of being and doing things together. Both objectives prompted the organization of a group of handicapped teen-agers as "The Real Cool Cats," whose primary interest was in conducting parties and dances. The theme for one dance was "Autumn Twist Around the World." The dance area was decorated for the event with streamers, autumn leaves, and posters depicting scenes and people from other countries. Each person twisted in a costume representing the country of his choice.

Special interest groups usually result when several persons express an interest in a certain activity such as photography, sewing, or journalism. Unlike the general interest club, whose members are usually in the same age range, many special interest clubs have members in different age groups. For example, one group of handicapped adults, whose ages ranged from twenty-one to fifty, became interested in painting with water color and oils. As a group, they were invited to show their paintings at the San Francisco Art Festival, and although their paintings were no better than average, the members enjoyed being together and sharing a common interest.

One of the greatest values of special interest groups, whose appeal commonly centers in a particular hobby, is the opportunity they afford the handicapped person to acquire or develop an interest which he can pursue at home. Such interests and hobbies can help to enrich the everyday life of handicapped persons who have a great deal of leisure, oftentimes spent alone. Hobbies cover a wide range of activities, and among the various types conducted by public recreation departments there are certain to be some that appeal to the handicapped. Some departments maintain hobby centers, where skilled leadership is provided in activities such as photography and art.

Hobbies may be considered to be of four fundamental types, although these overlap and can be broken down into groups and subgroups:

1. Those which acquire knowledge; i.e., literary and study clubs.
2. Those which collect things; i.e., stamps, phonograph records, and so on.
3. Those which encourage creativity; i.e., sculpture, creative writing, and so on.
4. Those which encourage performance; i.e., archery, chamber music ensembles, and so on.

Selected Activities

Types of activities for clubs and special interest groups are as varied as the field of human interest. Each particular group selects activities peculiar to its own needs and desires. Following are accounts of groups that have been formed to engage in reading, writing, speaking, and service projects, four activities that have achieved popularity in a number of handicapped programs.

Reading

Literary activities have been extremely popular with young and older adult handicapped groups, particularly those with members whose educational backgrounds have been quite limited. Some adults have actually learned to read in an informal educational program, and many have improved their reading, writing, and speaking skills. One group requested instruction in reading, writing, basic grammer, spelling, and arithmetic. Instructors were provided by the Adult Education Department, and participants were able to earn high school credits. The group thoroughly enjoyed reading aloud and progressed from simple short stories, poems, and plays to the study and reading of Shakespeare. They also enjoyed reading to one another, and some of them were eventually able to assist the leaders by reading stories to tiny tots.

Writing

Writing is a tremendous outlet for creative expression, and writing for fun can bring a great deal of personal satisfaction. Because a handicapped person has spent most, or all, of his life in a wheel chair or a bed, however, it does not necessarily mean that he is capable of writing for publication. Handicapped persons interested in writing should be encouraged to channel their efforts into areas where they can find satisfaction such as the writing of short stories and poetry.

The desire or need for some type of publication provides an incentive for groups interested in expressing creative ideas to undertake the study of journalism. One group of twenty-five severely handicapped adults expressed an interest in publishing a newspaper for the Recreation Center, which they chose to call the *Center Highlights*. With the help of a staff advisor, the group organized themselves to function with a business manager and news and feature writers.

ADAPTATIONS. Most of the members were severely physically handicapped as a result of cerebral palsy. A number were bedfast with severe speech impairments which made communication most difficult. Some were unable to read or write because of the lack of formal education, and only a few were physically able to type or write. Each member of the group, however, assumed some responsibility for the publication of the paper. For example, those who were able wrote or typed the copy

Publishing a newspaper.

for others as it was dictated to them. Some who could not type stencils were able to work the hand-operated mimeograph machine; others assembled, stapled, and stamped the paper for mailing. One boy, aged sixteen, was able to type with a special head attachment. A bedfast person who was unable to speak or to use his hands but could nod his head to indicate yes and no, expressed a desire to design a cover for the teen-age publication. This was achieved through the help of the advisor, who worked with him for many hours looking through magazines to find designs he liked. He then indicated, by various yeses and noes, certain combinations of designs he wished and their location on the cover sheet.

MATERIALS PUBLISHED. For the most part, the participants were interested in writing about themselves, their experiences, and the activities conducted at the Center. Specifically, they enjoyed writing features such as gossip columns and special articles such as "Volunteers of the Month," features about the staff, original short stories, and poetry. "The History of the Center" was a special project. Writing editorials was also a popular activity because it enabled them to express opinions about various subjects. Writing news articles and designing art work for covers were other activities of the group.

The benefits of writing activities for the handicapped were numerous. Many of them improved noticeably their style of writing; some discovered abilities for writing poetry and short stories. All who participated improved in their reading and writing skills, while some learned the techniques of interviewing, observing, and research. An introduction to journalism was the incentive for one handicapped young adult to enter college and study creative writing. Eventually, she was able to obtain the job of writing a local gossip column for a small-town newspaper.

Publishing the *Center Highlights* not only provided many of the participants with a worthwhile activity, but it was a source of real enjoyment for the group as well as the reader audience. The children, as well as the adults, enjoyed reading about themselves in the paper and were interested to learn of plans and activities conducted by other groups at the Center.

Playwriting and play production became a popular activity as a result of reading plays. Some members of the writing group wrote short plays which were ultimately produced by the group. Plays were also written by the entire group, which proved to be a great deal of fun.

Speaking

Some handicapped persons are thrilled with the opportunity to just sit and chat with one another. Consequently, informal conversations and discussion groups have been extremely popular with handicapped persons, even for those with whom it is difficult to communicate. Social conversation in the form of a "sharing" period was used with one group to encourage each person, even those with severe speech impairments, to share with other participants a highlight of his last week's experience. Discussion periods were also held during which participants were encouraged to select topics and which were then moderated by the person who suggested the topic selected for discussion. "What Causes Earthquakes?" "Should a Handicapped Person Marry Another Handicapped Person or a Nonhandicapped Person?" and "What Educational Value has TV?" are typical of the topics chosen.

One group discussion concerning social manners and good grooming resulted in a request from the group for an activity in Personal Grooming and Social Conduct. Specifically, the group asked to study and discuss "How to Dress for Different Occasions," "How to Entertain at Home," "How to Order from a Restaurant Menu, and How to Tip," "The Correct

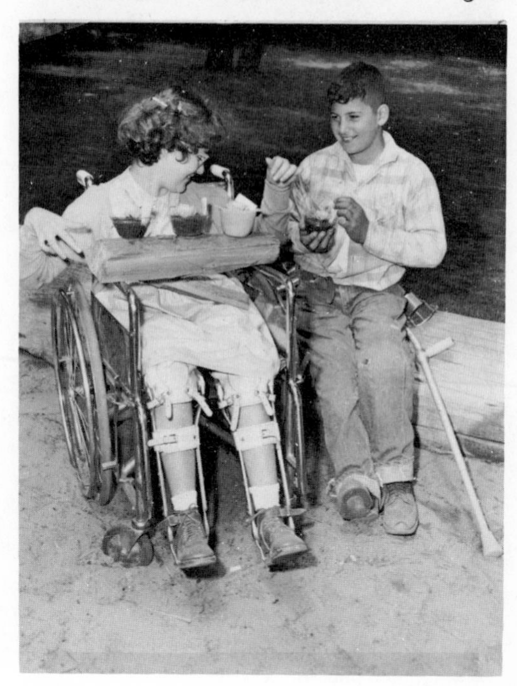

A service project — planting succulents for residents of an old folks home.

Use of Tableware," and "Good Manners at Home and in Public." Approximately six months were devoted to the study, demonstration, and discussion of each specific topic. During this time the group visited restaurants and were responsible for choosing, ordering, and paying for their own meals. In addition, group dinners were prepared by the participants, and guest speakers were invited to attend.

Service Projects

The handicapped, as all other people, need the opportunity to help others. Chapter 2 stressed the importance of providing service activities for the handicapped so that this basic need may be fulfilled. Many types of service activities are suitable for all groups as well as for individuals of all ages. Handicapped persons may be able to share a specific interest or skill with other members of a recreation program. For example, persons skilled in pottery, music, storytelling, or other areas may lead a group or assist the recreation staff in such activities. Service projects are especially suited to group activity, as each participant can contribute in some way to the total effort. One such project for persons in a home for

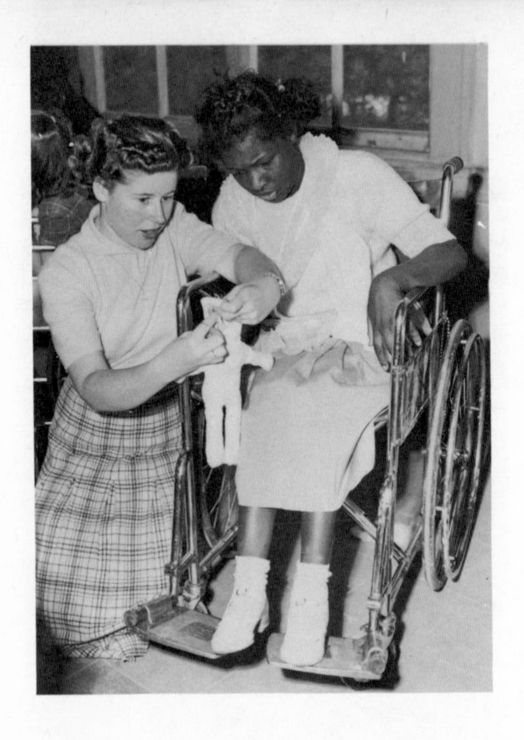

Another community service project—making dolls for the infant shelter.

the aged was undertaken by a group of fifteen handicapped pre-teen children. The children first made pottery bowls, which they designed themselves and then potted with succulents and other plants which they presented to the residents of the home. Another group made bed trays for patients at the local Crippled Children's Hospital. A group of twenty-five handicapped adults enjoy Christmas caroling each year in a convalescent home for elderly women.

The organization and use of an advisory council in a recreation program make possible a valuable service project. The council serves the dual purpose of giving participants in the program a share in planning and carrying out the activities and in evaluating the results. Such an advisory council at the Recreation Center consisting of representatives from various age groups plans with the staff the over-all program of the Center. The committees and subcommittees are particularly active in long-range planning and in preparing for special events such as circuses, carnivals, Christmas pageants, and others which appeal to children as well as adults. Standing committees include Invitation and Publicity, Decorations, Games and Activities, Refreshments, and Clean Up. The council has adopted by-laws and has established a nominal membership fee for each participant in the program. Although activities are planned and conducted within each respective age group, the council has been invaluable in establishing certain procedures, standards, and policies for the over-all program. (See illustration on p. 295.)

A Strike!

CHAPTER 21

Active Games and Sports

One of the basic drives of man is for physical activity; it is a fundamental function of life. Handicapped persons need not be deprived of opportunities for fulfilling this urge, so games and sports should be an important phase of every recreation program for them. Even though activities may have to be adapted, persons with physical limitations can derive a great many of the benefits experienced by all other people from participation in active games and sports.

Objectives

Enjoyment, satisfaction, accomplishment, and fellowship are primary objectives of sports programs for this group as for the nonhandicapped. Additional objectives include the improvement of skills in a specific sport, the practice of leadership, and the development of good physical and mental health habits. To participate in a wide variety of games, sports, and athletics, to learn fundamental motor skills, to plan games and sports programs, and to have freedom of choice in the activity itself are important values of games and sports for everyone.

Experience with the physically handicapped has indicated that the majority of them have been deprived of opportunities to participate in games and sports or in physical recreation of any kind. Many persons associated with the handicapped, including parents and teachers, seem to believe that they cannot take an active part in physical recreation. As a result, many handicapped persons who have been greatly sheltered are not aware that they can actually have fun taking part in games and sports. This situation is particularly prevalent among older persons. Handicapped children at a very early age should be given every possible opportunity for physical recreation in school and out, the same as all other children.

Stafford states that "sports and games give expression in a socially accepted manner, to those more primitive forces which have been suppressed by the necessities of modern society. The experiences and training which one receives in sports and games are indispensable to the well-adjusted personality. If these are necessary for normal individuals, they are even more necessary for the handicapped who have frustrations to overcome."[1]

[1] George T. Stafford, Ed. D., *Sports for the Handicapped* (New York: Prentice-Hall, 1950), p. 5.

An encouraging tendency on the part of some schools today is the establishment of adapted games and sports programs for the atypical student. Emphasis is being placed on their recreative value rather than on their corrective value. According to Stafford, "the objective is the education of the whole individual. It has in mind the adjustment of the student to his defect and to his environment. Many of the student's desires, urges and drives find healthful expression through adapted sports."[2]

Particular Values

The inherent values of games and sports are numerous, but one of the greatest benefits for the handicapped is the opportunity to learn good sportsmanship. Recreation leaders have repeatedly been appalled at their lack of understanding of fair play, respect for the rules of the game, and tolerance for group decisions. Handicapped persons who have been overly protected and sheltered have not been taught that they can't always win. Through games and sports, they learn to be good losers, to take turns, and to have consideration for others. Games and sports for the handicapped also offer opportunities for them to develop and to practice leadership. This is of great benefit to some handicapped persons who have strong leadership abilities but have had little or no chance to exercise them. Physical activity not only enlarges the scope of recreation pursuits for the handicapped, but it helps them to acquire the skills needed in vocational and trade training.

Experience has also indicated that participation in forms of active recreation under qualified leadership is beneficial to the health and physical condition of handicapped persons. For example, a group of multiple handicapped children at the Recreation Center, aged seven to twelve, showed noticeable improvement in physical coordination and in quality and speed in walking after participation in a program of active games over a period of several years. Some children using crutches learned to walk at almost a running speed by playing baseball. Others acquired the ability to move about freely and confidently in their wheel chairs.

Suggested Adaptations

Most structured games and sports activities were created for non-handicapped persons, but certain variations and modifications may be made in most of them so that the handicapped will derive the kind of

[2] *Ibid.*, p. 44.

fun and physical recreation which the activity was intended to provide. However, when adapting activities, leaders should approximate the true game situation as nearly as possible. The less change made in an activity, the more will handicapped persons feel that they are like others. Leaders should keep in mind (1) that adaptations should be made to suit the *physical ability* rather than the *disability*, and (2) that many handicapped persons and groups can themselves suggest adaptations. Some persons will be able to participate easily in one type of activity, while others will do better in another. As is true of the nonhandicapped, personal likes and preferences vary with individuals. In all instances, health and safety measures and special precautions indicated for each individual should be strictly observed.

The general principles governing adaptations discussed in Chapter 6 apply also to modification in games and sports. However, some specific suggestions may be helpful for leaders.

1. Substitute walking, "wheeling," or rolling (a bed for example) for running or skipping.

2. Use a bounce, a roll, or an underhand toss to replace throwing. Catching and batting may be modified in the same way. For example, a person in a wheel chair may be allowed to hit the ball by holding the bat on the side of his chair and swinging at a ball rolled to him by the pitcher. In tennis, a player may be permitted to hit the ball on the second or third bounce.

3. Substitute sitting down, kneeling, or lying down for standing. For example, a postpolio boy on crutches found that he could bat exceedingly well from a kneeling position. Some persons have been able to bowl from a lying down position.

4. Decrease distances as in horseshoes, ring toss, baseball, tennis, or volleyball.

5. Reduce the size of playing field, court, or area.

6. Restrict player or players to a definite place or position.

7. Substitute lighter and more easily controlled equipment. Balls, bats, duck pins, bowling balls, and many other such equipment may be purchased in plastic materials, which have been used successfully with handicapped persons. Plastic equipment is easy for them to manipulate, and it is practical and safe for playing indoors in small areas. Some persons who use crutches find that they can bat very well with a crutch and are therefore ready to "run" when the ball is hit.

8. Allow players to hit the ball any number of times, as in volleyball.

9. Permit players to hold the ball for a longer period of time, as in basketball.

10. Permit other players to run or to be wheeled for the batter. For example, persons who bat from a kneeling position need a runner.

Selected Games and Sports

There is a vast library of published material concerning games, sports and athletics, and there are numerous and various ways to classify them. Many of these activities are of such a varied nature and so interrelated that they may be classified under two or more headings. Games and sports may be classified by their space requirements, by the type of equipment used, by sex and age of persons and groups participating, by seasons, by degree of organization, and in many other ways. Major headings selected for discussion in this chapter are: (1) Low-Organized Games and Activities, (2) Individual and Dual Games and Sports, (3) Team Games and Sports. The few activities described under each classification afford examples of adaptations and illustrate types of games and sports that have been enjoyed by handicapped groups.

Low-Organized Games and Activities

Low-organized games are simple informal games that are played without official rules. They include many of the traditional children's games that vary with local customs and in different sections of the country. They are very popular on playgrounds. They can be played by small or large groups, both indoors or out. There are literally thousands of such games that can be adapted to all age groups, including adults. They offer opportunities for young children to learn basic game skills and coordination and serve as lead-up activities for the more highly organized group games and team sports. The low-organized games selected for discussion here are: (1) line games, (2) circle games, (3) relay races. The games described under each category were selected for physically handicapped persons. Comparable adaptations can be made in other similar games, which are described in books listed in the Bibliography.

Line Games

Descriptions of two line games follow.

RED LIGHT—10 to 15 players. Players stand on starting line and "it" stands about thirty feet away with his back turned and eyes closed. "It" counts out loud to ten and then says "Red Light." He then turns so that he can see the players. As "it" starts to count, players walk, run, or wheel toward "it" but must not be seen moving by "it" when he turns. All who are seen moving are sent back to the starting line. The action continues until some player advances close enough to touch "it." This player is next "it." Wheel chairs can be pushed by other children if a child is unable to wheel his own chair. The player reaching the starting line wins.

STATUES—10 to 15 players. The players are lined up in a single row, either standing or sitting. "It" stands about twenty feet in front. Each player demonstrates the statue or pose he will assume. "It" turns his back to the players, counts ten, and turns to observe players. Any player whom he sees moving, or whose pose is not like that demonstrated, exchanges places with "it." If "it" has difficulty turning himself around, he may be allowed to close his eyes and count to ten.

Circle Games

Fox and Squirrel and Crown the King are two circle games that have proved popular with the handicapped.

FOX AND SQUIRREL—10 to 20 players form a circle, either sitting or standing. Objects such as toy animals, bean bags, or rubber balls are given to two players opposite each other in the circle. One player is the fox and the other is the squirrel. At the signal "Go," players pass the fox around the circle, trying to overtake the squirrel. The fox may change his direction at any time. The squirrel must be careful to change his direction too, or he will be overtaken by the fox.

CROWN THE KING—10 to 20 players. All the players except two form a circle. One player is King, and he sits on a stool, chair, or wheel chair in center of circle; the other player stays in the circle and acts as guard. The players in the circle have a soft ball or a balloon with which they attempt to crown (hit) the King or his chair. The guard protects the King. However, if someone hits the King, he becomes guard, the guard becomes King, and the King goes to the circle, and the game is repeated.

Relay Races

Two well-known relays are:

BEAN BAG TOSS RELAY. The players sit or stand in line formation, with an equal number on each team. A large circle is drawn on the floor or ground about ten feet in front of each line. If the children have difficulty in moving about, a "runner," who stands at the circle, should be provided by each team. The first player of each team has two or three bean bags. At the starting signal the two players try to toss the bean bags, one after the other, into the circle. One or more points may be given for each bag resting in the circle or on the line. After the last bag is thrown, the player or "runner" for the team picks up the bean bags and gives them to the second player in line. After all players have thrown the bags, the winning team is declared by the highest score. Extra points may be given for the team that finished first.

ZIGZAG RELAY. Players sit on floor in zigzag formation. A rubber ball or volleyball is given to the first player. At the signal, the ball is rolled from player to player. When the end player receives the ball he rolls it back immediately. The team wins that first gets the ball back to the starting player.

Individual and Dual Games and Sports

One of the greatest values of individual and dual games and sports for the hadicapped as well as for others lies in the fact that they can be enjoyed at any level of skill and participation. They are excellent recreation activities, as they can be enjoyed by persons of both sexes and of almost all ages. Persons participating in such games and sports develop interests and skills that may continue throughout a lifetime. Dual games and sports, in particular, offer realistic opportunities for competition to even the most severely handicapped person. They also provide the basis for competition between individuals or groups in tournaments or contests, and can be correlated with other activities.

The following selection of individual and dual games and sports merely suggests some activities that have been enjoyed by a variety of handicapped individuals on crutches, in wheel chairs, or on beds and reclining chairs. Safety precautions, as always, should be observed.

Archery

Various types of indoor and outdoor archery can be adapted for handicapped individuals who are able to use their arms and hands. For example, the distance to the target may be shortened, and the weight of the bow modified. Wheel-chaired persons should be placed in a diagonal toward the target so as to allow greater space for the bow. Indoor archery in which small bows and arrows with suction cups are used can be played by persons lying on their backs or sides. Archery is considered an excellent activity for persons with partial or no vision, provided they have had the opportunity to inspect the equipment and have been given sufficient instruction in the game.

Badminton

Official rules may be used except for the number of players and for modification in the service. Four players on each side are recommended, particularly if all persons are in wheel chairs. The forward two players alternate on the service and the back two players rotate by moving forward to receive when the service goes to the other side. A form of badminton can also be played by substituting balloons for the shuttlecock and by using paddle tennis paddles instead of the regular badminton rackets.

Bicycling

Bicycling can be enjoyed by even severely handicapped persons. Tandem bicycles are particularly useful because children even with heavy braces can ride on the back seat by having their feet strapped on the bicycle.

Boating and Canoeing

Boating and canoeing are enjoyed by both children and adults, including handicapped persons even though they are in wheel chairs or in beds. Persons in wheel chairs who are able to propel themselves should be able to row; others who can control only one paddle still enjoy the feel of rowing. Even the blind and partially sighted have no special difficulty in learning to row. Special safety measures essential for all types of handicapped persons in boating programs include the wearing of life jackets as well as continuous alertness on the part of a sufficient number of qualified leaders.

Severely handicapped children getting ready for a tandem bicycle ride.

Bowling

Bowling is one of the most popular activities for the handicapped and is easily adapted for them, whether played as a table game, on the green, or in the bowling alley. Bowling in public facilities offers an excellent opportunity for the handicapped to participate with the nonhandicapped, and bowling clubs are popular among handicapped teen-agers and adults. The standard rules of the game are usually applied, with minor adaptations. Players using crutches may be able to balance themselves well enough on one crutch to bowl from a standing position, while others may have to sit in a chair or on the floor. Persons in wheel chairs or even in beds have played the game by using one or two hands to throw or roll the ball from the side of the chair or bed; others direct the ball by holding it between their feet. Players in a standing or a seated position may also be allowed to use their feet entirely to roll or push the ball. Lighter balls are commonly substituted for the standard balls. Ramps may also be designed to fit a chair or a bed so that the ball may be rolled down the lane. In public facilities, rubber floor mats are often recommended to prevent participants from slipping and wheel chairs, crutches, and heavy braces from marring the floors. Persons with partial or no vision should require few if any adaptations after they have been introduced to the game and have explored the area. Teams of sightless bowlers have been organized throughout the United States, and many of them have established excellent bowling records.

Croquet

Croquet is an excellent social activity, especially suitable for the handicapped to play with the nonhandicapped. Plastic equipment may be purchased, which is easier for some handicapped persons to manipulate, and persons with crutches may be allowed to use them as mallets. It may be necessary to allow more space between the wickets near the stakes so that people in wheel chairs can move in close enough to drive the ball.

Fishing

Fishing is enjoyed equally by very young children and very old adults. A fishing program can include a wide variety of activities which can be correlated with other phases of the program, such as arts and

Fishing is more fun with homemade fishing poles.

A blind multiple handicapped boy learned to putt.

crafts and camping. Children especially enjoy learning about fish, looking for bait, and making their own fishing gear. Even handicapped children can select their own poles, learn casting and fly and leader tying and how to put on the bait. Persons who have difficulty with hand coordination or a great deal of involuntary motion have more success by using drop lines or simple throw lines, which can be easily made. Fishing lends itself to contests, fishing derbies, and overnight outings, all of which are enjoyed by the handicapped.

Golf

The regular game of golf can be played only by persons in good physical condition, but adaptations such as putting and driving, clock golf, and miniature golf are enjoyable for handicapped persons. In *Active Games and Contests,* Mason and Mitchell[3] have described other variations such as bingo golf, croquet golf, sidewalk golf, and marble and hockey golf, all of which can be adapted to the handicapped. Persons using crutches may have to drive with one hand or from a seated position. Persons in wheel chairs may need a longer handle for driving, particularly if they cannot bend over. The use of a plastic golf ball may be of help to those who have little strength in their hands and arms. Visually handicapped persons enjoy golf or golf adaptations particularly as a social activity with the nonhandicapped.

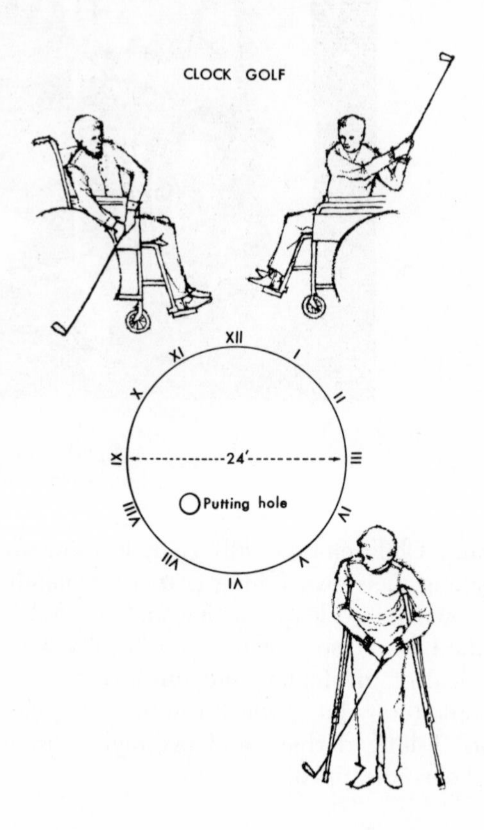

[3] Bernard S. Mason, Ph.D. and Elmer D. Mitchell, Ph.D., *Active Games and Contests* (New York: Barnes, A.S., 1935), pp. 127–130.

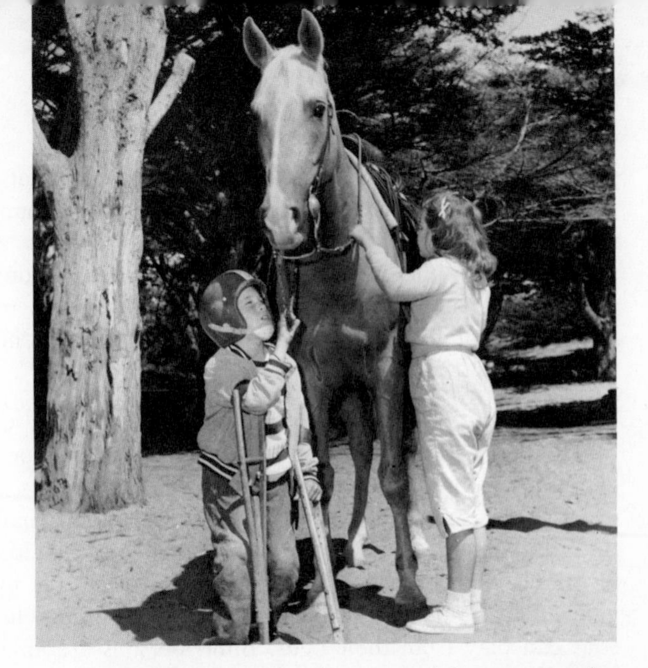

Horseback riding has been one of the most popular events for the severely handicapped. A blind girl mounts while a cerebral palsied boy holds the horse.

CLOCK GOLF. Clock Golf (see p. 314) has been most popular with a group of severely handicapped persons. It is essentially a putting game and can be played in small spaces in backyards, on the lawn, or on the ground. A circle twenty to twenty-four feet is drawn on the ground. Twelve numbers or markers are placed at regular intervals, representing the twelve numerals on the face of a clock. The markers can be tin cans with numbers painted on the bottoms set into the ground so that they are flush with the surface. The putting hole is placed off center within the circle so that the distances vary for each shot. The game consists of trying to get the ball into the hole from each numeral, starting with the one o'clock marker and so on around the clock. The object is to "hole out" from each successive numeral in the fewest number of putts. When everyone has played around the clock, the player with the lowest number wins. Contestants may play independently or with partners.

Horseback Riding

Horseback riding can be enjoyed by severely handicapped persons even if they have to be held on the horse. Horseback riding proved to be one of the most popular activities for a group of severely handicapped children aged seven to nineteen, none of whom had ridden a horse or a pony before. Members of a horseman's club brought their horses to the day-camp site so that the children could ride around the grounds. In most instances the horses were led by their owners, and in cases where the child had difficulty sitting up, another person rode in the same saddle to hold him on. Blind children and adults have been quite proficient at horseback riding, and it is considered one of their most popular sports.

Horseshoes and Ring Toss

Horseshoes and ring toss are easily adaptable for all types of handicapped persons. Usually the only modification necessary is to reduce the distances between the stakes in horseshoes and from the target in ring toss. Rubber or plastic equipment is easier to manipulate for some persons, and bean bags are suitable for illustrating the tossing motion. Both games can be played sitting down or in reclining chairs, and some persons can play from their beds. Blind persons are able to play more successfully if some type of noisemaker is installed at the horseshoe stakes and on the ring toss pegs.

Kite Flying

All children should have the opportunity to make and fly their own kites, and handicapped children are no exception to this rule. Kite flying is a very popular sport among a group of severely handicapped children who enjoyed making their kites as well as flying them. When kite flying was introduced to the program, teen-agers as well as adults expressed considerable interest in the activity because they had never before had the opportunity to make or fly a kite. Many handicapped persons need help to put their kites in the air and to keep them up; however, their thrill in holding a kite when it is flying is worth the effort. Blind persons require little if any adaptations, especially after they have received thorough instructions and have become quite familiar with the playing area.

Marbles

The official game of marbles requires good hand coordination and sight, but some handicapped persons can play the game, while others may participate in variations such as Marble Football.

Table Tennis

Table tennis, which is a type of tennis played on a table, has been very popular with the wheel-chaired and others who have the use of at least one arm or hand. Standard equipment is usually suitable for most persons, but equipment may be adapted. For example, larger paddles may be of help to some, and securing a shield along the edges of the table near the net helps to prevent balls from bouncing off the table. The shield should be approximately four feet long and twelve inches high. Table tennis can be played by persons in bed or in reclining chairs, in which case the table usually must be shortened and adjusted to the height needed. An underhand shot may be used to start the volley. In all instances, the game can be played more successfully if someone who can move fast enough retrieves the ball for the handicapped players.

Shuffleboard

Shuffleboard can be played by persons who are able to use one or more limbs and can be played in a standing or seated position. Standard equipment can generally be used, but the distance may need to be shortened or widened. Persons unable to use their hands may be allowed to use the inside of their foot to push or kick the puck. Persons in wheel chairs should have their chairs stationary and on an angle, which allows for a stronger push of the puck. Persons in bed or reclining chairs may play from the side of the bed or chair. Partially sighted or blind persons can play shuffleboard after they have become familiar with the court and equipment. A sighted person is needed in most instances to inform the players of the location of the pucks. Table shuffleboard is also enjoyable for the blind and others with physical handicaps.

Swimming

A great deal has been written about swimming for the handicapped. Its therapeutic values are recognized to the extent that it is included in programs for the handicapped in hospitals, in special schools, and in adapted physical education programs. The American National Red Cross conducts swimming workshops for instructors of the ill and handicapped, and in some cities these programs are offered in cooperation with the National Recreation Association. Many public recreation departments became interested in recreation for the handicapped through swim programs, which they can offer more readily than some of the other activities. Many persons working with the handicapped believe swimming to be the recreation activity which is most applicable to persons with the widest range of physical disabilities.

In addition to its values, for all persons, swimming provides particular benefits for the handicapped. One of the greatest values is the opportunity for socialization with the nonhandicapped. Handicapped persons can enjoy swimming on an equal basis with others, and some have been successful in competitive aquatics. The bouyant effect of water is commonly recognized, and handicapped persons discover that they can move affected parts when immersed in the water. Learning to swim gives them a feeling of belonging and helps to maintain their contacts with the community environment. Swimming offers an opportunity for success in a sport, and the ability to swim means a great deal to a person who cannot engage in other sports such as skiing or skating. Through successful swimming experiences handicapped persons are further encouraged to participate in other types of recreation activities.

Many persons who use crutches and wheel chairs have well-developed shoulders and arms and consequently have a great deal of strength, which is an asset in swimming. Such persons often have little use of the hips and legs, but they are able to "crawl" with their arms. The side stroke may be used by those who have more strength in one side than the other; the breast stroke by those wishing a slower pace. Persons having upper limb involvement may find the use of swim fins helpful in propelling the body through the water. Some persons with this handicap have learned to wiggle their hips as a seal uses his tail, to facilitate this motion, but usually it is easier for them to swim on their stomach. Good breathing, of course, is essential. Persons who are more severely handicapped, such as bedfast individuals, have found real satisfaction by just being in the water.

In discussing methods of teaching swimming to the physically handicapped, the Connecticut Society for Crippled Children and Adults states that flotation devices may be a great aid in teaching, although they should not be overused. The Society contends that it is better for a handicapped person to use such a device and have his own independence than to have an instructor hovering over his every move. "This concept is especially important for the more severely handicapped persons who live in a world of braces, crutches, wheel chairs. The use of a flotation device opens up a whole new world to them."[4] Persons with partial vision and the blind may be taught diving and all of the various strokes. However, it is of utmost importance that the blind person have a thorough understanding of his surroundings, such as the shallow and deep ends of the pool, drinking fountains, doors, and all other important landmarks. Instruction should not begin until he is completely familiar with

[4] Connecticut Society for Crippled Children and Adults, Report of Third Institute on *Swimming for the Physically Handicapped,* New Britain, Connecticut, April 1958, p. 14.

Swimming is one of the most beneficial activities for the handicapped.

his surroundings and his landmarks firmly located in his mind, so that he will feel secure in his every movement. An important point to remember is that the blind must feel the demonstrations, as they cannot see them; explanation alone is not enough. Detailed methods for teaching the blind to swim are outlined by Mathews, Kruse, and Shaw in *The Science of Physical Education for Handicapped Children.*[5]

Some persons with auditory difficulty have poor balance in the water and perform better by using back or side strokes. A modified stroke which permits the head to stay above water is often recommended for these persons, who should not get water in their ears.

Swimming is an activity that must be adapted to the individual, as each person differs in his ability to move. The type of movement that a handicapped person can make will determine to a large degree the type of stroke that is suitable for him. Daniels has compiled certain teaching techniques for instructors in aquatics programs, as follows:

1. The group method of instruction should be used when possible. It should be supplemented by individual instruction when necessary.
2. The instructor should use a wide variety of teaching aids and equipment in capturing and holding the learner's interest.
3. The instructor should be informal, with periods of short duration.
4. The standard rules of health and safety should be observed and supplemented by special policies when necessary.

[5] Donald K. Mathews, Robert Kruse, and Virginia Shaw, *The Science of Physical Education for Handicapped Children* (New York: Harper, 1962), pp. 52–55.

5. Students should be classified according to swimming ability. It is not necessary or desirable to classify for swimming . . . according to type of disability.
6. The swimming period should represent a good balance between instruction and recreation.
7. Pleasure and successful accomplishment should result from each . . . experience.[6]

A wide variety of stunts, contests, relays, and tag games may be included in the aquatics program for handicapped participants. It has been recommended that pool temperatures for most handicapped persons should be around 85 degrees. Hunt believes that cerebral palsied persons should have a temperature in the low 90's to relax tense muscles common to many such persons.[7]

Tobogganing

Tobogganing in wheel chairs has been a very popular sport with children of the Recreation Center. The sport was first introduced to a group of severely handicapped youngsters who had never been on snow trips before. The staff worked out adaptations so that even persons who were bedfast could participate in tobogganing from wheel chairs or beds and in other phases of fun in the snow, such as building snowmen and making snowballs.

Tether Ball

Tether ball can be played by persons who have only the use of one arm and hand and from standing or seated positions. Occupants of wheel chairs and reclining chairs may need to have the rope lengthened and to start farther away from the pole. Use of a long rope for the ball enables persons who have upper limb involvement to kick the ball in order to wind it around the pole, or a lighter ball may be used so that they can manipulate the head or shoulders to hit the ball. Persons confined to their beds may have more success in playing the table game of miniature tether ball. (Described under Table Games in Chapter 22.) Persons with partial vision (and those who are blind) may have more success with a lighter ball, but the use of a bell ball is recommended for persons with no vision.

[6] Arthur S. Daniels, *Adapted Physical Education* (New York: Harper, 1954), pp. 227–229.

[7] Valerie V. Hunt, *Recreation for the Handicapped* (New York: Prentice-Hall, 1955), pp. 146–148.

Team Games and Sports

One of the most important values of team games for the handicapped is that they provide individuals with opportunities to participate in an activity as an important member of an organized group. Furthermore, they enable a group of severely handicapped persons—for example, in wheel chairs—to learn to move about and function as a unit. In such group participation, individuals may learn to accept responsibility, to cooperate with their teammates, and to respect their opponents. In addition, they may be guided in developing such social qualities as loyalty, self-control, courtesy, obedience, and the desire to play according to the rules. In particular, team games provide an excellent opportunity for handicapped persons to develop a spirit of competition, which is difficult for them to experience as individuals. Like all beginners in team games and sports, they should progress first through a series of lead-up games such as relay races and contests so that they will acquire a knowledge of the rules and some ability to perform the basic skills of the sport.

Handicapped persons derive the same satisfactions and pleasures from watching team sports as all other persons. While watching games such as baseball or football the handicapped participate with the general public in an activity that has become an important phase of the American way of life.

Following are selected team games and sports that have been popular with handicapped groups.

Baseball

Baseball may be played by handicapped groups, but various modifications are usually necessary. For example, some persons may be unable to bat well, while others may have great difficulty in running or in catching or throwing the ball. The roles of umpire, scorekeeper, and coach, who are important members of the team, can be assumed frequently by the most severely handicapped person. The use of plastic equipment such as balls and bats makes it easier for many handicapped persons to play. Persons who use crutches may prefer to bat with a crutch so that they are ready to run when the ball is hit, whereas persons in wheel chairs may have someone run for them or push them to the bases. Individuals in wheel chairs may pitch from the side of their chairs, but persons using crutches often find they can pitch better by sitting on the ground or floor. Individuals who are unable to use their hands or arms but have the use of their feet may be umpires or scorekeepers, or runners for other players.

Learning the techniques of baseball from the pros.

These persons are quite able to play some of the variations of baseball such as kickball baseball. Besides participating as umpires, scorekeepers, or coaches, bedfast persons and those in reclining chairs have enjoyed keeping scrap books of their favorite team and players and have become ardent baseball fans as well as experts on the history and rules of the game.

Baseball has been adapted for blind persons with fair success. Buell discusses adaptations that are used in various schools for the blind.[8] A softball is rolled on the gravel area to the batter who must be listening for the rolling sound so that he can hit the ball. When he has hit the ball, he runs to a teammate who is calling him from first base. If a totally blind fielder catches the ball while it is rolling, the batter is out. A large inflated ball with a bell in it may be used and bounced to the batter. Fielding is the most difficult phase of baseball for blind players.

Basketball

Wheel chair basketball has become very popular, due in part to the wide publicity received by various teams who travel throughout the nation and abroad. Severely handicapped persons find this game difficult, but they can enjoy many variations of basketball, such as twenty-one,

[8] Charles E. Buell, *Sports for the Blind* (Ann Arbor, Mich.: Edwards Brothers, 1947), p. 69.

keep away, guard ball, and goal shooting. Persons using crutches find it easier to perform with one hand or to use both hands from a seated position. The basket may need to be lowered for persons playing while seated, as in wheel chairs. Portable hoops may be set up for persons in bed or reclining chairs, and large softballs or rubber balls are better for shooting baskets.

Soccer

Soccer as well as kick ball can usually be played successfully by persons who cannot use their hands and arms but can use their feet and move about freely. Players using crutches and those able to use their feet should be able to kick the ball. The position of goalie can be played by persons in wheel chairs, who can use their chairs to block the ball. If the goalie is unable to kick the ball back into play, another person may kick it in from out of bounds for him. Modifications of both kick ball and soccer are available in table games that can be played by persons in bed or reclining chairs.

Partially sighted or totally blind persons can play soccer if the players call out words to assist their teammates in locating the ball and if bell balls are used for the same purpose.

Volleyball

Variations in the playing rules are also necessary or desirable when volleyball is played by handicapped groups. For example, players who are greatly restricted in movement may be permitted to catch the ball rather than to bat it; those unable to serve may throw the ball into play or may be given assistance on the serve. Players with upper limb impairment are permitted to hit the ball with their shoulders or head. In some cases it is necessary to lower the net and to use a lighter ball.

Volley newcomb and giant volleyball are modified forms that have been played successfully by persons who are partially sighted or blind. The ball used in giant volleyball is a large Navy rescue balloon with small bells attached to the air intake. The bells jingle when the ball is in flight. The game is played on a regulation volley court.

BALLOON VOLLEYBALL. This game is a simplified variation which requires only a balloon and a string or rope which is stretched approximately six feet above the floor or ground to serve as the net. It can be played indoors or out by persons in wheel chairs or on crutches. The court may be marked off with sidelines, and a serving line should be determined six feet from each side of the net. The width of the court should be determined according to the number of players, their mobility, and the space available. A court eight feet wide is suggested for six players (three to a side). Players in wheel chairs may be permitted light-weight paddles in order to extend their reach. Persons may be allowed to use their crutch to hit the balloon, but should be careful not to hit other players. The standard rules and scoring system for volleyball may be used, although players may be allowed two attempts to get the ball over the net.

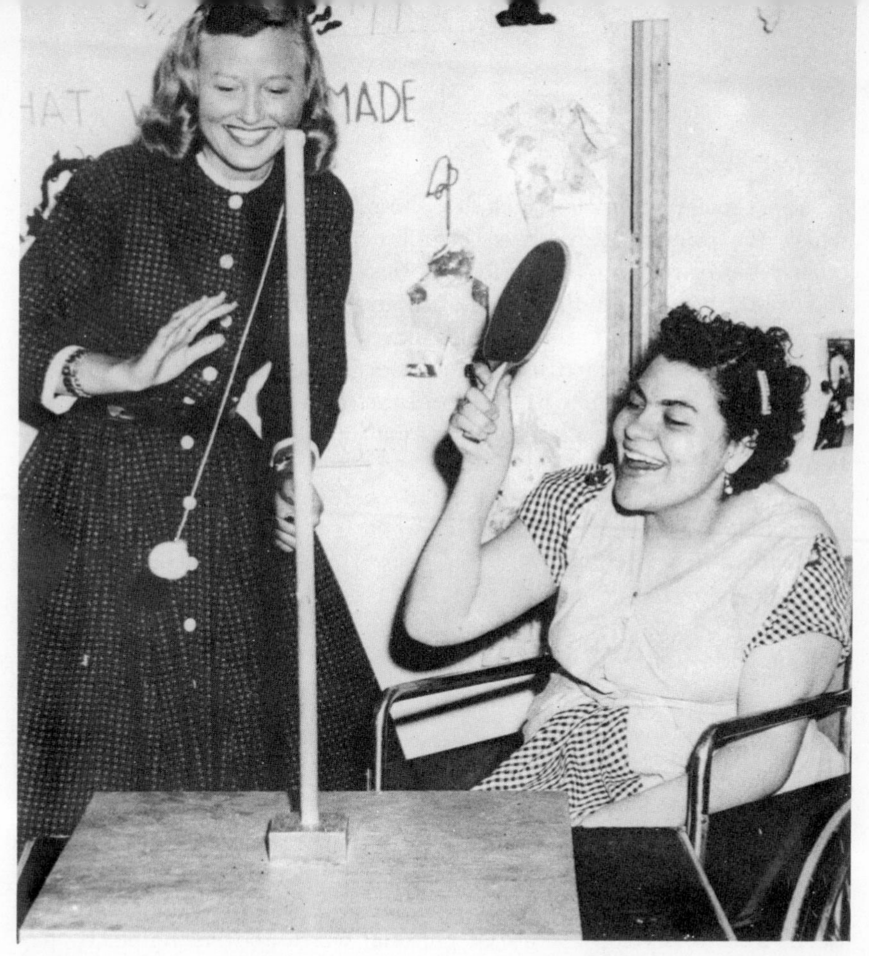

The author plays an adaptation of tether ball with a person in a wheel chair.

CHAPTER 22

Social Recreation

Social recreation includes those activities and experiences in which the primary purpose is sociability. Most persons engage in the other types of recreation described in this volume, such as drama, music, and sports because of their special interest in the activities themselves, although the enjoyment resulting from association with others in the activity may be a valued by-product. Social recreation activities, on the other hand, have as their basic appeal the satisfactions in fellowship and sociability which they afford to individuals as a direct result of participation in these activities.

The development of pleasant relationships among handicapped individuals by providing opportunities for them to engage in chosen activities with others having similar interests is one of the objectives of the recreation program. Social recreation, because of its informal approach, can be easily adapted for use with various age groups and by persons with a wide range of handicaps.

Values

A significant value of informal recreation for the handicapped lies in its opportunity for fulfilling their many social needs. For example, many handicapped persons have not had the opportunity to identify with others and to develop a sense of personal worth and belonging. By participating in social activities they can find satisfaction and enjoyment through contacts with other individuals. As previously mentioned, they are also frequently lacking in social graces. Those occasions when handicapped and nonhandicapped groups entertain one another, or when the handicapped welcome visitors to their programs, afford opportunities for instruction in social manners in order that the handicapped may feel at ease and enjoy the sociability of such events. Participation in such activities as parties and dances enables handicapped persons to find opportunities for self-expression, for emotional release, and for relaxation.

Few recreation activities can be adapted for use by persons with severe handicaps as easily as many forms of social recreation. Such adaptations do not always require advanced preparation on the part of the participants or leaders nor demand a predetermined level of performance.

Few types of social recreation require physical skills or special mobility; many of them, on the contrary, call primarily for quick mental reactions or for clear thinking. Many quiet group games enable handicapped individuals to enjoy group activity without the stress or strain that sometimes accompanies more highly competitive team play. Table games are usually played on an informal competitive basis, but the handicapped may be encouraged to improve their skill by the organization of tournaments, which also provide added interest in the activity. Unlike many activities in the recreation program which can be carried on successfully only by a group or under the guidance of a leader, some forms of social recreation such as card games, dominoes, or conversation can be enjoyed by two or more persons between scheduled group activities or for other brief periods. Puzzle solving can be a challenge to one individual or it can be shared with others. In fact, social recreation plays a significant though often secondary role in most phases of the recreation program, whether the activity be a dance, picnic, or holiday celebration.

Types of Activities

Social recreation functions through many different types of activities and special events. Activities include various types of games such as quiet, table, card, and others; informal drama such as skits, stunts, and charades; music such as singing and musical mixers; corecreation sports, arts and crafts of various types, and preparty activities. Special events include seasonal and special parties, banquets, suppers, outings, such as picnics, tea and coffee hours, and family recreation.

Three types of activities and events included in this section are quiet group games, table games, and parties.

Quiet Group Games

A few examples of quiet group games are described here.

GIVE. Give can be played by a variety of handicapped individuals of all ages and in groups as large as forty or more. Players are divided into teams, and each team has a captain; for example, if there are ten or twenty players, the group is divided into two groups with a captain or runner for each group. If there are more than twenty players, the group can be divided into three or four groups. The runner could be a person on crutches or in a wheel chair; however, the runners should be fairly equal in their ability to walk, run, or manipulate a wheel chair. The leader stands about fifteen or twenty feet away, facing the several groups. The leader then calls for some object that one of the players might be wearing or that he might have with him (hairpin, a crutch, something red, black, or white, a sweater, a shoe, or shoelace). Anyone on the team having such an object hands it to the runner, who runs, wheels, or walks with it to the leader. The runner arriving first with the desired object wins a point for the team. The team which accumulates the greatest number of points wins. The actual number of points required to win should be determined in advance by the contesting teams.

The leader must be alert and observant enough to ask for items which are visible in each group or for those items that he is quite certain the participating groups would have available. Also, he must consider the physical ability of each group and the individual participant's ability to obtain such articles. For example, if he asks for a shoe, he must be sure that in each group there is equal ability to unlace or take off a shoe.

Give played out of doors can be a tremendous aid in teaching the group to appreciate nature. For example, the leader could say, "Give me a maple leaf, or a pebble, or a certain type of wood."

GUESS THE LEADER. In Guess the Leader players sit in a single circle. The person chosen to be "it" leaves the room or retires to a safe distance until he is called back. While he is gone, the players choose a leader. The leader begins some action such as clapping hands, rocking back and forth, or nodding head, which the group imitates. "It" comes back to the circle and tries to discover who is starting the motion. "It" should change the motions quite frequently, and players should be cautioned to look at other players for the change of actions in order to fool "it." "It" should have three chances to guess the right leader. A new "it" is then chosen. If "it" fails to guess after three guesses, he goes out again.

HUMAN TIC TAC TOE. Nine pieces of paper are lined up on a square formation in rows of three between two opposing teams. The object of the game is for one team to get three of its own players in a straight line before the other team does, as in the paper and pencil Tic Tac Toe. Players on each team are given a number, and when the numbers are called out by a leader those players having that number walk and stand or wheel themselves onto a piece of paper. On the first number called, the player must take a position in the line opposite his own team's position on the sidelines. No coaching should be allowed on either side, as this spoils the suspense.

WHO AM I? Who Am I? is an excellent game to use as an ice breaker for large parties and dances. A slip of paper is pinned on each person's back so that he can't see it, with the name of some famous person written on it. The players go around the room asking questions about their identity. The questions must be such that they require only yes or no answers. Such questions as "Am I a man?" or "Am I alive?" or "Am I a movie star?" may be asked until the player guesses his identity. Names selected should be appropriate for the age group playing the game.

COLORS. One player in the group says, "I am thinking of an object in this room or near here, which is red," and so on. The others in turn name red objects, and the one who guesses correctly is next to choose an object. This game can also be used with foods. "I am thinking of a food that is yellow or brown," and so on. The person who guesses the food correctly chooses the next food.

FARMER'S BARNYARD. Number of players—10 or more, any age. One player is chosen to be the farmer. He is given a stick (crutch could be used) and is blindfolded. The players form a circle around him. The farmer goes about in the circle and finally points to someone with his stick or crutch. This person must take the other end of the stick, hold it, and do what the farmer says. For instance, if the farmer says, "Grunt, pig, grunt!" the player must grunt like a pig. The player tries to disguise his voice. Or the farmer may order, "Bleat, sheep, bleat!" or "Bray, donkey, bray!" or "Moo, cow, Moo!" If the farmer recognizes the player's voice, that person becomes the farmer. If not, the farmer points his stick to another person in the circle and tries again.

HIDE AND SEEK. Players sit in a circle. One person chosen to be "it" pretends to hide while the others close their eyes. When he has hidden in his imaginary spot, he states that he is ready, and the players open their eyes and guess. "It" could be hiding in a light bulb, in someone's shoe, in a flower pot, and so on. The one to guess correctly is "it" for the next play.

CHARADES. Charades, which is commonly called "The Game," is one of the oldest and most popular of all social games. It is the dramatic presentation of a word or a group of words that must be guessed by an audience. Charades have been especially popular with handicapped teen-age and adult groups. Players are divided into two or more teams, with a captain for each team. Each group meets separately and determines the method it will use in presenting its charades and the subject it will enact. For example, the group (1) selects a word with syllables that can be dramatized (i.e., dandelion: dandy makes syllable one, scene one; lion makes syllable two, scene two; the final scene is a dramatization of the entire word); (2) informs the other group or groups as to the part of speech the syllable represents (i.e., a noun, verb, adverb, and so on); (3) determines whether the syllable is to be presented by pantomime alone, by dialogue, or by a combination of the two; and (4) presents its dramatization. The groups make their presentations in turn, and the one whose offering takes the longest time for the others to guess is the winner. Under the direction of the captain, the team chooses the general subjects to be enacted by members of the opposing team.

Suggested categories for use in this game are:

Actors and actresses—TV or movie or stage
Advertising slogans
Bible stories or characters
Book titles
Comic strip characters
Movie titles
Mother Goose rhymes
Names of cities, states, or countries
Names of flowers and trees
Ordinary words which lend themselves to effective pantomime
Proverbs
People or events in the news
Vegetables

Various hand signals are used by players to transmit information to their team by pantomime. Following are signals that are commonly used to indicate the type of subject indicated.

1. Song—a grand opera pose with the mouth open.
2. Book—palms of hands together opened as a book.
3. Play—pulling an imaginary curtain.
4. Movie—pantomiming a camera by placing fingers to the eye with one hand and by turning the crank with the other.
5. Quotation—by holding up two wiggling fingers from each hand.

The number of words or syllables is indicated by holding up fingers; if words are similar in sounds, point to ear; if a word is a small word, indicate it with fingers. If audience is warm, indicate "keep coming" with hands. If audience is wrong, indicate "wash out" with hands; if right, indicate "go ahead" or "O.K." signal. When the word is too long, indicate "chopping off" or "scissors" sign. Fingers twiddled in the air indicate a plural word. Hands pulled apart as if stretching indicate "add on to the word," and hands brought close together from far out indicate "lessen length of word."

Another way of playing charades is for members of one team to choose a subject to be enacted by each member of the opposing team. The subjects are written on slips of paper and handed to the opposing team, one slip to each member. These individuals in turn make their presentation of the subject assigned, attempting to help their teammates guess it promptly. The groups decide upon a time limit for each presentation and a timekeeper is appointed. The team that guesses the subjects of its members' presentations in the shorter time is the winner.

LEOMONADE (TRADES). This game, which is somewhat of an adaptation of charades, is suitable for about 16 to 20 players. Two captains are chosen, by counting out, who in turn choose sides. Players are divided into two equal lines facing each other, about twenty or thirty feet apart. The group to be first decides upon some action like washing a window, flying a kite, eating ice cream, or any other familiar action. Then they advance saying "Here we come," the other side says, "Where are you from?" The advancing side replies, "New Orleans, New York," and so on. The other side says "What's your trade?" Advancing side says, "Leomonade." Then the other side replies, "Then show us some if you're not afraid." Whereupon the advancing side stands and acts out the idea they selected. The other group guesses what the action is, and if the guess is correct, they receive one point. If they guess correctly on the first guess they receive five points. After each side has had an equal number of turns, the side with the highest score is winner. If players have difficulty in moving they could sit on benches facing each other and whisper the action to be demonstrated.

Table Games

Table games are games that are played on a table by two or more people seated at it or standing about it. This section is concerned with table games that have been most popular with handicapped groups. It includes games played with small equipment, such as playing cards, and others requiring larger equipment. Many of the games described in this section are easily made at home; all of them can be purchased.

Table games are easy to play for persons in wheel chairs or even for those in bed or in reclining chairs. They are an excellent activity for large groups of handicapped persons, particularly when it is difficult for them to move about or when additional staff or volunteers are not available to give them a great deal of individual assistance. Table games are also excellent to use for integrated activities with the nonhandicapped.

Table games are easily adapted, and as with all other activities, specific adaptations should be made for each individual and group in order to assure enthusiastic participation. For example, checkers and chess can be designed on specially made boards that are easy to handle for persons having a great deal of involuntary motion. When persons cannot use their hands or feet to play, someone might move the checkers or chessmen for them. Card holders which make it easier for persons having difficulty with their hands can be purchased or made.

Many of the common card and other table games have been adapted for the blind so that they may play with the seeing as well as among themselves. Card games, for example, may be marked in braille. Checkers, chess, dominoes, and many other games may be purchased from the American Foundation for the Blind in New York.

One of the more popular table games requiring small equipment is miniature tether ball, which is described as follows:

Miniature Tether Ball

The outdoor game of tether ball can be scaled down to an indoor table game and provide plenty of fast action. A ball made from a cotton practice golf ball or from yarn can be used. The ball is batted with table tennis paddles or by hand, and the game can be placed on a table between two individuals in wheel chairs.

The pole, 30 inches in length, may be either a dowel or length of broomstick set in a 4″ length of 2″ × 4″, which, in turn, is nailed to the center of a piece of ⅜″ or ½″ plywood 2 feet square. The base of the pole is whittled so that it will fit snugly into a ½″ hole bored through the center of the block. The ball is fastened by a length of strong cord, such as carpenter's or mason's line, to a small staple or screw-eye in the top of the pole. It should clear the block at the bottom by two inches. A narrow piece of adhesive tape wrapped around the pole 1 foot from the top marks the foul line.

Ping-pong paddles may be used, or they can be made from 11-inch lengths of ½″ plywood about 6 inches wide. The handles can be made from a 9″ section of ¾″ × 1″ pine with the outer edges planed or whittled off to form a thick octagon before it is "ripped" down the center

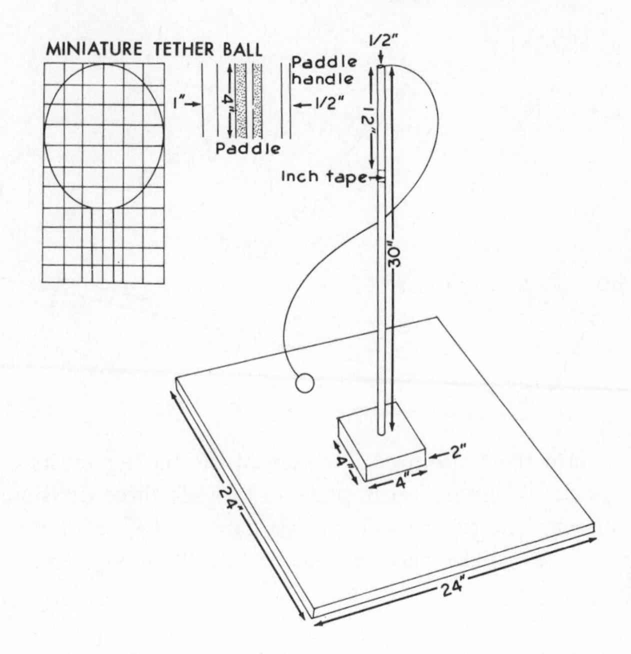

of its narrow edge. Cut into 4½″ lengths, the two sections are glued, bradded, and clamped to each side of the plywood paddle. After the glue has set, countersink all brads and sand smooth. Do not use varnish.

The object of the game is to wrap the tether cord around the pole above the taped line, one player trying in one direction while his opponent tries the opposite direction. The winner is the first player to wind the cord completely around the pole above the tape line in his chosen direction. Players toss for serve, and the loser chooses the direction of play. (See illustration on p. 325.)

Box Hockey

Box hockey is a game which has been used successfully, and it can be easily made. The box hockey rink is made of ¾″ plywood and forms an open box approximately six feet long by three feet wide, with sides and ends approximately six inches high as shown in sketch.

Three barriers as shown are required to complete the rink. The barriers, made from ½″ plywood, should measure 34½″ × 5⅞″. The end barriers should have a semicircular 6½″ cut into the bottom edge of the barrier 7″ from each end. The center barrier should have one 6½″ semi-

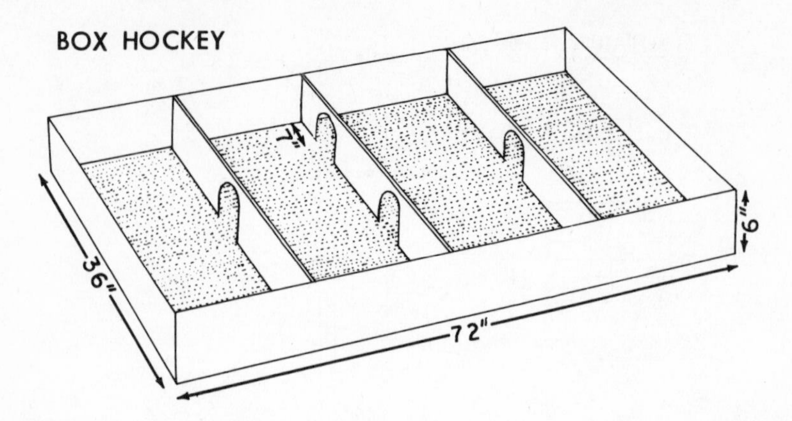

circular cut into the bottom of the edge of the barrier on its center line. The barriers should be nailed in place to provide three divisions of equal width as shown. The puck used for this game is 1½″ in diameter and ½″ thick. The hockey sticks may be made from 1″ dowel stock about two feet long.

TO PLAY. Box hockey can be played by two to four persons, but two is usually best. It can be played from a table, the floor, or ground. For the ritual of the face-off, the two contestants face each other across the center rink, tap the floor of the box with their sticks, then the opponent's stick above the puck, alternating three times. After the third time each endeavors to strike the puck into his opponent's court. If one of the players "jumps the gun" before the third tap, repeat the entire process. The object of the game is to try to knock the puck through the opening in the end barrier to the left, which is the opponent's goal. If the puck is knocked outside the rink it is replaced in the section it was in and playing resumes. The game is won by the first player to make three goals.

Top Spinning

A commercially available version of top spinning in the form of a table game has proved very popular with the handicapped. One eight-year-old boy who had no use of his hands learned to pull the top string with his mouth and was able to compete successfully with other less handicapped boys.

Other table games that have been popular with handicapped groups and may be purchased commercially are table cricket, skittles, marble football, and paddle pool.

Parties

Parties are a form of social recreation popular with both large and small groups of all ages. They are usually planned around a special occasion such as a birthday or holiday, although they often have a central theme such as a May Day Party or a Nursery Rhyme or Come As You Are Party. Party activities commonly include quiet group games, table games, informal stunts and charades, and the serving of refreshments.

The type of party or social depends upon certain factors such as the facilities, space, equipment and supplies available, the budget, the number, age level, and sex of the persons attending, and the likes and dislikes of individuals and groups.

The fact that committees are needed to plan and conduct a party is one of the primary values of such an activity for the handicapped. Party planning affords another opportunity for handicapped persons to serve on committees and to learn to assume responsibility. They should be encouraged to plan and conduct their own parties and to evaluate the results. Typical committees needed for party planning are invitations, publicity, finance, decoration, refreshment, entertainment, clean-up, and program. Not all committees, of course, are needed for all socials or parties.

Parties of all types are easily adaptable for a variety of handicapped groups and have proved to be one of the most popular activities. Holiday and birthday parties should be conducted year around, but parties built around themes, beach parties, and pizza parties have been greatly enjoyed.

The following description illustrates how one group learned to give a very successful party. A group of fifteen handicapped young adults requested a formal class in "party planning and socials." Most of them had had little, if any, previous experience in giving parties, but all wanted to learn how. The course was given over a period of approximately six months so that individuals could gain experience serving on the various committees. The success of several small parties encouraged them to attempt a May Day Party, complete with May queen and Maypole dancing, for approximately one hundred persons. "Shower of Flowers" was selected as the theme and committees formed were Invitation, Publicity, Decoration, Program, Finance, Refreshment, and Clean-Up. The invitations, which were stenciled and run off on the mimeograph machine by the committee members, were decorated with crepe paper and glitter umbrellas and flowers to indicate the "Shower of Flowers" theme. The large social hall was decorated with flowers made from

A May Pole Dance in wheel chairs.

tissues and crepe paper. Large tree branches painted green were also sprinkled liberally with flowers. A wishing well was made by members of the group from large cardboard cartons, painted on the outside to resemble rocks. Crowns of flowers for the queen and her attendants were made from crepe paper and plastic bands. The Maypoles, designed and made by the program committee, were of doweling which was attached to the ceiling and secured to the floor. Streamers were made from pastel-colored paper. The Refreshment Committee baked cupcakes and made strawberry punch for the event. The program committee, which assumed a great deal of responsibility, planned and carried out all of the games played and worked out the procedure for dancing around the Maypole in wheel chairs and on crutches. This was achieved primarily by assigning certain numbers of ambulatory men and women to each Maypole to assist with chairs and/or streamers as needed. Party games chosen were "Name That Flower Quiz," with prizes to winners, and "Cross Questions." The ice breaker used at the beginning of the party was "Who Am I?" described in this section under Quiet Group Games. The various committees worked approximately three months planning the party. The results, which were extremely good, were their own, and each person felt a real sense of achievement and satisfaction, in addition to the fact that each had fun.

The Social Setting

The setting for social recreation is an important aspect of the total program since an attractive setting is conducive to an atmosphere of sociability. An ideal social hall or room should be flexible enough to provide for a variety of needs such as a meeting place for groups, a lounge, and a place for conversation, semiactive games, and informal dancing and eating. If the area is large enough to provide for a variety of table and floor games, this will encourage participation of individuals and groups, frequently without personally directed leadership.

Types of equipment should include sturdy, comfortable chairs and sofas, tables for games of all types, a jukebox or record player, a piano, and appropriate decorations that contribute to a warm, friendly, and cheerful atmosphere. A snack bar or some type of cooking area provides an opportunity for many excellent social activities to be planned around food and is an asset to any social recreation program.

Trading wheel chairs for a soft ride on the hay.

CHAPTER 23

Outings and Trips

Outings and trips are among the most popular recreation activities for handicapped children and adults. Their popularity is due primarily to the fact that few handicapped persons have had opportunities to take trips and to participate in forms of outdoor recreation that most people take for granted.

In addition to the tremendous satisfaction and pleasure gained from these outdoor recreation experiences, severely handicapped individuals have been challenged—through camping, for example—to develop resourcefulness, self-reliance, and adaptability in the out-of-doors. Organized recreation programs have given children, as well as many older handicapped persons, their first opportunity to appreciate the natural environment and to use it to develop outdoor skills, to understand conservation, and to learn some of the principles of natural science. The desire for new experiences and adventure in particular can be fulfilled by participating in outdoor recreation activities, and the belief that all of these values contribute to the physical and mental health of each individual cannot be questioned.

Taking trips away from their neighborhood or community can be a thrilling and exciting experience for handicapped persons. Hiking through the woods to look for wild flowers can be achieved by persons on crutches and even in wheel chairs. Trips to the museum, visits to a farm, and hayrides are experiences that are long remembered by handicapped persons.

Discovering sea life at the beach.

Suggested Outings and Trips

Exploration, observation, and discovery trips can be exciting adventures as well as learning experiences. Most communities have a botanical garden, a zoo, and parks that are suitable objectives for group outings. The fact that exploration trips to the beach can be a great deal of fun is illustrated in the words of a blind child who said:

> I asked the recreation leader "What's on the beach?" and a few days later I found out. I felt some dead fish and some shells and some broken sand dollars under my feet. . . . I picked up a sand dollar and felt the round design. . . . The waves sounded like people swishing their hands back and forth. We saw a dead crab and a jellyfish, too. . . . The jellyfish was slippery.[1]

Hayrides

Horse-drawn haywagons and children without their crutches and wheel chairs have the ingredients for one of the most enjoyable of outings. One recreation program for the handicapped includes an annual hayride, which has become so popular that each year additional wagons must be provided to accommodate all of the children who wish to attend. The hayride is an all-day outing and picnic which is conducted in a nearby city park. Wheel chairs and crutches, which are abandoned for a soft ride on the hay, are transported to and from the picnic area by cars and buses. Over one hundred children participate in this annual event. (Illustration.)

Hiking

Hiking on crutches or even in wheel chairs in selected areas can be an enjoyable experience. Some groups must limit themselves to easily accessible areas and terrain, while others may be encouraged to explore mountainous areas and wooded trails. One group of handicapped teenagers, some on crutches and some in wheel chairs, "hiked" across the Golden Gate Bridge in San Francisco. Although transportation was close by in case it was needed, the majority of the participants completed the hike.

[1] *Center Highlights,* Camp La Playa Edition, Recreation Center for the Handicapped, San Francisco, 1961. (Mimeographed.)

Picnics

Picnicking is a popular feature of almost all outings, particularly if they are conducted for the entire day. The food may be ready to eat or may be cooked over outdoor fires. Because picnicking has become one of America's favorite outdoor recreation activities for families, informal groups, and organizations, many picnic sites are available. Some recreation departments maintain a picnic bureau which assists groups in selecting a site, provides wood for fires, gives advice in organizing picnic games and entertainment, lends program equipment, and in some instances, provides a leader to conduct the picnic program. A developed picnic area, however, is not essential, as some of the most enjoyable picnics may be held in a densely wooded area, in a meadow, or on the banks of a small stream. Even though certain areas suitable for a picnic might seem quite inaccessible to persons in wheel chairs and portable beds, every effort should be made to give them opportunities for enjoying these secluded spots.

Feeding a new-found friend at the farm.

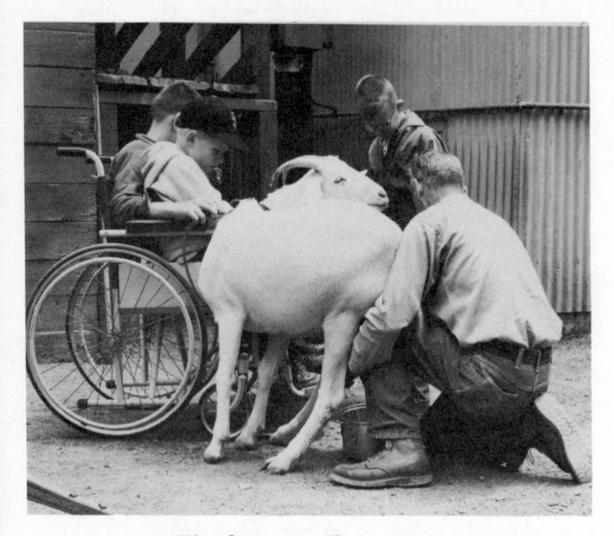

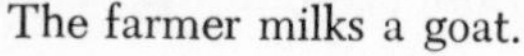

The farmer milks a goat.

Their first ride on a cable car.

Trips to Farms

Opportunities for all children to visit farms and ranches are becoming increasingly rare, yet these experiences are among the most enjoyable as well as educational. One group of handicapped youngsters is invited each year to a farm where it spends the day visiting baby animals such as calves, kid goats, colts, and baby lambs. An added thrill for the children is to watch baby chicks, ducks, and pheasants and to see mother hens sitting on their nests. The children also ride horses and ponies and help feed the farm animals. The highlight of the day occurs when they put aside their wheel chairs and crutches and slide down hay stacks. (See illustrations.)

Historical and Educational Trips

There are many interesting places to visit in every community, and handicapped persons welcome the opportunity to enjoy them. Trips to art galleries, industrial plants, museums, parks, public buildings, and areas of historic interest enrich the recreation program. Persons interested in a specific activity such as journalism have enjoyed visiting newspaper offices; others have visited television and radio stations, police and fire stations, libraries, and local airports. Such trips are not only of recreational value but they are educational as well, and they provide another opportunity for the handicapped to participate with others.

Preliminary Arrangements

Trips and outings for the handicapped should be carefully planned, and all precautions should be taken to insure the comfort and safety of the participants. It is desirable for staff to become familiar with facilities before handicapped persons are taken to them. In particular they should check entrances, exits, eating accommodations, and toilet facilities. Buildings such as museums, for example, may have a great many stairs at the front entrance but usually have elevators which can be used by persons in wheel chairs, crutches, and portable beds. The terrain of outdoor areas should also be checked to make sure there are no hazards and that it will permit circulation by the handicapped. A report form for outings appears in Chapter 13, and additional suggestions relating to outings are included in Chapters 11 and 12.

On his first plane ride, a blind boy "sees" the cockpit.

Day camping can provide many of the values of long term camping.

CHAPTER 24

Day Camping

Day camping has long been recognized as having a unique place in the community recreation program. Where it is developed for its own merits, rather than as a substitute for resident camping, it can provide many of the values of long-term camping in addition to its own special contributions, which are particularly suited to the needs of many of the physically handicapped.

Aims and Benefits

One of the greatest benefits of day camping for this group is the opportunity it affords for them to learn to adjust to group living. Many handicapped children, because of lack of previous experiences for developing social maturity, have difficulty in making the adjustment required in being away from home with large groups of strange children in a residential camp.

Through attendance at a day camp, a handicapped child—and his parents as well—is helped gradually to gain confidence in his ability to become somewhat independent and to be willing and able to be separated from them. This is especially true if the day camp experience includes an occasional overnight campout. Children and parents are thus conditioned to the idea that the children can ultimately participate in a residential camping program. It should be kept in mind, however, that all handicapped children are not capable of benefiting from attendance at a resident camp, whereas they may secure the enjoyment and values of a camping experience through a day camp program.

Day camping experiences for the handicapped can also stimulate the beginning of the development of other recreation interests, since they often reveal significant abilities and aptitudes of which they were unaware.

The objectives of day camping, as well as the values derived, are the same for the handicapped as are those for nonhandicapped children. "Camping provides a creative educational experience in cooperative group living in the out-of-doors. It utilizes the resources of the natural surroundings to contribute significantly to mental, physical, social and spiritual growth."[1] Briefly the specific aims may be defined as follows:

[1] Grace Mitchell, *Fundamentals of Day Camping,* Association Press, 1961, p. 217.

1. To provide fun in the out-of-doors.
2. To offer satisfying contacts with nature, so that the camper may acquire a sense of being at home in the out-of-doors.
3. To provide opportunities for group and individual experiences in a natural environment; to join in and contribute to a plan of living for a day, a week, or more.
4. To foster the growth of independence and self-direction in each camper.
5. To acquire new skills, hobbies, and interests that have long-time values.
6. To arouse a sense of curiosity, stimulate spontaneous expression, provide enjoyment, and accelerate the learning process.
7. To provide opportunities for new experiences, for emotional satisfaction, and for spiritual growth.
8. To foster better mental and physical health, courage, and confidence and to exercise mind and body in healthful activity.
9. To offer a range of experiences that will help to prepare the campers for resident camping.
10. To provide opportunities for the development of initiative, leadership, and a sense of responsibility.

In order to assure the type of experience for every camper as described above, groups organizing day camps should be guided by the Day Camp Standards as established by the American Camping Association, Bradford Woods, Martinsville, Indiana.

Day Camp Organization

Before a day camp program can be carried on many factors must be considered and a number of essential procedures must be established. Several of these are described briefly.

Day Camp Committees

Most agencies conducting day camp programs for the handicapped have some type of committee that helps to plan and organize the camp. The agency that administers the camp determines the kind of committee members needed as well as their functions. Such a committee might include parents of the handicapped, teachers, board members, camping experts, and other professional and lay community leaders. Subcommittees may be appointed to assume responsibility for specific phases of the camp as needed. Typical of these subcommittees are enrollment of campers, site, budget and finance, transportation, food, equipment and supplies, staff, and program. A medical advisory committee is frequently established to assist the camp committee. If the camp committee is composed of persons who are familiar with the resources of the community, there is no limit to the possibilities for obtaining the assistance necessary to conducting a successful camp.

Camp Seasons and Schedules

Day camp sessions for the handicapped, as well as for others, frequently range from one to three days a week for eight weeks to five consecutive days for four to eight weeks. Some communities attempt to provide at least two weeks of summer day camping for each child. While the length of the season varies with each locality, wherever feasible, day camping should be conducted throughout the year.

In planning the day camp program, it is advisable to think in terms of the whole day. Programs usually start between nine and ten o'clock in the morning and continue until three or four o'clock in the afternoon. The hours depend largely upon the climate, transportation arrangements, and other variable factors. Providing some overnight campouts in a day camp program offers the handicapped an opportunity for trial separation from their parents, as well as the unique experiences gained through overnight camping.

Trip camping, which is described later on in this chapter, has been especially popular with teen-age handicapped persons who have more or less progressed beyond the usual day camp routine and are more interested in participating in advanced camping.

Sites

Almost every city has public and private parks, recreation buildings, churches, schools, camps, and other areas and facilities that may be used as a site on which a day camp may be conducted. In one city the Girl Scout summer day camp was loaned for two two-week sessions to a group of handicapped children for conducting a day camp program. Hunting, fishing and social clubs, an estate with buildings which could be utilized, a pond, a lake or the seashore, are all possible sites for conducting a day camp.

A regular city day camp site is used by the handicapped.

Insofar as possible, the camp program should utilize the natural resources afforded by the site and environment. If a day camp is located in a wooded area, it probably affords numerous opportunities for living close to nature and for nature lore activities such as leaf collection and identification, bird study, and construction of nature trails, shelters, and exhibits. By the same token, a camp located near or at the beach may also provide numerous, but different, opportunities for nature activities such as the collection and identification of sea shells, the study of marine life, the use of beach sand in crafts, and fishing.

To conduct a day camp for the handicapped, areas must be large enough to provide space for desired camp activities and to accommodate persons in wheel chairs, beds, and so on. They must have adequate shelter to permit carrying on the program in case of rain or bad weather. An adequate water supply and toilet facilities should measure up to the highest standards of health and safety as established by the American Camping Association. A natural wooded area is ideal, of course, but successful day camps have been conducted by imaginative and intelligent leaders on less attractive areas. Even a makeshift camp can present a challenge to the nature counselor who can bring various nature materials to the campsite.

Finance and Budget

The cost of a day camp for the handicapped will vary according to the number of children, the paid staff, method of transportation, equipment and supplies, camp food, insurance and other considerations. Camper fees are usually expected of the participants and should be considered a primary source of financing. Fees should be established by the governing body or set by the camp committee. Fees should not be too large to keep children away, but equally, no child should feel that he is supported by charity. Camperships for handicapped children are frequently obtained from various interested individuals and groups in the community and from health and welfare agencies serving the handicapped. Camperships should be obtained especially for children whose families are unable to bear the expense.

Enrollment of Campers

The camp committee, having selected the camp site and determined the aims and objectives of the day camp, may establish with the camp director and medical advisory committee the policies for selecting campers. The usual rule for selecting handicapped children for any camp is

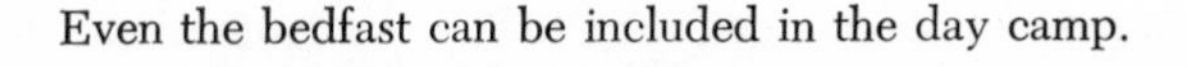

Even the bedfast can be included in the day camp.

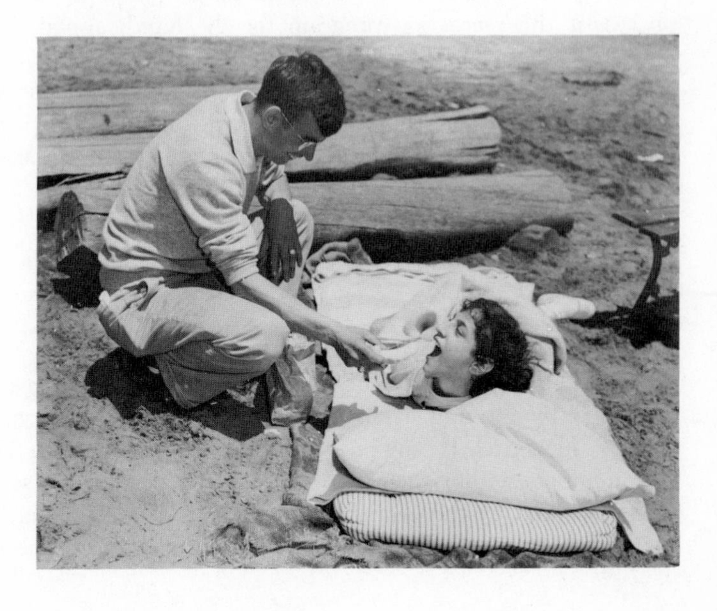

that children are selected who will secure the greatest benefit from camping and group living. The committee must determine the minimum and maximum age, the type of handicapped children the camp is equipped to serve, i.e., the nonambulatory, the ambulatory, or mixed, and if it is to include both boys and girls, which is the usual pattern for camps for the handicapped.

If information about the campers has not been obtained previously, the committee should develop an application blank that will provide the type of information it needs. Such committees usually specify that children must be examined and judged to be able to attend day camp either by their own physician or by one in attendance at schools, clinics, or other designated agencies. Parents must also furnish certain information that is essential for the camp staff, particularly where overnight campouts are included. See Chapters 13 and 14 for typical forms and required information.

Prospective campers may be referred to the camp committee by individuals or by groups within a community, such as health and welfare agencies serving the handicapped, hospitals, clinics, and schools. Referral agencies are discussed in detail in Chapter 3.

Camp Personnel

Camp personnel should conform to the same standards for personal qualities, training, and experience as are required in other comparable phases of the recreation program for the handicapped. These are discussed in Chapters 5 and 6, relating to leadership standards and of personnel procedures. In-service training sessions should be a prerequisite to selection as a staff member and should include a review of the aims and objectives of day camping for the handicapped, discussion of campers and their handicaps, physical handling, and various aspects of program planning and day camp activities. Further discussion of in-service training is included in Chapter 6, "Personnel Procedures."

Camp Units

One of the best ways of separating the participants into congenial groups is by forming camp units. These are usually organized by age groups, such as 5 through 7, 8 through 12, 13 through 17, and so on. The numbers within each group are determined by the severity of their handicaps and by the available trained staff and volunteers. Some camping programs have established standards that require one professionally

ng under the stars was a thrilling experience.

The Day Camp Program

he day camp program for the physically handicapped must, as with other group, be thought of in terms of the campers themselves as rate and distinct persons. Each individual camper has interests, both essed and unconscious, and needs, recognized and unrecognized. successful program satisfies these interests and needs through day-ay living of a camping experience.

gram Planning

The campers must have a share with the professional staff in plan-g the camp life and program. Helping to initiate plans, sharing in the ponsibility for carrying them out, and evaluating results are not only damental to learning, but for many of the handicapped they afford a e opportunity to participate in group planning and group living. Long-ge planning of this type may be accomplished with the total camper oup if the camp is small or through a representative camper council if camp is large. Where the camp is organized in units, each should velop its own daily or weekly program according to the interests, eds, and age of its members, but within the framework of the over-all mp schedule and program.

Camp personnel should conform to the same standa
phases of the recreation program for the handicappe

trained staff worker to every four handicapped p
they are severely handicapped. Groups who are
be organized in larger ratios, such as one staff
campers.

It should be remembered however, that in
should the ratio of staff to handicapped be so
independence of handicapped participants.

In one area, county school officials for the han
that summer recreation and camping programs, al
well meaning citizens of the community, caused th
This was due to the fact that too many staff and vo
the program and they gave more assistance to th
necessary.

Sleepi

T
any
sepa
expr
The
to-d

Pro

nin
res
fur
ra
ra
gr
th
de
ne
ca

The program should emphasize and be planned around activities that are based upon a camp setting such as nature study, outdoor cooking, and pioneering. Children, even though severely handicapped, should have opportunities to climb trees, to study plants and animals, to sleep and eat in the out-of-doors, and, in general, to have experiences in primitive living. Following are some suggested activities to help them achieve these aims.

Nature Study

Nature study is the most important part of a day camp since through it the primary objective is achieved—that of living close to nature, pleasantly, healthfully, and comfortably.

The purpose of the nature program is essentially to arouse curiosity in the campers and to help them to satisfy it. Janet Nickelsburg states, "nature study is not so much the learning of names and classifications as it is an attitude of mind. It is the ability to see a story in a drop of water, to construct an adventure from the silver ribbon left on the ground by a passing snail, to watch and wonder at the banking and turning of the gull in flight, and to interpret the coming storm by the movement of the clouds."[2]

Most handicapped children, as well as many nonhandicapped, have had very little experience with the world of out-of-doors. They must be stimulated to see, hear, smell, taste, and touch. The nature program should start with what is at hand, and nature lies about us all the time. Every day camp can have something interesting to stimulate these senses in the way of insects, birds, grasses, seeds, butterflies, flowers, weeds, clouds, rocks, and the wind. "The primary objective of a nature counselor is to stimulate children to make their own observations, to notice likenesses and differences, and to discover and correlate what they find to where they found it and in what surroundings."[3]

One group of handicapped children spent literally hours in a summer day camp lying on the ground observing ants and snails. After learning a great deal about the ant and snail, their habits, what they ate, how they built their homes and other information, they became interested in having a snail race. This interest was a highlight of the nature program for

[2] Janet Nickelsburg, *The Nature Program at Camp,* A Book for Camp Counselors (Minneapolis: Burgess Publishing Company, 1960), p. 1.

[3] *Ibid.,* p. 7.

several days. Overnight campouts provided them with the opportunity to hear the chirps of crickets and other night creatures and to identify their sounds. Trips to the zoo, aquarium, and to a farm greatly enhanced their knowledge of nature, including birds, fish, and animals, which was tested through games and quizzes built around identification of animals and birds. Trips to the farm, as described in Chapter 23 was a thrilling and educational experience. Milking and feeding the farm animals and seeing vegetables and fruit growing in fields and orchards were a rare treat for all of them.

Campers should be encouraged to be curious about trees—the variety, the bark, the color, the leaves, where and how fast they grow, how tall they are, what the leaf bud looks like and the shape of the flower the trees bear, whether the wood is hard or soft, and what it is used for. The discussion of these and other pertinent matters stimulates wonder about trees and creates the desire to feel, look, and climb them. Tree climbing in one day camp for the handicapped was an unforgettable experience, especially for a blind girl of thirteen who had never had the opportunity to climb a tree. She had heard sighted campers talk of climbing trees, and suddenly, she disappeared from the immediate camp grounds. As the search for her began, the camp counselors called and called. Finally, someone heard her giggling from the top of the highest oak tree. It was an experience she still talks about and will long remember.

Most camps have some type of plant life, and so much the better if there are wild flowers, weeds, ferns, mosses, vines, and shrubs. Children can take nature walks, even in their wheel chairs, to observe, study and compare plant life. The study of plant life can lead into collecting leaves, twigs, and stones, and to mounting and exhibiting these objects. One handicapped child collected objects by carrying a paper bag in his mouth because he couldn't use his hands. He was assisted by another camper in putting the objects in the bag, but he selected and carried his own specimens.

The building of terrariums and aquariums has been very popular with handicapped children of the Recreation Center. Specimens brought in by the children during a six-week camping period included a variety of animals and plants such as tadpoles, toads, turtles, insects, beetles, leaves and twigs, as well as rocks, shells, and many types of sea life.

Bird watching can be an exciting event in the day camp particularly if the children notice how they feed, what they eat, their patterns of flights and songs, and how their coloration conceals them from their enemies. Where birds are scarce, children can visit a bird sanctuary, listen to records of bird songs, make scrap books of bird pictures, stories,

A blind girl and boy enjoy the shelter they helped to build.

and poems. Plaster casts of tracks in mud, or at the beach, may be made. Frequently, feathers may be found which will provide sufficient curiosity to go in search of its owner or to learn of its habits and kind.

Sleeping under the stars was one of the most thrilling of all experiences for a group of handicapped children. They saw the Milky Way, identified the Big and Little Dippers and planets such as Venus and Mars. They saw the Plain of Grimaldi on the moon and learned about the weather, the wind, and the rain.

Pioneering

Most children have a strong desire to live as the frontiersmen, the Indians, or the prospectors, and handicapped children are no exception. Day camping can satisfy this romantic instinct for them while simultaneously teaching them the basic essentials of real camping. On the first day at camp the children should be oriented to the camp facilities by becoming acquainted with trails, camp boundaries, dangers, and directions of the camp site. Making a map of the camp site is an excellent means of orienting the children to the area. Notes may be taken while they are being shown the site and the map constructed later. Maps are excellent group projects and correlate with crafts as described later in this chapter.

Pioneering should also include learning how to use camp tools such as the hand ax and jackknife with skill and safety. Making shelters, lean-

Fire building and cooking should be a part of pioneering in the day camp program.

to's, trail blazing, hiking, signaling, tying knots, and learning to pitch a tent are all part of pioneering and deserve a place in the day camp program.

Fire Building and Cooking

Cookery and fire building are phases of pioneering in the day camp program. Handicapped campers should be taught where and how to build the various types of cooking fires, such as the tepee or wigwam, the crisscross, fire in a hole, or tin can fires. One group of handicapped children found great delight in cooking their breakfast on the tops of large tin cans with air vents punched in the bases. This experience led to an interest in learning to build the council fire for the evening campfire program.

Some day camps for the handicapped provide hot lunches already prepared, but advantage should be taken of the opportunity for campers to cook the noon meal at least some of the time. If an occasional overnight campout is provided, campers may also learn to prepare the evening meal as well. In many day camps, the campers bring a paper bag lunch, and milk and fruit juices are served at noon and in the midafternoon. One-pot meals have been very popular with a group of handicapped children, who found them fun to prepare. The main dish, such as stew or chowder, is cooked in one big pot and includes meat, potatoes, and vegetables. Children may be made responsible for planning the meal and for bringing certain parts of it from their homes. Toasting marshmallows and hot dogs is always an easy and favorite way to cook part of the lunch or afternoon snack.

One group of fifteen severely handicapped teen-agers made themselves responsible for cooking their entire meal for an overnight campout. Although some were seemingly helpless, as a unit they found ways to adapt so that everyone had some responsibility. For example, one severely handicapped boy of fifteen, unable to use his hands or arms, found that he could hold a long skewer in his mouth to cook shishkebab and to roast hot dogs and marshmallows. Some were able to pare vegetables with assistance from volunteers or staff in holding the vegetable peeler. Others were able to roll the vegetables in tin foil for cooking over coals. Several undertook group projects such as baking bread and cookies in aluminum reflector ovens, while others tried the more advanced type of cooking underground.

Hiking

Hiking even in wheel chairs and on crutches can take on the spirit of fun and can be an enjoyable part of the day camp program. Hikes are more interesting if they have a specific objective. Collection hikes, identification hikes, pioneer hikes, picnic or map-making hikes can all be fun with a purpose.

General Crafts

Crafts in the day camp program should, insofar as possible, make use of the natural resources. For example, wooden pins, beads, buttons, and buckles may be made from bits of bark, pods, rocks, pine cones, and shells. One day camp for the handicapped, which was surrounded by eucalyptus trees, provided many native materials for use in the craft program. Eucalyptus buds were painted and strung for necklaces. The dead leaves, which were shaped like feathers, were painted and stapled to head bands for Indian headgear. The clay and dirt were used to make coarse pottery pieces. In another camp, near the beach, sand painting (described in Chapter 18) and sand building became enjoyable activities.

Relief maps of the camp site can also be made of clay. Crafts may be correlated with other camp activities such as music, drama, games and sports, and service projects. Musical instruments such as the shepherd's pipe, flutes, and whistles can be made of bamboo; drums and rattles, from gourds, cans, or boxes. Fishing poles and drop lines may also be made from native materials, and learning to tie flies is an important part of campcraft.

Music

Singing is the most popular form of music in the day camp, as it goes on almost continuously during hikes, while cooking, and around a campfire. Action songs, as described in Chapter 16 are very appropriate and enjoyable, but folk songs, ballads, rounds, and many other types are also popular. Rhythm bands, especially if the instruments are made by the campers themselves, will furnish many delightful hours of pleasure. The ukulele, guitar, banjo, and harmonica are commonly associated with camping, and, if campers or staff members are able to play them, they can make a real contribution to the camp music. Singing games also have a place in the camp music program.

Dramatics

The day camp provides an excellent opportunity for informal and simple dramatics that are popular with all age groups. Pantomimes, skits and stunts (described in Chapter 15), monologues, dialogues, and charades are frequently used for the campfire program, and are an excellent means of entertaining parents and guests. One group of handicapped children created their own skits and stunts for the campfire program, based on the funny situations or gossip that happened during the weekly camp. Pantomimes of camp members building their first fire or cooking or rowing a boat can be presented in the spirit of fun and good fellowship. The same group of handicapped campers enjoyed pantomiming the camp counselors and planned one campfire program around a "Turnabout Day," when the campers became the camp counselors and the counselors became the campers.

Storytelling is one of the most enjoyable of all activities for the day camp, and can be a part of all camp activities—not limited just to the story hour. There are many occasions for telling stories, as on hikes or walks, when someone finds an arrowhead or a fossil and it brings to mind a story of long ago. There are wonderful stories about animals, birds,

Storytelling.

trees, rocks, lakes, the moon, the sun, and the stars; also myths, legends, fairy tales, and folklore of every country. Every section has its own folklore and tales of early settlers, Indians, or pirates. The use of local color in storytelling makes the area come alive to the campers. Ghost stories became a favorite of one group of handicapped preteen children, who particularly enjoyed hearing them at the weekly campfire, just before bedtime. Pirate stories told at one camp site near the ocean prompted the campers to look for buried treasure in the sand. This interest ultimately resulted in the planning and conducting of treasure hunts and in the selection of a pirate theme.

Games and Sports

Many of the games and sports described in Chapters 21 and 22 can be included in the day camp program. Swimming, boating, fishing, horseback riding, archery, horseshoes, quoits, and ring toss are excellent day camp activities. Informal and quiet games may also be used and adapted to camp themes and camp surroundings. For example, Give may be adapted to the nature program, and many of the guessing games and relays can be built around animals, birds, fish, and nature lore.

Service Projects

Service projects which give the handicapped camper an opportunity to do something for others can also be included in the day camp program. Campers might wish to make something useful and enjoyable for a local underprivileged group, to have letter or card exchanges, or to develop some type of project with children from foreign lands. CARE, 20 Broad Street, New York, N.Y., or UNESCO, 405 East 42nd Street, New York, N.Y., are sources of suggestions for service projects. These and similar agencies frequently have local offices.

The Camp Newspaper

The feasibility of developing a camp newspaper may depend on the length of the camp period and types of activities conducted. However, production of a camp paper can be an enjoyable activity and provides a record of camp highlights for campers, parents, and their friends. A group of seventy-five campers published one newspaper during a four-week day camp session under the guidance of a counselor who was responsible for coordinating the efforts of various units.

Flag Ceremonies

Most day camps begin and end their program with flag ceremonies. Other flags are also used in the camp, such as the state flag, unit flag (designed and made by campers), and safety flags. Handicapped children have been eager to assume responsibility for flag ceremonies, and they should be taught to conduct them properly. In one day camp for the handicapped, the flag ceremonies were assigned to the various units so that each camper had the opportunity to take part as a member of the color guard and to learn the proper procedure for flag raising and lowering.

Health and Safety

Campers should learn good health practices as a part of camp keeping and living. They should be taught that maintaining good health and safety is a responsibility of every camper. Instruction in the proper methods of handling tools used in crafts and pioneering activities and of participating in water sports and many other camp activities is essential to the safety of the campers. Safety councils are frequently organized as a way of emphasizing the importance of safety and health for campers. The council may be small in number but representative of the different units. Its responsibility is to inspect the camp and its surroundings, reporting any safety violations or omissions and safety hazards. In one day camp, a partially sighted camper was elected the leader for this type of council, and the children loved assuming the responsibility as council members.

Special Programs by Handicapped Groups

Children at the Recreation Center's day camp, over a period of years, have enjoyed all of the activities previously mentioned. A great many of these activities have been conducted around camp themes, which help greatly to develop group unity and provide an excellent framework for a variety of activities. Such themes as pioneers, beachcombers, gypsies, Indians, or cowboys lend themselves to an unlimited range and scope of activities such as songs, campfire skits and stunts, arts and crafts, games, and camp cookery. The following pages describe several examples of programs built around a theme.

A Pirate Theme

The location of the camp unit and the telling of pirate stories inspired a group of twelve seven-to-nine-year-old children to select a pirate theme. On the first day of camp, when the children were taken to their unit, they noticed that a large oak tree at their unit site was shaped like the bow of a pirate frigate. Their imaginations soon labeled it a pirate ship, and they decided to call themselves pirates. The unit counselors discussed pirate lore with them, and the children began to develop their theme by making pirate symbols for identification. They made a black flag with crossbones and skull, black pirate hats with the same symbol, black boots, and scimitars to carry out the theme. Neckerchiefs and eye patches were also made by each camper. A large black flag was made from an old sheet dyed black, and white tempera paint was used to make the crossbones and skull. The hats and scimitars were made of black cardboard and the boots of black oilcloth stapled together. Bits of old costume jewelry and other trinkets were buried in "jewel boxes" together with silver and gold-wrapped candy coins. Treasure hunts were

"Pirates" digging for treasure.

the highlights of the camp theme. Pirate songs such as "Come Let's Play We're Pirates" and "Three Pirates Came to London Town" were sung regularly, and stories of pirates were told by campers and camp staff. Simple pirate ships were made in the crafts program, and the campers had ship races on a nearby lake. Pirate skits and stunts were worked into the campfire program, and pirate games were also played by the group.

South Sea Islanders

A teen-age group chose the theme South Sea Islanders. They learned Hawaiian songs and games and presented the play "Lava—or Love" (See Chapter 15) during the campfire program. They had a Hawaiian luau on the beach and invited guests. Hawaiian leis were made in the crafts program, and, as a culmination to the activity, the group had dinner at a restaurant called "The Waikiki Beachcomber."

Early California

At a summer day camp for handicapped children, which was conducted at the school site, an "Early California" theme was selected by a group of forty-five campers, ranging from five to twenty-one years of age.

The camp was in session for six weeks. The various age units chose certain phases of the theme which they wished to develop. For example, the younger children chose a California Indian theme; the older children, an early Spanish theme. The Indian theme was based on authentic culture of California Indians. The children became Indians of the Yurok, Hupa, and Pomo tribes. They learned authentic dances and rituals, songs, and games, made bows and arrows as these tribes did, and used authentic mortars and pestles to grind corn. Some of the children wove baskets, made shell necklaces, and headbands of quills, which they dyed in bright colors as the California Indians did for their headdresses.

The group selecting the Spanish theme became señoritas and señores. They made Spanish sombreros for the señores; fans, mantillas, Spanish shawls, and flowers for the señoritas. Although the school ground was bare, except for small patches of concrete and grass, the children and camp counselors were delighted to find that the hard, clay soil was actually adobe. The group proceeded to mix the adobe with straw and water, shape the mixture into miniature "bricks," and dry them in the sun, just

An Indian war chant.

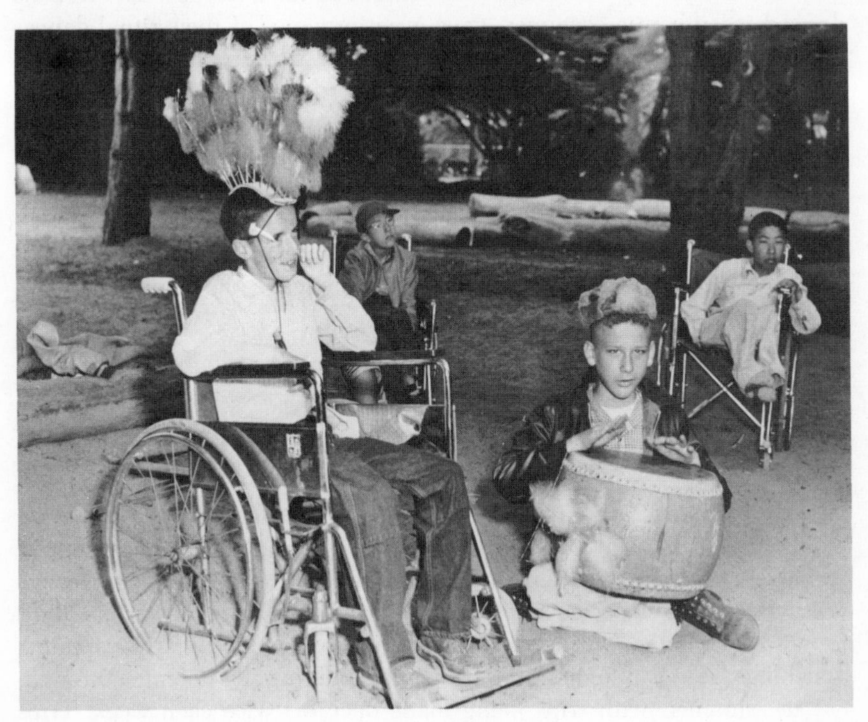

as the Spanish padres and their helpers had done nearly two hundred years before. From these "bricks," the children constructed "missions," which became the highlight of the Spanish theme. During the creation of the missions, the children who were interested were taken to visit some of the famous California missions in order to secure background information for their project.

At the end of the six-week period, both groups contributed to the culmination of the theme, which took the form of an all-day fiesta. The Spanish group cooked a Mexican meal, complete with refried beans, enchiladas, and tortillas. After lunch came the procession, led by the padre, followed by the Indians and the others. Then came the bullfight. The señores and señoritas filed into the "stands" to watch and cheer for their favorite bullfighters. The matadors and toreadors entered grandly, bowing to the audience. Then the "bulls" were brought in (in their wheel chairs), looking ferocious with papier-mâché horns attached to head bands, and the fight was on. One of the most appealing of the bullfighters in this event was "The Bashful Bull," who was, in fact, a little cerebral palsied boy who was incapable of holding his head up. He played his part to perfection, to the delight of the audience. The Indians dressed in authentic costumes, gave a performance of their ritual dances and games. The smaller wheel-chair-bound girls performed a "scarf dance," accompanied by appropriate recorded music. Their colorful scarves waved realistically as the girls were wheeled through the intricacies of the dance. They were attached by their corners to the ends of dowels, which, in turn, were attached to the backs of the wheel chairs. The afternoon's entertainment was rounded out by a guest artist's rendition of the Mexican Hat Dance. The many well-deserved *oles* from the audience, at the conclusion of the program, gave the children a rare feeling of accomplishment.

Trip Camping

Trip camping, over a period of several years, has proved to be the most successful and popular type of camping for groups of handicapped teen-agers at the Recreation Center. It was inaugurated as a progressive type of camping experience, especially for older teen-agers who had outgrown the regular routine of day camping for children. Trip camping, which has been conducted by the summer staff, usually operates throughout the summer, with trips being made once or twice each week. Trips

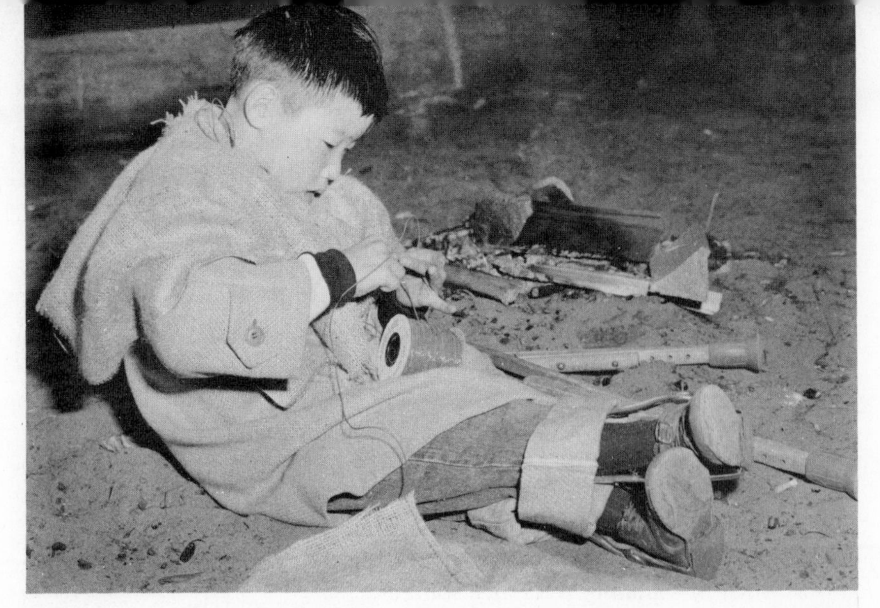

An "Indian" making a burlap serape.

have been limited primarily to camping out in various state parks in northern California.

One of the many values a well-organized trip has for the handicapped lies in the planning and working together for group living. Planning the trip in itself has been a thrilling experience for many of the handicapped persons, who for the first time in their lives, were taken to supermarkets to purchase food and to various stores for bedding and other camping equipment and supplies. Most of the group, who were very severely handicapped, had never experienced this type of planning and purchasing together, but they have learned to be independent and self-reliant and have developed a real sense of shared group living in the out-of-doors.

The background, experience, and training of the "trip counselor" is of primary importance. He must be a mature, seasoned person, who is well-versed in his field through wide experience. He should be thoroughly familiar with camp crafts, pioneering, wildlife craft, and woodcraft. As previously mentioned, such a camp staff must be familiar with the various sites before groups of handicapped children are transported to them.

A progressive set of skills in campcraft and woodcraft, which campers must pass before going on trips, can also be established for the handicapped. However, these must be geared to the various types of handicapped persons and to their physical abilities.

Trip camping for the handicapped, wherever possible, should follow the pattern of trip camping for the nonhandicapped.

Bibliography

The following bibliography is offered as a guide to supplementary reading on various aspects of recreation for the physically handicapped and as a list of valuable reference sources.

The titles are grouped under three headings, which correspond with the three major divisions of this volume. Each publication has been listed under the heading that is most appropriate; however, some of the listed references, particularly those in Part III—"Activities and Programs"—deal with several activities described in this section.

Magazines and periodicals frequently carrying articles dealing with various aspects of recreation for the physically handicapped are: *Recreation,* issued by the National Recreation Association, New York; *American Recreation Journal* and *Recreation in Treatment Centers,* issued by the American Recreation Society, Washington, D.C.; *Journal of Health, Physical Education and Recreation* and *Research Quarterly,* published by the American Association for Health, Physical Education and Recreation, Department of the National Education Association, Washington, D.C.; *Journal of the Association for Physical and Mental Rehabilitation,* issued by the Association for Physical and Mental Rehabilitation, Rehoboth Beach, Delaware; *Exceptional Children,* issued by The Council for Exceptional Children of the National Education Association, Washington, D.C.

PART I. THE HANDICAPPED AND RECREATION

Apton, Adolph, M.D. *The Handicapped, A Challenge to the Nonhandicapped.* New York: Citadel Press, 1959.

Butler, George D. *Introduction to Community Recreation* (rev. ed.). New York: McGraw, 1959.

Buell, Charles E. *Recreation for the Blind.* New York: American Foundation for the Blind, 1951.

Chapman, Frederick M. *Recreation Activities for the Handicapped.* New York: Ronald, 1960.

Cruickshank, William M., and G. Orville Johnson. *Education of Exceptional Children and Youth.* Englewood Cliffs, N.J.: Prentice-Hall, 1959.

Conference Proceedings. Golden Anniversary White House Conference on Children and Youth. Washington, D.C., 1960.

Focus on Children and Youth. Golden Anniversary White House Conference on Children and Youth. Washington, D.C., 1960.

Girl Scouts of the U.S.A. *Working with the Handicapped: A Leader's Guide.* New York, 1954.

Hunt, Valerie V. *Recreation for the Handicapped.* Englewood Cliffs, N.J.: Prentice-Hall, 1955.

Kessler, Henry H. *Rehabilitation of the Physically Handicapped* (rev. ed). New York: Columbia U. P., 1953.

Mallinson, Vernon. *None Can Be Called Deformed.* London: Heinemann; 1956.

Martmer, Edgar E., M.D. *The Child with a Handicap.* Springfield, Ill.: Thomas, 1959.

The Education of Exceptional Children. The 49th Yearbook, Part II, The National Society for the Study of Education. Chicago: U. of Chicago, 1950.

PART II. ORGANIZATION AND OPERATION

American Recreation Society, Inc. *Personnel Practices for Recreation Departments and Agencies,* 1404 New York Avenue, N.W., Washington 5, D.C.

———. *The Recreation Program,* 1404 New York Avenue, N.W., Washington 5, D.C.

———. *Credo for the Recreation Profession,* 1404 New York Avenue, N.W., Washington 5, D.C.

Ball, Edith. *Developing Volunteers for Service in Recreation Programs.* National Recreation Association, New York, 1958.

Bright, Sallie E. *Public Relations Program.* New York: National Publicity Council for Health and Welfare, 1950.

Butler, George D. *Recreation Areas; Their Design and Equipment* (rev. ed.). Profusely illustrated. New York: Ronald, 1958.

Gabrielsen, M. A., and Caswell M. Miles (eds.). *Sports and Recreation Facilities for Schools and Community.* Illustrated. Englewood Cliffs, N.J.: Prentice-Hall, 1958.

Hutchinson, John. *Principles of Recreation.* New York: Ronald, 1951.

Hjelte, George, and Jay S. Shivers. *Public Administration of Park and Recreational Services.* New York: Macmillan, 1963.

Kraus, Richard. *Recreation Leaders' Handbook.* New York: McGraw, 1955.

Meyer, Harold D., and Charles K. Brightbell. *Recreation Administration: A Guide to its Practices* (rev. ed.). Englewood Cliffs, N.J.: Prentice-Hall, 1961.

National Recreation Association. *The ABC's of Public Relations for Recreation.* New York, 1946.

———. *Communications and Public Relations.* New York, 1959.

———. *Personnel Standards in Community Recreation Leadership* (rev. ed.). A Committee Report. New York, 1957.

———. *Know Your Community.* New York, 1955.

Planning Facilities for Health, Physical Education, and Recreation (rev. ed). The Athletic Institute. A Workshop Report. Illustrated. Chicago, 1956.

Professional Preparation of Recreation Personnel. American Association for Health, Physical Education and Recreation. A Conference Report. Washington, D.C., 1957.

The Recreation Program. The Athletic Institute, Chicago, 1954.

PART III. ACTIVITIES AND PROGRAMS

DRAMA AND SPECIAL EVENTS

Ellis, Mary Jackson. *Finger Play Approach to Dramatization.* Minneapolis: Denison, 1960.

Hecker, Fred A., and Prescott W. Eames. *How to Put on an Amateur Circus.* Minneapolis: Denison.

Hake, Herbert Y. *Here's How* (rev. ed.). Evanston, Ill.: Row, 1958.

Holbrook, Marion. *Play Production Made Easy.* National Recreation Association, New York, 1933.

Murray, John. *One Act Plays for Young Actors.* Boston: Plays Inc., 1959.

Musselman, Virginia. *Informal Dramatics.* National Recreation Association, New York.

———. *Simple Puppetry.* National Recreation Association, New York.

National Recreation Association. *Easy Stunts and Skits.* New York (undated).

———. *For the Storyteller.* New York, rev. 1961.

———. *Fun and Festival Series.* New York.

———. *Pageants and Programs for School, Church, and Playground,* New York (undated).

———. *Planning and Producing a Local Pageant.* New York, 1952.

———. *Storytelling, Techniques for the Leader.* New York, 1952.

———. *Stunts Series.* New York.

———. *88 Successful Play Activities.* New York, Rev. 1951.

———. *Suggestions for an Amateur Circus.* New York, 1951.

Pels, Gertrude. *Easy Puppets.* New York: Crowell, 1951.

Schonberger, Emanuel D. *Fundamentals of Play Production.* Evanston, Ill.: Northwestern U. P., 1949.

Sheldon, George E. *The Big Time Circus Book.* Evanston, Ill.: Northwestern U. P., 1939.

Ward, Winifred (ed.). *Stories to Dramatize.* Anchorage, Ky.: Children's Theater Press, 1952.

———. *Playmaking with Children.* New York: Appleton, 1947.

MUSIC AND DANCE

Barr, Lillian J. *Motion Songs for Tots.* Minneapolis: Denison, 1958.

Burchenal, Elizabeth. *Folk Dances and Singing Games.* New York: G. Schirmer, Inc., 1909.

———. *Folk Dances from Old Home Lands.* New York: G. Schirmer, Inc., 1922.

Camp Fire Girls. *Music Makers.* Delaware, Ohio: Cooperative Song Service, Radnor Road (undated).

Girl Scouts of the USA. *Sing Together.* New York, 1949.

———. *Skip to My Lou.* New York (undated).

Leisy, James. *Abingdon Song Kit.* New York: Abingdon Press, 1957.

Let's All Sing. Delaware, Ohio: American Camping Association, Cooperative Song Service, Radnor Road (undated).

Mettler, Barbara. *Materials of Dance—As a Creative Art Activity.* Tucson, Ariz.: Mettler Studios, 1960.

Musselman, Virginia. *Mixers to Music for Parties and Dances.* National Recreation Association, New York (undated).

National Recreation Association. *Action Songs.* New York (undated).

———. *The Golden Book of Favorite Songs; A Treasury of the Best Songs of Our People.* New York, 1946.

———. *Singing Games.* New York (undated).

A New Treasury of Folk Songs. New York: Bantam Books, 1961.

The Recreation Program. The Athletic Institute, Chicago, 1954.

Stuart, Frances R. and John S. Ludlam. *Rhythmic Activities.* Minneapolis: Burgess Publishing Company, 1956.

Tobitt, Janet E. *The Ditty Bag.* Janet E. Tobitt, 228 East 43rd St., New York 17, New York, 1946.

Twice 55 Community Songs, The Brown Book. Evanston, Ill.: Summy-Birchard Publishing Company, 1957.

Zander, Carl E. and Wes H. Klausmann. *Camp Songs 'N' Things.* 1950 Addison St., Berkeley 4, Calif., 1939.

Zanzig, Augustus D. *Roads to Music Appreciation.* National Recreation Association, New York, 1948.

———. *Starting and Developing a Rhythm Band.* National Recreation Association, New York, 1954.

ARTS AND CRAFTS

Allen, Doris and Dione Lee. *Sunset Mosaics.* Menlo Park, Calif.: Lane Book Company, 1962.

Benson, Kenneth R. *Creative Crafts for Children.* Englewood Cliffs, N.J.: Prentice-Hall, 1958.

Ellis, Mary Jackson and Gene Watson. *Creative Art Ideas.* Minneapolis: Denison, 1959.

Isenstein, Harold. *Creative Claywork.* New York: Sterling Publishing Company, 1960.

Jenkins, Louisa M. and Barbara Mills. *The Art of Making Mosaics.* Princeton, N.J.: Van Nostrand, 1957.

How to Make Pottery and Ceramic Sculpture. The Museum of Modern Art. New York: Simon and Schuster, 1947.

Hunt, Ben W. *Indian and Camp Handcraft* (rev. 1945). New York: Golden Press, 1938.

———. *Golden Book of Crafts and Hobbies.* New York: Golden Press, 1959.

———. *Golden Book of Indian Crafts and Lore.* New York: Golden Press, 1954.

Kit V. Crafts that Last. Delaware, Ohio: Cooperative Recreation Service, Radnor Road.

Lewis, Shari. *Paper Puppets.* New York: Citadel, 1958.

Marks, Mickey Klar. *Sand Sculpturing.* New York: Dial, 1962.

National Recreation Association. *Craft Projects for Camp and Playground.* New York, 1953.

Powell, Harold. *The Beginner's Book of Pottery Series.* New York: Emerson Books, Inc., 1960.

Sanders, Herbert H. *Sunset Ceramic Book.* Menlo Park, Calif.: Lane Publishing Company, 1953.

Staples, Frank H. *Arts and Crafts Program Manual—A Planning Guide for All Ages.* National Recreation Association, New York, 1953.

CLUB AND INTEREST GROUPS

Higgins, Winfield. *Tourplay.* New York: Wm. Frederick Press, 1949.

Hyde, Margaret O. and Frances W. Keene. *Hobby Fun Book.* New York: The Seashore Press, Inc., 1952.

The Recreation Program. The Athletic Institute, Chicago, 1954.

U.S. Commission for UNICEF. *Hi, Neighbor* (Books 1–4). U.S. Commission for UNICEF, United Nations, New York.

ACTIVE GAMES AND SPORTS

American Association for Health, Physical Education, and Recreation. *Recreational Games and Sports.* Washington, D.C., 1957.

American National Red Cross. *Swimming for the Handicapped, Instructors' Manual.* Washington, D.C., 1955.

Buell, Charles E. *Active Games for the Blind.* Ann Arbor, Mich.: Edwards Brothers, 1947.

———. *Recreation for the Blind.* American Foundation for the Blind, New York, 1951.

Cureton, Thomas K., Jr. *Fun in the Water.* New York: Association Press, 1949.

Daniels, Arthur S. *Adapted Physical Education.* New York: Harper, 1954.

Donnelly, Richard J., William G. Helms, Elmer D. Mitchell. *Active Games and Contests.* New York: Ronald, 1958.

Fait, Hollis F., Ph.D. *Adapted Physical Education.* Philadelphia: Saunders, 1960.

Hindman, Darwin A. *Handbook of Active Games.* New York: Prentice-Hall, 1951.

Mathews, Donald K., Robert Kruse, and Virginia Shaw. *The Science of Physical Education for Handicapped Children.* New York: Harper, 1962.

Rathbone, Josephine Longworthy, Ph.D. *Corrective Physical Education.* Philadelphia: Saunders, 1954.

The Recreation Program. The Athletic Institute, Chicago, 1954.

Stafford, George T., Ed.D. *Sports for the Handicapped.* New York: Prentice-Hall, 1947.

SOCIAL RECREATION

Bowers, Ethel (ed.). *Parties for Special Days of the Year.* National Recreation Association, New York, 1936.

Borst, Evelyne and Elmer D. Mitchell. *Social Games for Recreation.* New York: Ronald, 1959.

Eisenberg, Helen and Larry. *Handbook of Skits and Stunts.* New York: Association Press, 1962.

———. *Omnibus of Fun.* New York: Association Press, 1956.

Handbook for Recreation. United States Department of Health, Education, and Welfare, Social Security Administration, Children's Bureau, Washington, D.C., 1960.

Handy Party Book. Delaware, Ohio: Cooperative Recreation Service, Radnor Road, 1932.

Handy Stunts—Kit I. Delaware, Ohio: Cooperative Recreation Service, Radnor Road, 1932.

Kemmerer, James W. and Eva May Brickett. *Games and Parties for all Occasions.* Minneapolis: Denison, 1962.

Mason, Bernard S. and Elmer D. Mitchell. *Party Games for All.* New York: Barnes and Noble, 1946.

National Recreation Association. *Games for Quiet Hours and Small Spaces.* New York, 1938.

———. *Parties, Plans and Programs.* New York, 1936.

Social Recreation Leadership—Kit B. Delaware, Ohio: Cooperative Recreation Service, Radnor Road, 1932.

The Recreation Program. The Athletic Institute, Chicago, 1954.

DAY CAMPING

Camping for Crippled Children. Elyria, Ohio: The National Society for Crippled Children and Adults, 1945.

Day Camping for the Cerebral Palsied. United Cerebral Palsy Association, 321 West 44th St., New York (undated).

Hammett, Catherine T. and Virginia Musselman. *The Camp Program Book.* New York: Association Press, 1951.

Hammett, Catherine T. and Carol M. Horrocks. *Creative Crafts for Campers.* New York: Association Press, 1957.

Joy, Barbara Ellen. *Camp Craft.* Minneapolis: Burgess Publishing Company, 1961.

Mitchell, Viola A. and Ida B. Crawford. *Camp Counseling.* Philadelphia: Saunders, 1961.

Mitchell, Grace L. *Fundamentals of Day Camping.* New York: Association Press, 1961.

Musselman, Virginia. *Day Camping.* National Recreation Association, New York, 1963.

Nickelsburg, Janet. *The Nature Program at Camp.* Minneapolis: Burgess Publishing Company, 1960.

Price, Betty. *Adventuring in Nature.* National Recreation Association, New York, 1939.

A Report on an Experiment in Camping for Children with Muscular Dystrophy. Muscular Dystrophy Association of America, 39 Broadway, New York 6, New York, Dec. 15, 1955.

Welfare Council of Metropolitan Chicago, Division of Recreation and Informal Education. *First the Person Then the Disability.* A report of the consultant project on camp and city leisure time activities for the handicapped. Chicago (undated).

INDEX